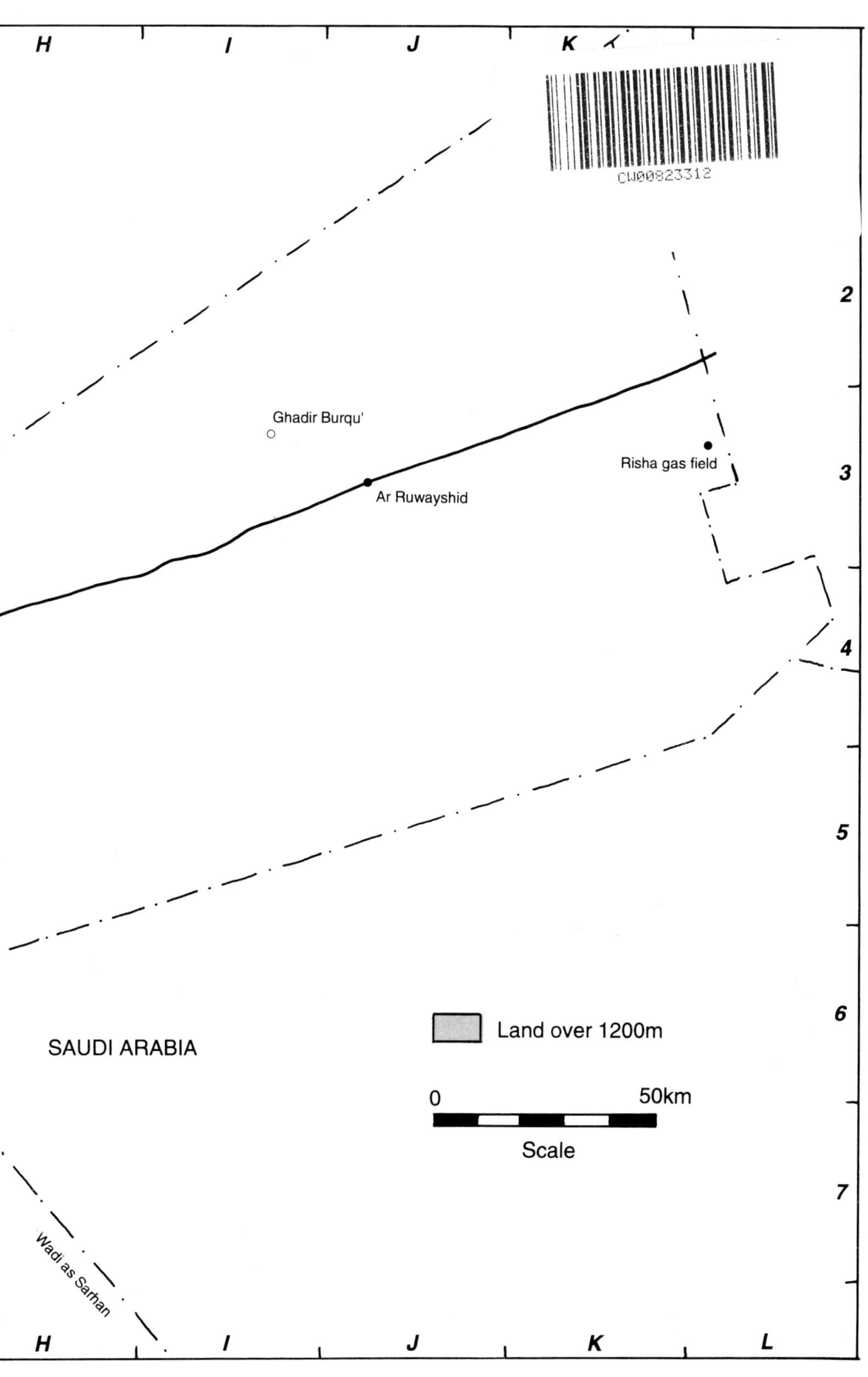

H
I
J
K
L
2
3
4
5
6
7
Ghadir Burqu'
Ar Ruwayshid
Risha gas field
SAUDI ARABIA
Land over 1200m
0
50km
Scale
Wadi as Sarhan

The BIRDS of the Hashemite Kingdom of JORDAN

Ian J Andrews

Published by I. J. Andrews, 1995

ISBN 0 9524978 0 8

First published in 1995 by
I. J. Andrews
39 Clayknowes Drive
Musselburgh
Midlothian EH21 6UW
Scotland

British Library Cataloguing in Publication Data.
A catalogue record for this book is available from the British Library.

Text set in Times (9/10pt)

Typeset and printed by
Burns & Harris (Print) Limited, Dundee, Scotland

Cover illustrations:
Wadi Umm Ishrin at dusk (Author)
Male Sinai Rosefinch, Dana, October 1994 (Tim Loseby)

CONTENTS

FOREWORD *by His Majesty King Hussein I*

God Almighty has blessed our country with priceless treasures, primary among them is a long and rich history and a charming natural environment. The land of Jordan is the birthplace of the world's three great monotheistic religions. Located at the crossroads of Asia, Africa and Europe, this land has also historically served mankind as a bridge for trade, travel, communication and understanding. The usefulness of this natural land bridge has not gone unnoticed by the dwellers of the skies, either, and Jordan is a favourite resting point for large numbers of migratory birds. The Kingdom's remarkable geographic and ecological diversity has endowed it with a bountiful variety of life, including a flourishing array of avian species.

Ian Andrews' interest in the birds of Jordan has blossomed from a hobby into the first comprehensive summary of the Kingdom's bird population. While the amateur birdwatcher will find this study to be an indispensable guide to the birds of Jordan, the work also fills an important niche in Jordan's efforts to preserve its natural heritage. I hope that this book will inspire bird-watchers and nature lovers everywhere to visit our country and discover its marvels for themselves. With this book, another step has been taken to ensure that the treasures of today will be preserved for the generations of tomorrow.

Hussein I

LIST OF COLOUR PHOTOGRAPHS, MAPS AND ILLUSTRATIONS

UNLESS OTHERWISE CREDITED ON THE PLATE ITSELF, THE FOLLOWING PHOTOGRAPHS WERE TAKEN BY THE AUTHOR IN JORDAN.

PLATES 1-8 CAN BE FOUND BETWEEN PAGES 30 AND 31, AND PLATES 9-16 BETWEEN PAGES 62 AND 63; PLATES 17-24 ARE LOCATED BETWEEN PAGES 94 AND 95 AND PLATES 25-32 BETWEEN PAGES 126 AND 127.

Common Sandpiper
Curlew Sandpiper, adult

Plate 17
White-eyed Gulls
White-winged Black Tern, adult
Whiskered Tern, juvenile
Whiskered Tern, juvenile

Plate 18
White-winged Black Terns
White-winged Black Tern, adult
White-winged Black Terns
White-winged Black Tern, juvenile
Spotted Sandgrouse, female

Plate 19
Barn Owl
Long-eared Owl
Scops Owl
Little Owl
Hume's Tawny Owl

Plate 20
Nightjar
Egyptian Nightjar
Egyptian Nightjar
Little Green Bee-eater
Bee-eater
Smyrna Kingfisher
Roller

Plate 21
Hoopoe Lark
Desert Lark, *annae* subspecies
Dunn's Lark
Desert Lark
Bar-tailed Desert Lark

Plate 22
Calandra Lark
Temminck's Horned Lark
Short-toed Lark
Thick-billed Lark, juvenile
Thick-billed Lark, adult

Plate 23
Rock Martin
Rock Martin
Red-throated Pipit
Red-throated Pipit, winter plumage
Long-billed Pipit
Tawny Pipit

Plate 24
Yellow Wagtail, male *feldegg* subspecies
Yellow Wagtail, male "*superciliaris*" subspecies
Yellow-vented Bulbul
Yellow Wagtail, male *beema* subspecies
Citrine Wagtail, first-winter

Plate 25
Rufous Bush Robin
Thrush Nightingale
Bluethroat, male
Blackstart
Redstart, male *samamisicus* subspecies

Plate 26
Isabelline Wheatear
Black-eared Wheatear, male
Desert Wheatear, male
Finsch's Wheatear, male
Red-rumped Wheatear, male
White-crowned Black Wheatear, first- or second-year bird

Plate 27
Mourning Wheatear
Mourning Wheatear, black morph
Rock Thrush, winter-plumaged male
Spectacled Warbler
Scrub Warbler
Arabian Warbler

Plate 28
Red-breasted Flycatcher
Ficedula flycatcher, first-winter
Blue Tit
Orange-tufted Sunbird, juvenile
Orange-tufted Sunbird, male
Golden Oriole, male

Plate 29
Red-backed Shrike, first-winter
Masked Shrike, adult
Masked Shrike, first-winter
Woodchat Shrike, adult
Jay
Fan-tailed Raven

Plate 30
Dead Sea Sparrow, male
Rock Sparrow
Indian House Crows
Spanish Sparrow, winter plumage
Tristram's Grackles

Plate 31
Trumpeter Finch, female or immature
Tristram's Serin
Yellowhammer and Chaffinch
Sinai Rosefinch, male
Sinai Rosefinch, female
Desert Finch, male

Plate 32
House Bunting, male
Ortolan Bunting, female/immature
Cretzschmar's Bunting, male
Black-headed Bunting, male
Corn Bunting

List of Maps

List of Illustrations

by ***John Busby***

INTRODUCTION

For a relatively small country, Jordan has a great variety of dramatic bird habitats, ranging from mountain forests to desert oases, from mountains and cliffs to sweeping deserts, and from deep gorges to broad wadis. The country is located on the junction of the Mediterranean and Arabian faunal regions, and it lies on one of the world's major bird migration routes, that from Africa to Eurasia. It is not surprising therefore that Jordan possesses a large and varied avifauna, sufficient to rival any Western Palearctic region of similar area. Despite this the birdlife of the country remains surprisingly little studied.

In the eyes of travelling western ornithologists Jordan's birds have long been overshadowed by those of its neighbour – Israel. Scholars of the Arabian Peninsula's birds have also tended to concentrate on the more 'interesting' areas of the south-west Arabian mountains and the Arabian Gulf. Jordan has for too long remained a gap in our knowledge of the region. This is even more surprising given the country's easy access, its striking tourist attractions, and its welcoming and generous peoples. Birdwatching in Jordan, as in any other Arab country, has its challenges, but it is not without its rewards.

For a foreigner to live in a country for three years and claim to be an expert on its birds is presumptuous. In the case of Jordan, however, so little has ever been published on its birds that the efforts of just one birdwatcher can make significantly important advances. The author lived in Jordan from 1989 to 1992 and visited most of the gross habitat types at all four seasons, but does not claim that coverage was by any means complete. There are a small number, probably as few as five local amateurs with a growing interest in birds, and hopefully this interest will develop sufficiently to enable a more comprehensive survey to be undertaken in the future.

Without doubt, visiting birdwatchers can still add significantly to our knowledge of Jordan's birds, and they may wish to consider carrying out more detailed survey work at specific sites. Until such time as a Jordanian wishes to take over, the author is willing to collate all bird sightings made in Jordan.

In order to make this book as definitive a summary as possible, many observations by local and foreign ornithologists have been combined with personal sightings to provide the framework of knowledge as it stands today. 374 species are detailed in the main list, of which about 220 are migrants or winter visitors, and possibly as many as 150 are known to have bred at least once.

Field identification is outwith the scope of this book and visitors to Jordan are initially directed towards the following selection of modern field guides.

Jonsson, L. 1992. *Birds of Europe with North Africa and the Middle East.* Christopher Helm, London.

Heinzel, H., Fitter, R. and Parslow, J. 1972. *The Birds of Britain and Europe with North Africa and the Middle East.* Collins, London.

Génsbol, B. 1986. *Birds of Prey of Britain and Europe, North Africa and the Middle East.* Collins, London.

Hollom, P.A.D., Porter, R.F., Christensen, S. and Willis, I. 1988. *Birds of the Middle East and North Africa.* Poyser, Calton.

The Drawings

The author is indebted to the artist John Busby, whose drawings not only enliven the text, but also help to conjure up an image of Jordanian birds in their respective habitats.

The Photographs

Wherever possible the bird photographs chosen for this book were taken in Jordan, and the majority were taken by the author. For those interested in technical detail, the author's photographs were taken with a Nikon F301 camera, Tamron 500m mirror lens and Kodachrome 200 ASA slide film. Additional Jordanian material made available by Tim Loseby, Peter Boye, Damian Debski, Richard Porter and Steve Harley is gratefully acknowledged, as are a small number of non-Jordanian photographs taken by Paul Doherty, Dr Mike Hill and Roger Tidman.

The Sites Guide

Visitors to Jordan will doubtless be aiming to see a wide cross-section of the country's breeding and migrant birds. To achieve this it is necessary to visit a selection of habitat types over a period of at least ten days. Spring offers the best opportunity for a combination of large numbers of birds and good weather, and any time from late March through to early May can be recommended. However, autumn and winter should not be ignored, with many discoveries doubtless still waiting to be made during these seasons.

The sites illustrated here are a selection of the most productive and easily accessible, with representatives from most of the main habitat types. The descriptions are based on visits made during 1989-92. Foreseeable changes for the future include improved access to the shore of the Dead Sea from Suwayma, south to As Safi when a proposed new highway is completed. Conversely at Azraq wetland sites have now become increasingly difficult to find as underground water is currently being extracted at excessive rates. Periodic winter flooding provides ample compensation at that site. Development of the southern beaches at Aqaba for tourism may also have an effect on the distribution of shorebirds and other migrants.

Sites in the Jordan Valley, Dead Sea, Wadi Araba and Aqaba areas are close to a currently peaceful, but potentially volatile border. Whilst every attempt has been made to select non-sensitive sites, a change in circumstances could restrict access to any of the sites illustrated. Please respect the requests of the military, and perhaps ask if there are alternative places nearby that you can visit.

Breeding Distribution Maps

The daunting task of systematically surveying Jordan's breeding birds has yet to be undertaken and it is fair to say that, at present, relatively little is known about the detailed distribution of the 141 to 154 species proven or thought to have bred in Jordan. Indeed 42 species (about a third of the total) were added to the breeding list during 1979-92 alone. A quick glance at even the 1988 *Birds of North Africa and the Middle East* shows that there are uncannily Jordan-shaped holes in the range maps of many common species, whilst other guides suffer from so-called 'liberal mapping'.

The distribution maps produced here are preliminary, although based on the best available information. To avoid the false impression of accuracy, the breeding distributions are mapped in terms of the avifaunal regions in most cases. Areas of proven or common breeding (solid red on the maps) are differentiated from areas of probable or scarce breeding (red stipple), and suspected breeding is indicated by a question mark.

Sequence and Nomenclature

In most cases, the sequence of the species and their English and scientific names are those used in "The 'British Birds' List of Birds of the Western Palearctic" (1984) which is itself based on Professor Dr K.H. Voous' "List of Recent Holarctic Bird Species" (*Ibis* **115**, 612-638 and **119**, 223-250, 376-406). A limited number of commonly used, alternative English names are also given.

At the time of writing many changes are taking place with regard to the splitting and lumping of some species and subspecies. For instance, it is now generally accepted that the Steppe Eagle is distinct from the Tawny Eagle, the Isabelline Shrike is distinct from the Red-backed Shrike, the Semi-collared Flycatcher is distinct from the Collared Flycatcher, and the Water Pipit is separate from the Rock Pipit. Conversely, Yellow-legged and Armenian Gulls are still treated as subspecies (of the Herring Gull) by some authorities. Pied and Cyprus Pied Wheatears are also included as subspecies by some workers despite their geographical isolation. However, the Barbary Falcon currently remains distinct from the Peregrine. In addition, it is the author's opinion that the status of the dark wheatears of the Basalt Desert is still not conclusively resolved and requires further study. Distinct subspecies such as the *samamisicus* Redstart and *semirufus/phoenicuroides* Black Redstart are described separately here.

The German species names are taken from "Die LIMICOLA-Liste der Vögel der Westpaläarktis" (*Limicola* **2**, 12-36). The Arabic names have been transliterated by Jad Al-Younis largely from the Arabic translation of the Vere Benson *Birds of Lebanon* published by the International Council for Bird Preservation.

Migration Timings

Passage birds make up a large percentage of Jordan's birds, and the timing of the migration season for such species is shown by means of a bar-diagram. These diagrams are designed to show the timing and relative abundance of each species over the 36 ten-day periods of the year (early, mid and late periods of each month). Times when a species is most frequently seen, or particularly common, are shown in solid red; a red stipple denotes that it is less frequent or rare.

The dataset from which the histograms have been constructed contains 13,000 records involving 248,000 individuals of 312 species seen by the author during the 34½ months from 9 July 1989 to 14 May 1992. Additional records of vagrants and early, late, or out-of-season migrants are taken from other sources. In the case of the rarer migrants and seabirds the charts may be observer-biased and the true patterns of occurrence will only become clear in future years.

Abundance and Status

An indication of the relative abundance of each species is given, largely based on the number of birds seen during the author's stay in Jordan. In increasing order of abundance the terms used are: vagrant, rare, scarce, uncommon, common, very common and abundant.

The status of each species is also summarised by means of a code in the Jordan checklist (page 47).

Useful Addresses

The Ornithological Society of the Middle East (OSME) was established in 1978. It aims, amongst other things, to collect, collate, and publish data on all aspects of the birds of the Middle East. It publishes the journal *Sandgrouse,* as well as the biannual *OSME Bulletin.*

Ornithological Society of the Middle East
c/o The Lodge, Sandy,
Bedfordshire SG19 2DL, U.K.

The Royal Society for the Conservation of Nature (RSCN) is the only organisation in Jordan dedicated to the conservation of nature, including birds. It publishes the quarterly magazine *El-Reem*, which is in Arabic with brief English summaries.

The Royal Society for the
Conservation of Nature
P.O. Box 6354, Amman, Jordan
Telephone Amman 811689
Fax Amman 847411

Acknowledgements

I must thank the many people who have helped in producing this book. It could not have reached its final form without the observations, suggestions, corrections and encouragement given by so many. Of these, several require special mention. Jörg Wittenberg is thanked by the author for sharing his knowledge of Jordanian birds, for giving an invaluable introduction on where to birdwatch in Jordan, and for providing numerous trip reports and publications by himself covering many years between 1978 and 1994. He also carried out an extensive review of a draft, for which I am most grateful. Peter Sherrington accompanied me on many trips in 1989-90 and his tireless enthusiasm never failed to find good birds. His records from the Ar Ruwayshid Desert fill a large gap in my personal coverage.

Of the local Jordanians I must particularly acknowledge the help given by Arslan Ramadan Bakig in showing me some of Jordan's lesser known and least accessible sites (for example, the Al Khirba as Samra sewage works and the Jordan River). My thanks also go to Darwish M. Shafei for showing me the skin collection of the Jordan Natural

History Museum and to Jad Al Younis for sharing his knowledge of Jordan. As a result of his work on the Important Bird Areas of the Middle East project, M.I. Evans of BirdLife International was also able to inform me of some important observations made by Ali Sutari. Khalil Ibrahim generously helped with some translations.

Following published requests by Jörg Wittenberg (Germany) and myself, many people sent details of their own observations from Jordan; without these contributions this book would have been far less complete. I thank and fully acknowledge the following for supplying trip reports (year in brackets) and valuable correspondence: L.N. Andersen (1979), G. Bennett/Ornitholidays (1984-86, and 1988), A. Bräunlich (1985), Mr Bucknell (1989), J. Busby (1992), M. Cocker/ Naturetrek (1994), P. Conder (1981), R. Coomber/ Ornitholidays (1992), D. Debski (1994), D.J. Evans (1987 and 1989), M.I. Evans, R.I. Bashford and RSCN survey team (1994), I.J. Ferguson-Lees/ Ornitholidays (1987), Dr M. Griffin (1990, 1991 and 1992), P. de Grissac (1985), S. Harley (1994), C. Hays, R. Hofland (1994), R. Kinzelbach (1975 and 1977), E. Lipkow (1989-90), D. McAdams (1980), A.M. Macfarlane (1976), E. Massiah (1990), M. Massetti (1990 and 1992), C. Milner/ Ornitholidays (1988), Dr D.A. Murdoch (1992), Dr R.D. Oades (1994), R.F. Porter (1994), H. Schaub (1993), D.A. Scott (1991 and 1992), H. Shirihai, M. Siering (1986), A. Smith (1993), J.L. Swallow (1989), C. Tack (1988), M. Ullman (1989), C. Violani, D.I.M. Wallace, C. Waller/ Cygnus Wildlife Tours (1985 and 1986) and J. Wittenberg/Natur-Studienreisen (1987-94).

My thanks go to Dr T.D.J. Cameron and Dr M. Griffin for proof reading the manuscript.

Finally, I must thank John Bannon and Colin Richardson, who did much to encourage this project in its early stages. It was the successful layout of Colin's *Birds of the United Arab Emirates* that ultimately influenced the format of this book.

THE COUNTRY OF JORDAN

The Hashemite Kingdom of Jordan[1] lies at the junction of the Levantine and Arabian areas of the Middle East. The country has borders with Israel (including the occupied territories of Gaza, the West Bank and the Golan Heights), Syria, Iraq and Saudi Arabia. The Gulf of Aqaba is its only outlet to the sea. Jordan is located between 29° 11′N and 33° 22′N latitude, and between 34° 59′E and 39° 18′E longitude. It is a small country, compared to most of its neighbours, and occupies an area of 89,411 km², similar to that of Austria or Portugal.

CLIMATE

The climate of western Jordan is essentially of Mediterranean type with a hot dry summer and cool wet winter, with two short transitional seasons. However, 80% of the country can be described as having a desert climate with less than 200mm of rain. There are three main climatic areas: (a) the highlands, (b) the Jordan Valley and (c) the desert.

The Northern Highlands have a cool temperate climate with quite hot summers (the average July maximum is 26-29°C, but with extremes up to 43°C) and rather cold winters (the average January maximum is 8-10°C). Rainfall is mainly orographic, associated with Mediterranean depressions, and it mostly falls in the winter and spring. On average the first invasion of cold air and the start of unsettled weather occurs on 20th October, and it can rain any time from then until mid-May. However, the amount and period of rainfall are very variable and fluctuate from year to year. Rainfall reaches a maximum of 500-600mm on the western slopes of the northern hills, where remnants of the forests of pine and oak still grow, but it decreases rapidly eastwards to 100mm. The Southern Highlands receive up to 300mm of winter rainfall, but are off the track of the majority of depressions. Ground frost is common, but snowfall is rare. It snows on average one to three times a winter in Jordan and a maximum of 1.2m has been recorded at Ajlun. The winter of 1991/92 was particularly severe in Jordan with over 900mm of rainfall at Amman (more than twice the average) and five separate heavy snow falls.

By contrast, the Jordan Valley climate is essentially sub-tropical with an extremely hot summer (the average July maximum is 39°C and the country's maximum recorded temperature of 51.2°C was measured here) and a pleasant winter (the average January maximum is 18-20°C). Over 300mm of winter rain falls in northern parts, but this amount decreases southwards.

The desert areas in the east and south have a continental climate, characterised by clear skies during most of the year, hot dry summers (high diurnal range) and rather cold winters (the average January maximum is 13-15°C), with very little annual precipitation (less than 200mm). An extreme low temperature of –12°C has been recorded in the desert in January, and an extreme high of 46.4°C in summer. Dust storms are common, especially in the summer.

There has been a tendency of decreasing rainfall since measurements have been taken in Jordan, but this should be seen against a background of variably very moist, moist, dry and very dry periods throughout the Christian and Islamic eras. However, the impact of this most recent decrease in rainfall has been exaggerated by man's misuse of the environment. For example, at Azraq over-pumping of the underground water has seen a cessation of flow from the springs, and misuse of the fragile semi-desert and steppe habitats has seen an increase in soil erosion.

GEOLOGY

The geology and bird life of Jordan are surprisingly closely linked. The bedrock of an area is often the foundation on which specific habitats develop and on which avifaunal diversity is ultimately dependent. Some bird communities are restricted to the sandstone cliffs of the Rift Margins; others can be linked to subtle differences in the rocks of the desert floor, and yet others are restricted to the Dead Sea Rift fault system. Even the Azraq oasis owes its existence to a geological boundary at the edge of a basalt area. In other cases species have evolved a distinctive coloration in response to the geological characteristics of the desert they occupy. Of particular note is the Desert Lark, which has a dark race (*A. d. annae*) found only on the dark flint and basalt deserts.

The rocks of Jordan span a huge range of ages; the oldest are at Aqaba and the youngest are in

Footnote [1] in this book Jordan excludes the West Bank, the area west of the River Jordan occupied by Israel since 1967. The modern boundary also incorporates a 1966 agreement with Saudi Arabia whereby Jordan gained a longer Gulf of Aqaba coastline in exchange for the Kilwa-Tubayq desert area. Minor changes have also recently taken place to the Jordan-Iraq border in the Risha area.

the Rift Valley and at Azraq. For convenience they can be grouped into the following classification:

(a) The granites which form the mountains behind Aqaba are of Precambrian age (that is they are more than 570 million years old). They are criss-crossed with sheets of intruded igneous rock, known as dykes.

(b) Palaeozoic sandstones (Cambrian to Silurian age – 590 million to 408 million years old) crop out along the Rift Margins, from the shores of the Dead Sea south to Petra, and also in the Rum Desert. At Petra the sandstones are spectacularly colour-banded in yellow, orange, red, grey, brown and mauve. This pattern was formed by the rhythmic deposition of various iron and manganese compounds from mineral-rich water that once flowed within the rock. In Jordan the Sinai Rosefinch breeds exclusively on this rock type.

(c) Mesozoic limestones (Triassic to Palaeogene age – 248 million to 25 million years old) extend across most of the Highlands and Desert areas of Jordan. In many cases the limestones contain significant amounts of hard chert (or flint) which, being less easily eroded than the limestones, often form a remnant surface layer of shattered pieces.

(d) The basalts of northern Jordan are the products of volcanic activity which began 25 million years ago and ceased less than one million years ago. The various lava flows radiate from the Jabal ad Druz centre in Syria, but there are small cones and fissures within Jordan. Erosion of this volcanic rock in the extreme temperatures of the desert climate has formed the extensive boulder fields found there today.

(e) Jordan's youngest rocks are to be found in the Rift Valley and Azraq Basins. They are typically soft siltstones and mudstones deposited in the extensive lakes which formerly occupied these sites until just a few thousand years ago. In the Jordan Valley these rocks have been easily eroded into a bad-land landscape of gullies and cliffs.

Vegetation

Four vegetational regions are generally recognised in the Middle East, based on climate and vegetation characteristics. Broadly within this general scheme 13 more detailed vegetation types can be defined as follows:

1. The Mediterranean region (highland areas with over 300mm of annual rainfall)
   Pine forest
   Evergreen oak forest
   Deciduous oak forest
   Juniperus forest
   Mediterranean non-forest

2. The Irano-Turanian region (steppes surrounding the highlands)
   Steppe vegetation

3. The Saharo-Arabian region (interior deserts)
   Hammada vegetation
   Mud flats
   Saline vegetation (Azraq)

4. The Sudanian region (the Rift Valley from Dayr Alla to Aqaba and the Rum Mountains)
   Tropical vegetation
   Saline vegetation
   Acacia and rocky sudanian vegetation
   Sand dune vegetation

In addition, water-dependent vegetation is found along flowing rivers which cross many of the other zones.

AVIFAUNAL REGIONS

Ranging in height from 407m below sea-level (–1335 feet) at the Dead Sea to 1860m (6102 feet) at Jabal Umm Adaami near the Saudi Arabian border, Jordan boasts a large altitudinal range. It also possesses a large range of habitats, lying as it does on the junction of the Mediterranean area and the Arabian Desert, and this partly reflects its varied geological basement.

In this report the country is divided into a series of 'avifaunal regions' based on a combination of topographical, geomorphological, climatical and vegetational criteria, as well on as the avifauna they possess. These zones differ in detail from schemes that might be defined on the basis of any single criteria, but they allow a subdivision into broad avifaunal assemblages.

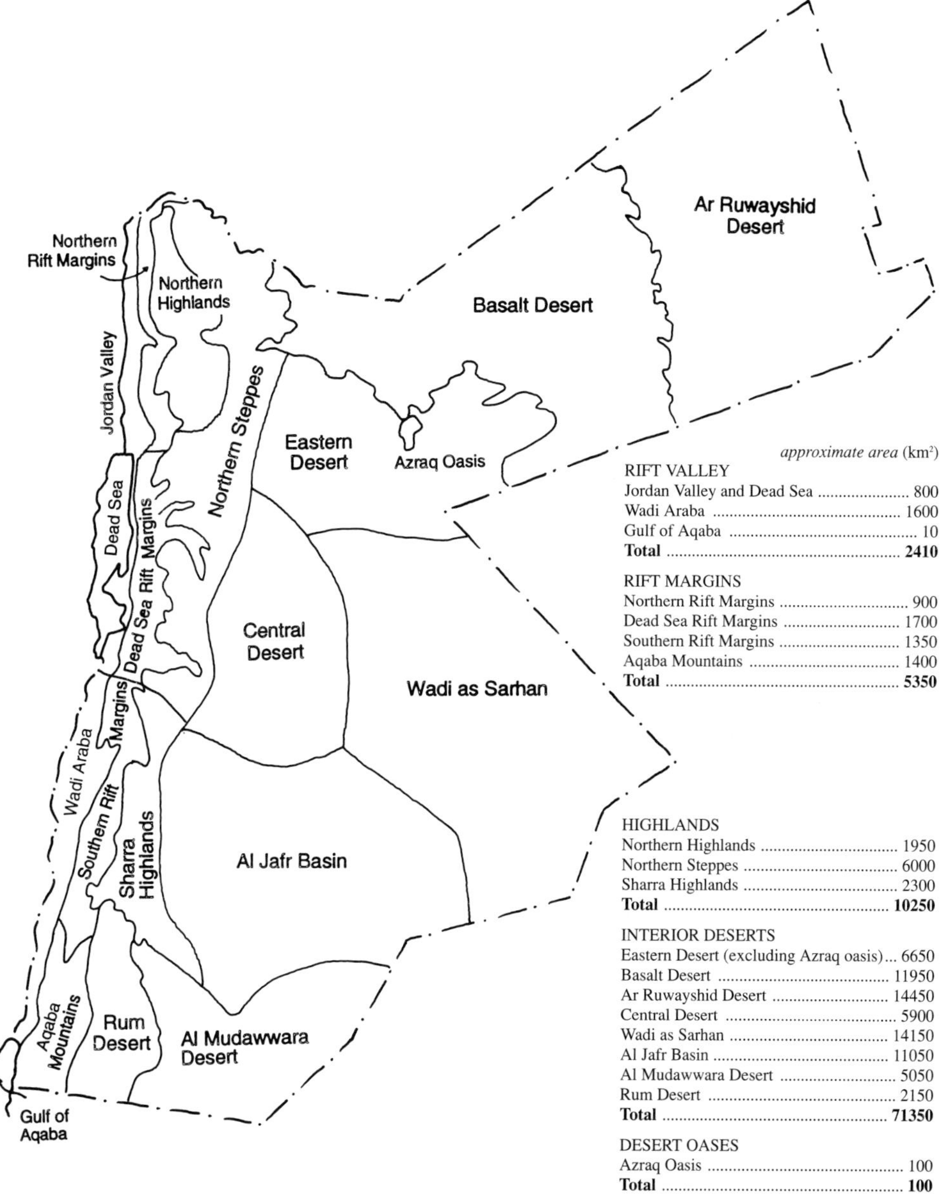

	approximate area (km^2)
RIFT VALLEY	
Jordan Valley and Dead Sea	800
Wadi Araba	1600
Gulf of Aqaba	10
Total	**2410**
RIFT MARGINS	
Northern Rift Margins	900
Dead Sea Rift Margins	1700
Southern Rift Margins	1350
Aqaba Mountains	1400
Total	**5350**
HIGHLANDS	
Northern Highlands	1950
Northern Steppes	6000
Sharra Highlands	2300
Total	**10250**
INTERIOR DESERTS	
Eastern Desert (excluding Azraq oasis)	6650
Basalt Desert	11950
Ar Ruwayshid Desert	14450
Central Desert	5900
Wadi as Sarhan	14150
Al Jafr Basin	11050
Al Mudawwara Desert	5050
Rum Desert	2150
Total	**71350**
DESERT OASES	
Azraq Oasis	100
Total	**100**

Jordan Valley (the 'Ghor') and Dead Sea

The Jordan Valley forms the northern segment of the Rift Valley and contains the Jordan River draining into the Dead Sea. There is little natural vegetation remaining, and the area is now extensively irrigated for fruit and vegetable production, a majority of the latter under plastic. In the north, from Al Adasiyya to Dayr Alla, higher winter rainfall together with extensive summer irrigation means that agriculture covers most of the valley from the Jordan River to the foothills. Water is taken mainly from the Yarmuk River to supply the King Abdullah Canal. Wetland areas are very few. In the 1940s the birds of the Yarmuk estuary reservoir was described where the Yarmuk River joins the Jordan River, but it is unfortunately not known if this productive site still exists.

The southern Jordan Valley, from Dayr Alla to the Dead Sea, has a hot arid climate and was formerly treeless desert. Irrigated crops such as banana plantations now cover large areas. Water is provided by reservoirs on dammed tributary wadis (for example, at Wadi al Arab, Wadi Shu'ayb and Kafrayn).

The Jordan River meanders the 105km from Lake Tiberias to the Dead Sea, a journey that takes it from 210m (689 feet) below sea-level to 407m (1335 feet) below sea-level. The river is between 20m and 30m wide. The flow of the river is now much depleted and its water saline since significant amounts of water are diverted for irrigational uses. The river meanders across an incised flood plain (the 'Zor'), which flooded in 1991/92 as it used to in the past. The banks of the river itself are well vegetated with *Phragmites* beds and *Tamarix* woodland.

At a depth of 407m below sea-level the Dead Sea is the lowest place on the Earth's surface. It is land-locked, and is fed by the Jordan River and runoff from side wadis. With no outlet to the sea, intense evaporation concentrates its mineral salts making its waters hypersaline. However, with more water now being diverted for irrigation before it can enter the lake, its level is lowering significantly and its area is also contracting. Around 1920 the surface lay at 392m below sea-level and its area was 1050km^2; in 1991 the level had dropped to –407m, it had separated into two lakes, and the area had reduced to 660km^2.

Birds do not, or rather cannot, use the lake, except in periods of flood when a plume of fresh water floats on the surface around the inflowing rivers. Otherwise fish die on reaching the hypersaline water, and herons and egrets are attracted to the easy pickings on the shore. The 55km of Jordanian shoreline is typically arid and rocky, but at Suwayma, on the northern shore, freshwater springs form a locally important marsh. Elsewhere small delta fans, such as that at Wadi al Mujib, are growing out into the Dead Sea.

Southern Ghor: From the Dead Sea south to the Khunayzira escarpment, extensive irrigated agriculture now covers the valley floor in Ghor Safi and Ghor Fifa. Little of the original tropical vegetation remains, except for acacias. There is a small natural marsh at As Safi. Potassium salts are currently extracted from barren and birdless evaporation pans south of the Dead Sea.

Breeding birds of the Jordan River and Valley include Spur-winged Plover, Black Francolin, Smyrna Kingfisher, Pied Kingfisher, Swallow, Reed Warbler, Orange-tufted Sunbird, Dead Sea Sparrow and Desert Finch. Indian Silverbill and possibly Nightingale and Clamorous Reed Warbler may also breed. Wintering species include Penduline Tit. The Yarmuk estuary reservoir of the 1940s held wintering Pygmy Cormorant, Darter, Great Crested Grebe and various duck; however the first two species have not been recorded in Jordan since that date.

Wadi Araba

Wadi Araba is the southern continuation of the Jordan Valley and Dead Sea rift. It is 155km long and rises from sea-level at Aqaba to a watershed at 355m (1165 feet) at Jabal Risha, then drops to –300m (–984 feet) at its northern end. Located in a military zone Wadi Araba is one of the least spoilt areas of Jordan; but for the same reason it is also poorly explored for birds. There are mobile sand dunes, vegetated wadis, sabkhas, and extensive gravel plains dotted with acacias which rise up the alluvial fans into the hills. Pure stands of acacia woodland, resembling savannah forests, occur locally at the foot of the mountains. The widest part of the valley occurs where the Dana and Abu Khushayba tributaries join the main wadi. There are only a limited number of irrigated agricultural projects in Wadi Araba; a small oasis with pools and palms occurs south of Rahma, and several small springs flow at Fidan.

Typical birds include Bar-tailed Desert Lark, Hoopoe Lark and Dunn's Lark (possibly erratic) in the desert, and Little Green Bee-eater and Arabian Warbler in the acacias. Crowned and Spotted Sandgrouse are also resident in the area. Lappet-faced Vultures may have occurred in the past, and small numbers of Houbara Bustard may still be resident.

GULF OF AQABA

Until 1949, when the Israeli settlement of Eilat was founded, Aqaba was the sole town at the head of the Gulf of Aqaba. It was originally located amongst a natural palm oasis which thrived along a line of springs fringing the north-eastern shore of the Gulf. Today the fields, palm plantations and salt pans of Eilat prove more attractive to many of the birds that formerly visited Aqaba, but it should be said that much of the area's natural habitat now remains only around Aqaba. The 27km coastline is largely taken up by hotels, built-up areas and docks, but has a few relatively unspoilt, broad, reef-fringed bays remaining towards the Saudi border. The rich marine life of the coral reefs, the most northerly of the Red Sea-Indian Ocean, provides excellent opportunities for snorkelling and diving.

There are no islands in Jordanian waters and no shorebirds nest here. In addition, unlike Eilat, there is little irrigated agriculture to attract newcomers to colonise. The few breeding species in and around Aqaba are therefore mainly desert dwellers, but the 'exotic' Indian House Crow and Ring-necked Parakeet are exceptions. The local species are outnumbered many times over by non-breeding and migrant birds of prey, seabirds and passerines especially in spring and autumn.

Rift Margins

From Umm Qays in the north to Aqaba in the south, a distance of 370km, the low lying rift valley is separated from the nearby highlands by a rather narrow zone of deeply dissected uplands. The altitudinal range is great, with a relative relief of up to 1700m (5577 feet) from the highland rim to the shore of the Dead Sea.

Across this range of latitude and altitude there are large variations in climate, geology and vegetation, allowing the rift margins to be divided into four zones from north to south, each with their own distinct character.

In addition to the breeding birds listed below under separate sub-headings, vast numbers of migrating birds fly over the area each spring and autumn, including at least 250,000 raptors which follow the physiographic line of the escarpment.

Northern Rift Margins

In the north the Rift Margins are composed of limestone, are more vegetated, and have gentler slopes than farther south. There are many tributary wadis, some of which have been dammed, for example Wadi al Arab. In spring the slopes receive rainfall allowing grass and flowering plants to flourish.

The reed-lined *Yarmuk River* flows in a steep-sided tributary valley, and forms the north-western border of Jordan with Syria. Apart from the settlement of Al Himma, the area is a military zone with limited access. A pool at Birket al Rais is a small, but locally important spring-fed wetland site.

The highlight of the riverine avifauna of the Yarmuk valley is the very rare Brown Fish Owl, which may still be found here. Also likely to occur are Griffon Vulture, Sand Partridge, Smyrna Kingfisher, Long-billed Pipit, Blackstart, Clamorous Reed Warbler, Fan-tailed Warbler and Orange-tufted Sunbird.

Dead Sea or Central Rift Margins

Major wadis dissect the Moab Mountains which flank the eastern shores of the Dead Sea. From the north, these include Wadi Zerqa Ma'in, Wadi al Hidan/al Mujib, Wadi al Karak and Wadi al Hasa. The wadis cut through the Northern Steppes, often forming dramatic gorges and sheer cliffs. Perennial rivers flow down the wadis creating a narrow strip of lush vegetation, dominated by oleanders. There are hot springs at Hammamat Ma'in and Zara.

On the higher ground and at the heads of the wadis are found Mourning Wheatear, Long-billed Pipit and Blue Rock Thrush. On the barren rocky hillsides and gorges there is a contrasting avifauna of Griffon Vulture, Bonelli's Eagle, Long-legged Buzzard, Barbary Falcon, Lesser Kestrel, Tristram's Grackle, Alpine and Little Swifts, White-crowned Black Wheatear and Rock Sparrow.

Southern Rift Margins

The high relief, mountainous areas which separate Wadi Araba from the Sharra Highlands are some of the most dramatic and remote in Jordan. They are characterised by rocky wadis, gorges and sandstone cliffs, and access is rather limited. Wadi Dana is one of the most picturesque and unspoilt wadis. A flora of *Quercus calliprinus, Pinus halepensis, Cupressus sempervirens* and *Pistacia palestina* is found on the higher, rugged terrain, whilst lower down *Lygos raetum, Nerium oleander* and *Pistacia atlantica* are found interspersed with *Artemisia inculta*.

Farther south, Petra is world famous for its ancient Nabatean city. It has a vegetation of *Artemisia* steppe on its rocky plateaux, typical Saharo-Arabian desert wadi spreads, lush growth at springs, and remnants of formerly more extensive Mediterranean *Quercus/Juniperus* forest on mountain slopes.

Characteristic species of the higher terrain include: Scops Owl, Cuckoo, Hoopoe, Black-eared Wheatear, Orphean Warbler, Great Tit, Orange-tufted Sunbird, Pale Rock Sparrow, Rock Sparrow, Cretzschmar's Bunting, Tristram's Serin, and possibly Woodlark.

On the cliffs and lower slopes are Griffon Vulture, Short-toed Eagle, Bonelli's Eagle, Sooty Falcon, Barbary Falcon, Chukar, Sand Partridge, Hume's Tawny Owl, Pallid Swift, Desert Lark, Rock Martin, Blackstart, Mourning Wheatear, White-crowned Black Wheatear, Scrub Warbler, Brown Babbler, Tristram's Grackle, Fan-tailed Raven, Rock Sparrow, Sinai Rosefinch and House Bunting.

Aqaba Mountains

To the south of Gharandal the Rift Margin hills take on a totally different character due to the change in geology from younger sedimentary rocks to older granitic rocks. The desert climate is severe, and there is little vegetation on the bare, rocky slopes. The mountains reach a maximum height of 1592m (5223 feet) at Jabal Baqir, north-east of Aqaba. Access is very limited, except by using the wadis which divide the range into distinct peaks. The most important of these is the major through-route of Wadi al Yutum, which contains many isolated acacia trees, the typical vegetation of the area. During floods, the wadis carry large amounts of sediment from the hills westwards to the gravel fans of Wadi Araba.

Typical birds of the wadis include Little Green Bee-eater, Desert Lark, Blackstart, Hooded Wheatear, White-crowned Black Wheatear and Arabian Warbler. The high mountain birds are largely unknown, but may include Lammergeier, Sooty Falcon, Hume's Tawny Owl and possibly Lichtenstein's Sandgrouse.

Highlands

The highlands of Jordan separate the rift and its margins from the desert plains, and extend the length of the western part of the country. The uplands are dissected by incised wadis, which divide them into the historical areas known as Ajlun, Balqa, Moab, Edom and Sharra. Altitudes are considerably higher than those west of the rift, with the highest points in the Northern and Southern Highlands 1247m (4091 feet) and 1736m (5695 feet) respectively.

These areas receive Jordan's highest rainfall, and are the most richly vegetated in the country.

Northern Highlands or Ajlun-Balqa Highlands

The highlands of northern Jordan extend southwards from Umm Qays to the Amman National Park, and they have a typical Mediterranean climate and vegetation. Large areas are now agricultural land, planted with olives and crops, and only scattered remnants of the formerly typical climax woodland vegetation remain. Pine *Pinus halepensis* forests (as found at Ajlun, Dibbin and Zai) and evergreen oak *Quercus calliprinus* forest, or maquis, (for example at Zubiya Wildlife Reserve) occur on differing soils at high altitudes, mostly over 700m. Deciduous oak *Quercus ithaburensis* forests occur at a lower altitude. Non-forest vegetation of shrubs and bushes, known as garigue, is also extensive. The area is crossed by many lush, vegetated wadi systems which flow westwards and ultimately into the Dead Sea (for example the Zarqa River, Wadi Shu'ayb, Wadi as Sir etc.).

The highest points are 1247m at Jabal Umm ad Daraj, between Ajlun and Jarash, and 1103m north-west of Amman. The annual rainfall, falling mainly in winter, ranges from c250mm to 550mm.

The breeding avifauna includes many eastern Mediterranean species as well as some with Middle Eastern affinities: Short-toed Eagle, Sparrowhawk, Hobby, Turtle Dove, Syrian Woodpecker, Wren, Yellow-vented Bulbul, Blackbird, Upcher's Warbler, Spectacled Warbler, Sardinian Warbler, Lesser Whitethroat, Bonelli's Warbler, Spotted Flycatcher, Blue Tit, Great Tit, Orange-tufted Sunbird, Woodchat Shrike, Masked Shrike, Jay, Cretzschmar's Bunting and Black-headed Bunting. Merlin, Woodlark, Robin, Black Redstart, Finsch's Wheatear and various finches arrive in winter.

Northern Steppes

This broad zone separates the Northern Highlands and Dead Sea Rift Margins from the desert in the east, and has an undulating, low relief terrain. It is transitional in character and was formerly covered in steppe vegetation. There is a gradual increase in altitude from 500m in the north to 1000m south of Al Karak and Al Qatrana, and there is a corresponding change in the vegetation from grassland steppe to *Artemisia* brush steppe. The dominant plant species are *Poa sinaica* and the sedge *Carex pachystylis*, which provide an erosion-resistant root mat; the wormwood or sagebrush *Artemisia herba-alba* also occurs in the south. Little of this natural vegetation remains, and as rainfall decreases eastward from 250mm to

100mm p.a. arable land now gives way to grazing land. Unfortunately, high levels of grazing, extensive ploughing and some land misuse, have caused large areas to suffer from desertification and loss of plant cover. As defined here, the area extends from Irbid through Al Mafraq, Az Zarqa, Queen Alia International Airport and Madaba as far south as Al Karak.

Breeding birds include Little Owl, Calandra Lark, Short-toed Lark, Brown-necked Raven and probably Stone-curlew and Desert Finch. Other birds of the Rift Margin community (for example, Blackstart, Mourning Wheatear and Tristram's Grackle) can be seen on the western limit of the Steppes, especially where large wadis have cut deep into the steppe plateau. Birds of the Interior Deserts often reach their western limit in the east of this region especially where the steppe habitat has been degraded and the desert is advancing; these include Hoopoe Lark, Temminck's Horned Lark and Red-rumped Wheatear. The winter bird community is poorly known, but in addition to an influx of larks, finches and Corn Bunting, significant species such as Imperial Eagle, Houbara Bustard and Dotterel are presumed to be present.

The Al Khirba as Samra sewage stabilisation lagoons north-east of Az Zarqa lie in this area. They were inaugurated in 1985 and attract a large number of water birds, especially in autumn.

Sharra Highlands or Southern Highlands

A high altitude, steppic plain with moderate relief extends from Ash Shawbak south to Ras an Naqab. The highest point, at 1736m (5695 feet) lies in the west, and in the east the 1200m (3937 feet) contour arbitrarily separates this zone from the deserts of the Al Jafr Basin. Scrub and garigue vegetation is widespread on the higher ground, and remnants of evergreen oak and juniper forest can be found. The region is mainly undeveloped, but has some agriculture including apple orchards. A treeless, steppe vegetation occurs at lower altitudes in the Ash Shawbak and At Tafila plains. Annual rainfall ranges from 100mm to 315mm.

Typical bird species include Isabelline Wheatear and Spectacled Warbler, but the habitat is one of the least well explored.

Interior Deserts (The 'Badia')

The deserts of Jordan cover an enormous area extending from the highland foothills to the Syrian, Iraqi and Saudi borders, and they comprise some 80% of the country's total area. Although united by their harsh desert climate and vegetation type, in detail the character of the desert varies considerably as a function of the underlying rock types. The following subdivision is based broadly on geology and drainage basins.

Eastern Desert or Azraq Basin

The desert floor is typically either flint or limestone hammada, but a multitude of wadis (generally broad and with scrub vegetation) cross the area and drain inland towards the lowest point of the Azraq Basin at 505m (1657 feet). One exceptional wadi, Wadi al Butm, is lined with mature *Pistacia atlantica* (or 'butm') trees; no other wadi has such an abundance of native trees. Planted casuarina and eucalyptus trees provide cover at the Shaumari reserve headquarters. Isolated hills, wadi bluffs and rare gorges and cliffs provide the only rocky environments, for example the Wadi al Jilat gorge and the chalk cliffs at Dakhikiya.

The wadi vegetation is dominated by bushes and woody herbs of *Tamarix* sp., *Retama raetam*, *Artemisia herba-alba*, *Achillea fragrantissima* and *Atriplex halimus*, and these can form relatively luxuriant bushland. However, the cover is often reduced by over-grazing and it is only preserved in its climax state within the Shaumari Reserve.

Large mudflats, or qas, are concentrated on the northern boundary with the Basalt Desert, and these flood when there is sufficient runoff in wet winters. The largest qas of Qa' Khanna, Qa' Hibabiya and Qa' al Azraq are surrounded by expanses of herb vegetation. Today Qa' al Azraq provides a valuable bird habitat now that the marsh is dry, but it floods only in wet winters. Qa' al Azraq did flood in March to May 1990, April to June 1991 and December 1991 to April 1992, but not in 1992/3 or 1993/4. The desert wadis also flow briefly in flood conditions, and small pools can remain well into the spring.

Characteristic breeding bird species include Cream-coloured Courser, Temminck's Horned Lark, Hoopoe Lark, Thick-billed Lark, Desert Lark, Red-rumped Wheatear, Scrub Warbler, and possibly Houbara Bustard. The qa' margins hold breeding Greater Sand Plover, Kentish Plover and occasionally other water birds.

Basalt Desert or Al Harra Desert

The Basalt Desert of northern Jordan (known in Arabic as the Harrat as Sham) covers a vast area stretching from Syria to Saudi Arabia. The undulating, sparsely-vegetated landscape is dominated by lichen-covered basalt boulders of varying sizes, but there are volcanic hills, and in some places wadis have cut small gorges. There are many variations: in the south there are distinctive basalt-capped hills, and in the east large mudflats are common. In the west, where the rainfall is slightly higher, the original vegetation is grassland steppe, and a few hawthorn bushes remain at Jawa. Here, some areas have been cleared of boulders, and the silty soil produced wheat under irrigation for some years before salination caused them to be abandoned.

The altitude ranges from 1234m (4049 feet) near Bir al Abwan on the Syrian border, to only 505m (1657 feet) at Azraq. Rainfall varies from 150mm in the west to less than 50mm (true desert) in the east.

There are only rare pools of permanent fresh water within the Basalt Desert, but Ghadir Burqu', on the eastern limit of the basalt outcrop, is the site of a large permanent lake some 500m wide by 2km long. However, large amounts of the lake's water are pumped by the bedouin and it occasionally dries out.

Typical breeding species of the Basalt Desert include Long-legged Buzzard, Golden Eagle, Little Owl, Bar-tailed Desert Lark, Thick-billed Lark, Temminck's Horned Lark, Desert Wheatear, and Trumpeter Finch. Dark races of Desert Lark and Mourning Wheatear are also resident in this area. Remote areas may still hold Houbara Bustards, most likely in winter but possibly also breeding. Crane and Finsch's Wheatear are known to winter in this area; Black Vulture, Imperial Eagle, Dotterel, Black-bellied and Pin-tailed Sandgrouse are also predicted based on their occurrence in adjacent parts of Saudi Arabia. Dunn's Lark, desert Eagle Owl and Hume's Tawny Owl could also be resident on the same basis. Ghadir Burqu' is important to migrant ducks, waders, raptors and passerines.

Ar Ruwayshid Desert or North-eastern Limestone Plateau

In the so-called 'panhandle' north-east of the Basalt Desert, an undulating limestone and chert plateau extends to the Iraqi border. In addition to the hammada, there are many broad, shallow wadis, extensive mudflats, and in the north-east there is surprisingly some steppe grassland. In Jordan attempts are continually being made to use the desert for agriculture and the Ar Ruwayshid Desert is no exception. Earth dams collect flood water for irrigating wheat, and wells provide water for trial plots of fruit trees. The altitude ranges from 650m to 900m (2133 to 2953 feet) and at Ar Ruwayshid the annual rainfall is 77mm.

The avifauna of this area is similar to that of the Eastern Desert, with Long-legged Buzzard, Cream-coloured Courser, Little Owl, Bar-tailed Desert Lark, Hoopoe Lark, Thick-billed Lark, Lesser Short-toed Lark, Temminck's Horned Lark, Desert Wheatear and Brown-necked Raven.

Central Desert

The Central Desert region is crossed by the Desert Highway from Suwaqa south to Jurf ad Darawish. It is a low-relief desert of hammada and mudflats, and is drained by several scrub-lined wadis which eventually find their way through the rift margins into the Dead Sea. Large areas have been disturbed by open-cast phosphate mining, and there is some irrigated agriculture at Al Qatrana. (The avifauna of this region is summarised with that of the Al Jafr Basin, below).

Wadi as Sarhan

Part of the eastern border of Jordan follows Wadi as Sarhan, a major NW-SE feature in the Arabian Desert which eventually drains into Qa' al Azraq. In Jordan, the wadi-spreads of its western tributaries form broad, well vegetated, silt-filled strips which separate areas of limestone and flint hammada. Higher ground farther west consists of rolling hills, escarpments and more confined wadis. (This region's birds are also summarised with those of the Al Jafr Basin, below).

Al Jafr Basin

Like the Azraq Basin in the north, the Al Jafr Basin is a low-relief, enclosed basin fed by a number of broad, sparsely-vegetated wadis. To the north and east the basin is bounded by low escarpments which reach a height of 1430m (4692 feet). Jordan's most extensive qa' is at the lowest point of the basin, at 852m (2795 feet) above sea-level, but this qa' only rarely floods. Here, at Al Jafr, there is also a small settlement with some irrigated horticulture. The annual rainfall at Al Jafr is only 38mm, half that of Azraq.

The avifauna of the Central, Wadi as Sarhan and Al Jafr areas is very similar to the Eastern Desert with Cream-coloured Courser, Hoopoe Lark, Temminck's Horned Lark, Desert Wheatear, Red-rumped Wheatear, Scrub Warbler and Trumpeter Finch. Long-legged Buzzard and Brown-necked Raven are also found. The higher escarpments along the watersheds provide habitats for Mourning Wheatear and Desert Lark.

Al Mudawwara Desert

East of the mountainous Rum Desert, and south of the prominent Batn al Ghul escarpment, is a low-relief desert with isolated hills and low rocky mountains separated by broad, sandy wadis. Altitudes vary from 650m (2133 feet) to 1150m (3773 feet) and as the climate is distinctly arid little natural vegetation can grow. Wheat is grown using centre-pivot irrigation at Sahl as Suwwan and at Al Mudawwara.

The western part of this area holds some representatives from the Rum Desert fauna such as Sand Partridge, White-crowned Black Wheatear, Mourning Wheatear and Trumpeter Finch. However, bird densities become very low in the Jabal Khishsha area east of Al Mudawwara. The only residents appear to be Brown-necked Raven, Kestrel, Little Owl, Trumpeter Finch, Hoopoe Lark and Desert Wheatear. Across the border in Saudi Arabia, the remote Tubayq mountains retain a population of Lappet-faced Vultures.

Rum Desert, Southern Mountainous Desert or Hisma Basin

The Rum Desert covers an extensive area of wide sandy wadis and mudflats separating towering, sandstone mesas, as typified by Jabals Rum and Umm Ishrin. These are two of Jordan's highest mountain peaks, rising up to 800m (2625 feet) above the surrounding valley floors. The area extends from the Ras an Naqab escarpment south to the Saudi border. The exact profile of the mountains is controlled by the geology. The most dramatic cliffs are found where red sandstone is capped by white sandstone domes. More pyramidal peaks occur further east, formed in an overlying red sandstone formation which has better developed jointing.

The area is arid with rainfall of about 75mm p.a., but there is locally significant shrub vegetation, especially White Broom *Retama raetam* in the wadis. Vegetation on the high peaks is impoverished, but includes scattered Acacia and Juniper trees. Somewhat lusher vegetation grows locally along spring lines as in Wadi Rum.

Typical species of this dramatic habitat include Verreaux's Eagle, Sooty Falcon, Lammergeier (at least in the past), Long-legged Buzzard, Sand Partridge, Hume's Tawny Owl, Tristram's Grackle, White-crowned Black, Hooded and Mourning Wheatears, Scrub Warbler, Sinai Rosefinch and House Bunting. Migrant raptors and passerines also use the area.

Extensive irrigated agricultural complexes are located on the silt flats at Disi, north-east of Wadi Rum, and attract a variety of migrants including some wetland species.

Azraq Oasis

There are a few small springs around the perimeter of the Basalt Desert, but none so large or important as the Shishan (Qaisiyeh and Souda) and Druz (Aura and Mustadhema) springs at Azraq. These springs owe their existence to the Azraq depression being sufficiently low to naturally tap the aquifer which lies beneath the basalt hills to the north. The springs once used to flow water at a combined rate of some 7.5 million gallons per day (or 12.4 million cubic metres per year), and this allowed an extensive marsh of meadows, bushes and pools to develop around them. Its former glory and importance can be judged by quoting Dr Bryan Nelson, who wrote in 1973: 'The heart of the Azraq wetlands, its pools, run into open, meandering creeks which feed the deep, permanent marsh. This eventually surrenders to the edge lagoons with their seasonal stands of sedges and rushes'. Two settlements, trade routes, agriculture, palms, and planted casuarina and eucalyptus also grew up around the springs.

During the last ten years the area of permanent standing water at Azraq has sadly reduced to virtually nothing. Increasing amounts of water from the same underground aquifer that sources the springs are being pumped to Amman and siphoned off by local agricultural projects (see page 26). Since the springs ceased to flow in 1989, the previously lush marsh has become a dusty, parched wasteland with dried-out bushes and periodic fires. Today, transects across the area reveal the depressing sight of dried pools and marshes with mud-cracked and salt-encrusted surfaces. Apart from the ever-shrinking pools in the villages themselves, no wetland sites remain except for a small, recently-dug area of fish pools.

Surrounding the former wetland and several metres lower than it, a crescent-shaped qa' forms the lowest part of the Azraq-Sarhan rainwater catchment and floods in wet winters. On the margins of the barren qa' itself, salt-tolerant plants such as the succulent *Halocnemum* and the pink *Halopeplis* together with low, woody shrubs, form a steppe-like habitat.

The oasis was formerly the site of a rich wetland avifauna, but many of the breeding species of the 1960s, especially those dependent on marsh vegetation and open water, can no longer breed there. The following 20 species were lost as breeding species by 1993: Little Grebe, Little Bittern, Squacco Heron, Purple Heron, Mallard, Garganey, Marsh Harrier, Spur-winged Plover, White-tailed Plover, Little Ringed Plover, Water Rail, Moorhen, Baillon's Crake, Blue-cheeked Bee-eater and Savi's, Clamorous Reed, Great Reed, Reed, Moustached and Fan-tailed Warblers. Several additional species including Black-winged Stilt, Avocet and Collared Pratincole can still breed if the flooding of the qa' allows. Lesser Short-toed Lark and Rufous Bush Robin are less reliant on the wetland habitat and still occur around the oasis.

A large number of migrant and wintering wildfowl and waders also used to frequent the oasis, but these are now forced to rely on the flooded qa' for temporary habitat.

Conservation and Environmental Threats

The Jordanian countryside and its wildlife communities have undergone significant changes over the centuries and continue to be under threat from various activities. In recent years a proliferation of development projects has occurred with little regard to the environmental impact. A rapidly increasing population and an expansion of agricultural production have together seen the death of the Azraq wetland (see page 26). Wildlife hunting, a popular and traditional activity, has eventually taken its toll of the larger mammals and game species, and habitat destruction has been rife. Litter is also a growing eyesore, and pollution is a potential threat in the Gulf of Aqaba.

It is only during the past 20 years that steps have been taken to conserve this valuable and irreplaceable aspect of the country's heritage.

Long-term change is difficult to assess due to the paucity of historical data. As in many countries, in Jordan only a minority of the population have an awareness and understanding of their native animals, plants and birds. The first detailed studies, which form the baseline of our knowledge, were carried out by an international expedition in the 1960s. The Royal Society for the Conservation of Nature (RSCN) was established in Jordan in 1966, and nine years later the government delegated to it the responsibility for the enforcement of wildlife legislation including the establishment and running of wildlife reserves.

Today the RSCN administers six official Wildlife Reserves in Jordan, although a total of 12 are eventually planned:

Burqu' (planned) – Basalt/Ar Ruwayshid Desert
Zubiya – Northern Highlands
Rajil (planned) – Basalt/Eastern Desert
Azraq Wetland – Azraq Oasis
Shaumari – Eastern Desert
Mujib – Dead Sea Rift Margins/Northern Steppe
Abu Rukbah (planned) – Northern Steppe
Bayir (planned) – Wadi as Sarhan
Dana – Wadi Araba/Southern Rift Margins
Jarba (planned) – Southern Highlands
Jabal Masadi (planned) – Wadi Araba/Southern Rift Margins/ Southern Highlands
Wadi Rum – Rum Desert

In addition to these Wildlife Reserves, 18 Grazing Reserves cover a further 20,000 hectares and provide some protection against overgrazing.

The 'National Parks' of Jordan should not be confused with other parks of that status in other countries. This term is used rather misleadingly in Jordan for recreational parks with the provision of restaurants and play areas.

Hunting

There is no doubt that the diversity of animals in Jordan and especially of grazing species and carnivores, was formerly more varied than at present. The abundance of rock art and mosaics depicting animals, presumably prey species, suggests that Ostrich, gazelle *Gazella* sp., Arabian Oryx *Oryx leucoryx*, Nubian Ibex *Capra ibex*, Syrian Wild Ass (Onager) *Equus hemionus* and Asiatic Lion *Felis leo persica* were widespread in the distant past. There is also historical evidence that Syrian Bear *Ursus syriacus* and Fallow Deer *Dama dama* were present in the Northern Highlands, and crocodiles used to inhabit the Jordan River.

The hunting of gazelle and other wildlife in the desert dates back thousands of years. The use of 'kites' or funnel-shaped, stone-built traps is well documented, especially in the Basalt Desert. These traps were strung out for vast distances to intercept the migration paths of the gazelle.

It was the advent of automatic weapons and motorised hunting that decimated the larger mammals and birds. The Ostrich was extinct as early as 1939, and the populations of gazelle, still seen in their thousands in the 1940s, were reduced soon after. The numbers of Houbara have also declined significantly. The large carnivores were always present in Jordan in low densities, and they suffered greatly during the last 25 years. The Leopard *Panthera pardus* was last reported in the Rift Margins in 1987, but may still survive there. The Asiatic Lion has been extinct for over a hundred years, and the last Cheetah *Acinonyx jubatus* was shot in 1962. It is probable that the Asiatic Jackal *Canis aureus*, Wolf *Canis lupus* and Striped Hyena *Hyaena hyaena* remain in small numbers.

Wildfowl shooting used to be a very popular sport at Azraq. In the 1960s an annual bag of 2500-3000 was recorded, or to put it in context, just 1% of the ducks passing through Azraq in any winter at that time. Most shooting took place during the early morning from hides on the fringes of the marsh.

Current hunting laws in Jordan date from 1973 and are under the control of the RSCN. They are comprehensive and include a complete ban on automatic guns and shooting from hides or vehicles – methods which had been most destructive in the past.

Hunting is not permitted east of the Hejaz Railway, except under licence from the RSCN. West of the railway, however, in the Highlands, Rift Margins and Rift Valley shooting of certain species is allowed, with a quota allotted for each hunting trip. For example, Chukar and Sand Partridge can be hunted between 15 September and 30 November; but with only three kills permitted each trip. Other permitted quarry include geese, ducks, sandgrouse, Quail, Turtle Dove, larks, Coot, Snipe, Woodcock, thrush and Skylark.

Falconry is a traditional hunting method which is still carried out in many Arab countries, particularly in the Arabian Peninsula. In Jordan today this sport is not that prevalent, and appears to be exclusively exercised by some bedouin tribal chiefs. Visiting hunters and falconers, however, do have an impact by trapping passage birds of prey at sites such as Ghadir Burqu' and Al Jafr.

Deforestation

Historically Jordan used to be renowned for its forests, but today these are much reduced in area, and remnants of ancient forest remain only in the remotest and most inaccessible corners of the Kingdom. The main causes for this deforestation are felling for wood, clearance for crops and prevention of regeneration by overgrazing.

It has been said that the Biblical 'wilderness' probably refers to the forested highland areas of Jordan in the 2nd and 3rd millennia before the Classic Period. By that time much of the easily cultivated land would have been farmed, but subsequently the area of forest would have decreased only slowly, largely due to charcoal burning.

The period from 1908-17 is often quoted as one of the most destructive periods for the Jordanian forests. The Turks carried out massive felling operations to fuel their Hejaz Railway which crossed Jordan on its route from Damascus (Syria) to Medina (Saudi Arabia). There was apparently enough woodland in the Sharra Highlands to justify building a branch line from Unayza to Ash Shawbak to transport the cut trees.

WATER

Water is a priceless resource in Jordan, both for man and for the natural environment. Underground aquifers are of the utmost importance, as are the winter rains which fill the country's reservoirs. However, an ever increasing demand has placed immense pressure on these limited resources, especially on the aquifers which are not being recharged.

The recent drying out of the Azraq Oasis is a great loss to the biodiversity of the region, and has occurred as a result of the over-exploitation of its underground water source. The water is pumped to both domestic and industrial users in Amman, as well as from 600 wells on local farms.

Small-scale pumping started in the 1960s, and a contraction of the wetland area was noted even then. For a period in 1980 and 1981 water was pumped directly from the Shishan springs. On this occasion it was environmental concerns that forced the pumping to be abandoned. The overflow from the spring pools had virtually ceased, but soon reverted to its previous rates when pumping stopped.

In 1981 a well field of 15 boreholes was constructed a few kilometres north of Azraq. Using this method it was hoped that a higher rate of abstraction could be achieved without affecting the springs. For about a year the discharge from the springs was stable; then in the mid-1980s flow rates began to diminish year by year as the level of the water table fell dramatically. This was apparently not only due to the high rates of pumping to Amman, but also to the ever-increasing amount of water which was being abstracted for local agriculture.

For short periods in 1986 and 1987 the Druz springs stopped flowing, but in 1988 the flow dried up completely at Druz, and in 1989 a similar situation occurred at Shishan.

During 1989-92 little, if any, water flowed from the spring pools to feed life into the marshes. The only permanent standing water during this period lay outside the Wetland Reserve and constituted a limited area of fishpools and a small marsh fed by an artesian borehole which had been allowed to flow since 1963. Even this latter borehole had ceased to flow by 1994 as the water table continued to fall.

DESERT

The marginal lands or semi-deserts (known in Arabic as the 'badia') are under great pressure. Some areas have suffered greatly from overgrazing by sheep and goats as, in addition to the now-static bedouin herds, flocks are transported into the marginal grazing land and watered by truck. Elsewhere, unnecessary ploughing of the desert to gain ownership rights causes the breakdown of the soil layer. Bushes are cut for fuel, vehicles destroy plant cover, and opencast mines extract phosphates – these all cause further damage to the fragile desert habitat. In an attempt to allow plant cover to be maintained, grazing is controlled in 18 grazing reserves within Jordan. However, attempts to halt grazing in the Azraq Grazing Reserve (including Wadi al Butm) have not been successful, and even this area now holds many flocks and bedouin camps.

Reservoirs and Sewage Works

By way of positive changes, the building of dams has created several reservoirs which collect river water flowing into the Jordan Valley. Although some habitat may be lost in the flooding process, the addition of wetland habitats in otherwise arid areas is some compensation. Although potentially good habitats, disturbance by shooting and damage by pollution sometimes decreases their attractiveness.

An extensive sewage plant on the desert fringe near Az Zarqa now offers a refuge for migrants crossing the Syrian Desert, and must to some extent fill the niche formerly offered by Azraq. Sympathetic management regimes have been proposed for this site, which could help attract many more birds. A similar sewage treatment plant provides valuable wetland habitat for migrants at Aqaba.

Tourism

In recent years Jordan has become a popular tourist destination. Numbers have increased from 0.7 million in 1975 to 2.6 million in 1990, and are set to increase further now that the border with Israel is open. Aqaba is the principle destination, and further hotels planned for the south beaches will inevitably intrude into relatively unspoilt areas. A trip to Wadi Rum or Petra is now included on most tours, and the pressure of tourism on some sites is being felt. Care will have to be taken to prevent over-exploitation from destroying the sense of wilderness the tourists come to see. The habitat in the immediate vicinity of the Rum settlement is now criss-crossed with four-wheel drive tracks, and the settlement itself does mar the empty landscape. Vast wilderness areas do exist in the vicinity of both Petra and Wadi Rum, however, and much of Jordan still remains well off the tourist trail.

A BIRDWATCHING SITES GUIDE

Jordan Valley and Dead Sea

WADI SHU'AYB AND SHUNA RESERVOIR

Wadi Shu'ayb can be reached either directly from As Salt, or from Wadi as Sir, Mahis and then following the tributary wadi of Wadi Bir as Sabil. There are several convenient stops on the way down both wadis, including public picnic sites, but as there are military camps be selective where you stop in the lower part. Higher up, there are oak woods with Syrian Woodpecker and Jay. On the rocky slopes with scrub and scattered trees you can find Cretzschmar's Bunting, Blue Rock Thrush, Sardinian Warbler and Red-rumped Swallow, as well as three species of shrike – Great Grey, Woodchat and Masked. The river is lined by oleander and reeds, and here it is possible to see Smyrna Kingfisher, Orange-tufted Sunbird, Yellow-vented Bulbul, Cetti's Warbler and Great Tit. Spanish Sparrows breed in colonies in the tallest poplars. Raptors often fly over in spring, using the wadi as a north-easterly route off the Jordan Valley. In winter, the area is visited by northern European species such as Black Redstart, Robin and Chaffinch.

Before reaching the Jordan Valley, the river enters the small Shuna Reservoir. Access is via the sign-posted Tourist Park. The reservoir usually floods in winter and spring, but dries out during the hot summer when the water is taken off for agriculture. A few Coot and ducks use the reservoir in winter, along with rare Great Crested Grebe. Little Swift and resident Swallows also assemble in cool weather. In spring, water levels usually decline to produce a muddy habitat suitable for many herons, waders, gulls and terns. Breeding birds include Spur-winged Plover and possibly Pied Kingfisher. Migrants can be found in the bushes of the Park.

KAFRAYN RESERVOIR

Kafrayn is a large, deep reservoir near the bottom of the road from Na'ur to the Dead Sea. At the military checkpoint, turn off right taking the road up the Jordan Valley. After 3km, turn right by a small bridge and a derelict hut. A marshy and bushy area between the road and the dam has breeding Reed Warblers, and is often productive for migrant warblers, shrikes etc. It is also a good place for Roller, Red-rumped Swallow, Graceful Warbler and Great Grey Shrike. Indian Silverbills nested here in 1990. Passage raptors can also pass over this site in good numbers.

From the dam, access is along a track on the west side of the reservoir as far as a muddy area at the northern end. Although this reservoir could have great potential, it suffers from excessive shooting, and any waterbirds soon become rather wary. A few Pied Kingfishers are resident. In winter, it can hold Great White, Little and Cattle Egrets, plus Great Crested and Little Grebes, Coot, and a few ducks. A vagrant Pomarine Skua was once seen in November. The barren hillsides hold Sand Partridge, Desert Lark and Blackstart.

SUWAYMA

A productive area of natural pools, marsh and *Tamarix* scrub occurs along a line of freshwater springs on the north-eastern shore of the Dead Sea. It lies 1km west of Suwayma Resthouse, in front of the funfair.

There is a small, but easily accessible colony of Dead Sea Sparrows in the *Tamarix*, and a few pairs of Spur-winged and Kentish Plovers breed by the pools. A wide variety of migrants can be concentrated at this site in spring, with herons, waders (including Greater Sand Plover and once a Jack Snipe), pipits, wagtails (including Citrine Wagtail) and warblers. This is also a good spot for Desert Finch, which may breed nearby. Winter visits can turn up Shelduck, and occasionally a single Greater Flamingo; ducks gather on the freshwater outflow of the Jordan River when it is in flood.

Dead Sea Shore

A new road follows the shore of the Dead Sea south for 20km (and will eventually join with the Wadi Araba road), but a military checkpoint beyond the Dead Sea Hotel only allows access to the southern sector until four o'clock. The specialities of this area are Brown Babbler, Tristram's Grackle, Sand Partridge, Fan-tailed Raven, Blackstart and White-crowned Black Wheatear, and it should be possible to see all of these from the roadside or by wandering up one of the side wadis. The lush vegetation by the Zara hot springs is worth investigating for resident birds and migrants, but the area is popular with the locals on Fridays.

With a military pass and a four-wheel-drive vehicle (at time of writing), it is possible to reach the mouth of Wadi al Mujib. Here, House Bunting, Little Green Bee-eater, and Sinai Rosefinch can be seen at the northern limit of their ranges. The surrounding barren, rocky hillsides are one of the best places in Jordan to see the elusive Hooded Wheatear. Smyrna Kingfisher and other water-birds make use of the fresh water, while Grey Herons pick out the fish that die on entering the Dead Sea.

Other Jordan Valley Sites

Access is not straightforward, and there are many army checkpoints. In general, the closer you get to the Jordan River the more difficult it gets to proceed. It is not surprising therefore that the birdwatching sites of this area are little known.

Smyrna Kingfisher, Swallow and Cattle Egret are resident. In winter, one cultivated area west of South Shuna (Ash Shuna al Janubiyya) has produced: Dead Sea Sparrow (flocks of up to 100), Spanish Sparrow, Skylark and Water Pipit.

Further north, Pella (known locally as Tabaqat Fahil) is famous for its ruins, but nearby wadis, streams and trees can be explored for birds. It is also possible to explore up the Zarqa River from Dayr Alla. Behind North Shuna (Ash Shuna ash Shamaliyya) is the Wadi al Arab Dam, and east of Waqqas is the Wadi Ziglab Dam.

Wadi Araba

In theory, the recently-built 'military road' gives access to the broad rift valley that runs from Aqaba to the Dead Sea. South of As Safi the area is patrolled by the army. Be very cautious at all times, and under no circumstances stray west of the road (despite what the maps say, the border fence is as close as 100m in places). Further north access is easier.

A military pass (*tasriya*) is essential to drive along Wadi Araba between Al Karak and Aqaba. This pass can be easily obtained in Aqaba (on Mut'a Street, behind the Al Amira Haya Hospital), or east of Al Karak (turn west off the King's Highway, 1km north of the main Route 35-50 junction near the Prince Ali Hospital).

Wadi an Numira

Some 4km north of the Potash Works, Wadi an Numira leads back into the hills through a dramatic, narrow gorge with a huge, suspended block trapped high above the small stream. There is a track leading off the main road north of the bridge over the wadi. White-crowned Black Wheatear, Blackstart and Rock Martin are amongst the resident species, and Little Green Bee-eaters occur immediately north of the Potash Works.

As Safi

The extensive irrigated agriculture of the Southern Ghor has a bird community dramatically different from that of Wadi Araba to the south, and it is a largely unexplored migrant trap. There are also small marshes at As Safi, such as those 6km south of the main bridge over the major wadi, and just west of the main road. Penduline Tit, Reed Bunting and Dead Sea Sparrow have been seen here in winter.

Fidan

Some 140km north of Aqaba, a tarmac road heads off east towards the Rift Margin foothills at Fidan, giving relatively easy access to the Wadi Araba avifauna. It is essential to get explicit military permission from Aqaba (see map on page 31); however, even this may not preclude problems with local army officers.

The first part of this road crosses flat desert (Wadi Abu Dubana) which holds Desert Wheatear, Scrub Warbler, Bar-tailed Desert Lark, Hoopoe Lark and Dunn's Lark (the latter has been observed in at least 1990 and 1994). Spotted and Crowned Sandgrouse are also a possibility, as there are drinking pools in the area. Further on, beside low hills (definitely avoid the military camp on the left!), acacias hold Little Green Bee-eater, Arabian Warbler, Brown Babbler, Great Grey Shrike and Orange-tufted Sunbird. The more rocky areas (for example, Jabal Hamra Fidan) are habitat for Sand Partridge, Desert Lark and Blackstart. Passage raptors, mainly Steppe Buzzards, can pass over in considerable numbers in spring and autumn. There are also several lush, marshy springs in this area, where Dead Sea Sparrows were seen in December 1989. The tarmac road ends at Qurayqira farm, which can be worth a look for White Storks and other migrants. From here, it is possible to head north-west on a track to the incised part of Wadi al Fidan, but a four-wheel-drive vehicle is required to continue east to the old copper mines at Feinan, and then up Wadi Dana (see page 34).

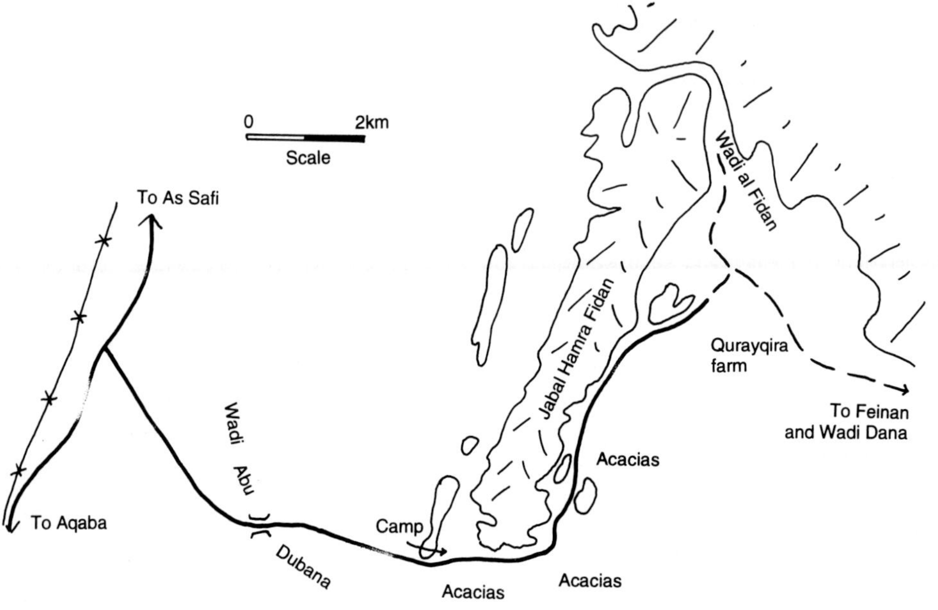

Gulf of Aqaba

Aqaba

Although Aqaba lies adjacent to Eilat at the head of the Gulf of Aqaba, it remains virtually unvisited by birdwatchers, and here you will have no choice but to find your own birds. Although the same variety of birds must pass over both Eilat and Aqaba, many vagrants are still waiting to be seen on the Jordanian side of the gulf. Although the situation may well change, be aware that the military and even the locals are not used to birdwatchers and their activities.

At least two areas have proved good for migrants (although there could be many more). One of these is in the old palms and irrigated smallholdings which stretch from the Ayla archaeological site south towards the port, including the area around Aqaba Fort. View from the pavement and various tracks. The other good area is in the undeveloped ground with scattered palms inland from the hotels, including the traffic islands and road-side bushes on the circular road to the Hippic Club, a small plantation and beyond.

Virtually any Western Palearctic migrant could turn up, but look out for warblers, pipits, wagtails, buntings, nightingales, shrikes, Wryneck, Bee-eater, Rufous Bush Robin, Golden Oriole, Rüppell's Warbler, Bonelli's Warbler and Spanish Sparrow. Rarer species include Corncrake, Namaqua Dove, Blue-cheeked Bee-eater, White-cheeked Bulbul and River Warbler. A few birds of prey do fly over, and more follow the ridge of mountains behind the town, but the main flow of birds in this region hugs the Israeli side of the Gulf of Aqaba until north of the town.

Resident species around Aqaba include Indian House Crow, Ring-necked Parakeet, Little Green Bee-eater, Brown Babbler, Tristram's Grackle

Aqaba

Palm trees at Aqaba (Jill Andrews)

Wadi Araba

South Shuna, Jordan Valley

Wadi Shu'ayb

Salt-encrusted rocks, Dead Sea

The Dead Sea from Mukawir

The Jordan River at Damiya

Wadi al Mujib

The mouth of Wadi al Mujib

Wadi Dana

High ground above Wadi Dana

Petra

Sharra uplands

Jabal Khishsha

Aqaba Mountains

Oak woodland, north of Ajlun

Dibbin Forest

Amman National Park

Wadi al Butm

Jabal Umm Ishrin

Wadi Rum

Qasr al Kharana

Flint desert, Thulaythuwat hills

Basalt-capped hills at Qattafi, east of Tell Qorma

Ghadir Burqu'

Basalt boulder fields, south-east of As Safawi

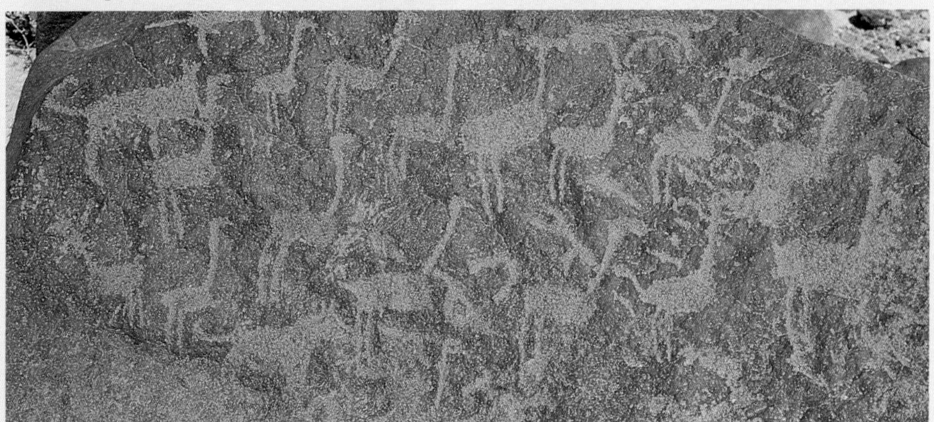

Rock art, Tell Qorma

Azraq marshes in the 1960s (Bryan Nelson)

The former marshes, Azraq Wetland Reserve, September 1994

The flooded qa', Azraq, April 1991

and Barbary Falcon. Few of the migrants stay to breed, but Sooty Falcon occurs rarely in summer.

A recent addition to the Aqaba birdwatching sites is the sewage treatment plant adjacent to the Israeli border. This can at present be visited only with military permission, but things may change. The plant was established in 1987, but there are already extensive irrigated palms in the vicinity.

The best site for seawatching appears to be the jetty of the Aquamarina Hotel, as it offers a clear view in all directions. The optimum time is probably in the first few hours after daybreak, as the light gets progressively more difficult for observing birds towards the afternoon. Although Israeli observations tend to suggest that the seabirds should be more easily seen off Aqaba than Eilat, when watching from Jordan the opposite seems to be the case – presumably they must be somewhere in between!

Most migrating seabirds track on a northerly course, which tends to take them towards Eilat. Scan from the direction of Fara'un Island right towards Eilat town – not only over the water, but also higher against the mountains (as birds often return higher). Other seabirds feed along the Aqaba shore and around the dock area, and during the day there are often flocks of ducks resting far out on the sea.

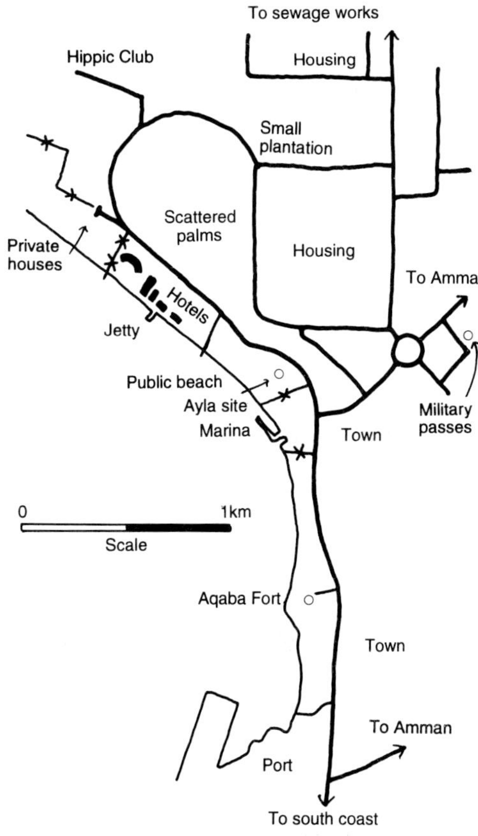

Of the seabirds, Black-headed Gull, Lesser Black-backed Gull and Common Tern are the most easily seen. Gull-billed Tern, Caspian Tern, Sandwich Tern, and Little Tern also occur fairly frequently. Rarities include Crested Tern, Bridled Tern (mainly in July-August), and White-cheeked Tern. Of the other gulls White-eyed Gull is the most regular visitor, with up to 12 present in recent years. Yellow-legged Gulls and Slender-billed Gull can also be seen. Cory's Shearwater is fairly regular, but Sooty Shearwater and Brown Booby cannot be guaranteed. Arctic, Pomarine and the rarer Long-tailed Skua can be seen on spring passage. Whilst seawatching, it is worth looking out for migrating herons, raptors, waders and passerines, which often fly low over the sea to make their first landfall at Aqaba. Green-backed Heron and Western Reef Heron have landed on the piers, and waders land on some of the beaches when they are sufficiently quiet.

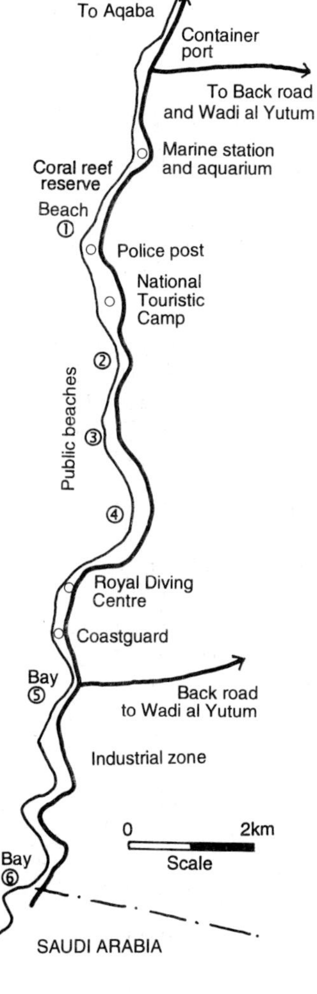

Aqaba South Coast

South of the Container Port, towards the Saudi border, there are several bays ①-⑥ good for roosting gulls, terns and waders (especially early in the morning), and promontories good for seawatching. Amongst the commoner gulls and terns, it is possible to see White-eyed and Slender-billed Gulls. Cory's Shearwater and Bridled Tern have been seen from the South Coast. Other interesting species seen along the shore include Western Reef Heron, and White-tailed, Caspian and Greater Sand Plovers.

There is cover for migrants at the Marine Science Station and Aquarium, and at the Royal Diving Centre. The latter site is excellent for snorkelling as well. There are single records each of Namaqua Dove and Isabelline Shrike at the Diving Centre. Migrating passerines can often be seen on seawatches.

The new 'back road' from the industrial zone and container port to Wadi al Yutum crosses some apparently barren gravel fans. Preliminary exploration of the acacia-lined wadis has revealed at least Little Green Bee-eater, Arabian Warbler and Hooded Wheatear.

Dead Sea Rift Margins

There is access from the King's Highway to all the major wadis flowing into the Dead Sea between Madaba and Al Karak. The three following routes offer good birdwatching opportunities:

(a) the road from Madaba to the hot spring resort of Hammamat Ma'in in Wadi Zerqa Ma'in.

(b) the road from the Wadi al Wala bridge down to Wadi al Hidan. This road has a dead end, but about half way back there is access north to the ruins and viewpoint at Mukawir, and from there it is possible to return along a ridge to the King's Highway at Lib. From Mukawir there are four-wheel-drive tracks down to the Dead Sea and Hammamat Ma'in.

(c) where the King's Highway crosses Wadi al Mujib, there is a viewpoint on the northern edge of the wadi (good for Griffon Vulture fly-bys). There is also potential to explore in the wadi bottom; this is easier to the east of the bridge.

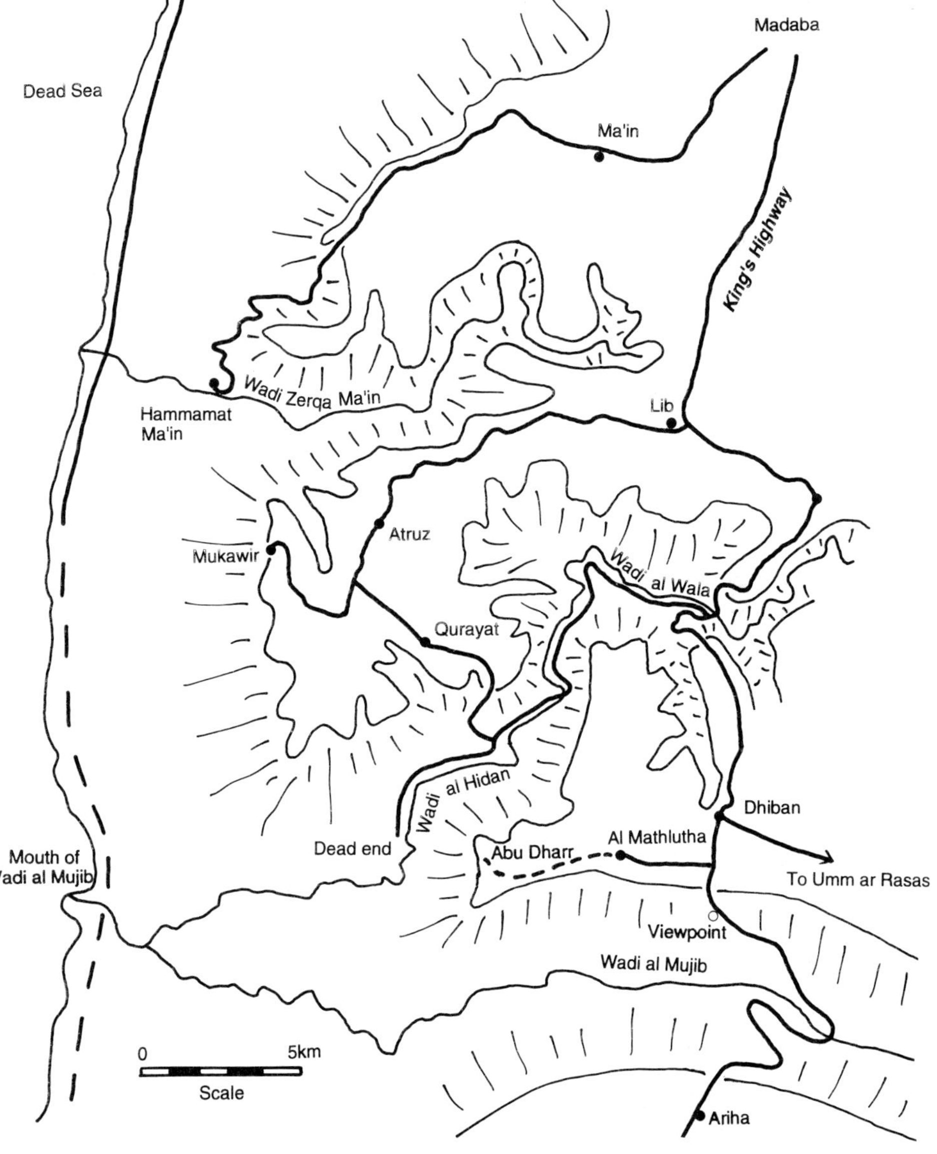

Resident birds of prey that can be seen over the hills, on cliffs, or in gorges include Griffon Vulture, Long-legged Buzzard, Bonelli's Eagle and Barbary Falcon. Egyptian Vulture and Lesser Kestrel are also present in summer, and large numbers of raptors pass over on spring migration. Alpine and Little Swifts, Rock Martin, and Tristram's Grackle can also be seen in the above habitats. Fan-tailed Ravens are a feature at Mukawir, but Brown-necked Ravens are also present.

The barren, rocky hillsides are habitat for Chukar, Sand Partridge, Roller, Desert Lark, Red-rumped Swallow, Blackstart, Mourning Wheatear, Blue Rock Thrush, Scrub Warbler and Rock Sparrow. A good place for Long-billed Pipit is where the King's Highway cuts through Wadi al Wala, as is the area of steep slopes west of Ma'in before the steep descent to Hammamat Ma'in. Lesser Kestrel and Woodchat Shrike also breed here. Woodlark, Black Redstart and Finsch's Wheatear can be found on this terrain in winter, particularly along the Lib to Mukawir road. Calandra Larks and Skylarks winter in the stubble fields of the plateaux (for example west of the village of Ma'in, and south of Dhiban), and a few Calandra Larks remain to breed.

Cetti's Warbler and Smyrna Kingfisher can be found in Wadi al Wala, and there are also Spanish Sparrow colonies in poplars there. All of these vegetated wadis are attractive to migrants, and in winter there are additional species such as Grey Wagtail, Bluethroat, Robin and Dunnock.

Southern Rift Margins

Wadi Dana

Wadi Dana is one of the most dramatic and unspoilt wadis in the Southern Rift Margins, and it is a reserve of the RSCN. The surrounding hills reach 1500m, and hold a rich and distinctive, high altitude avifauna. The wadi itself runs down to Wadi Araba, and contains a range of habitats which can only be reached on foot or by four-wheel drive. There is an official campsite, and several viewpoints on the northern rim overlooking the wadi. The camp is signposted, and is reached by taking the quarry road north and then west from Ar Rashadiyya cement works. There is a gate at the guard-house, before the road descends to the campsite.

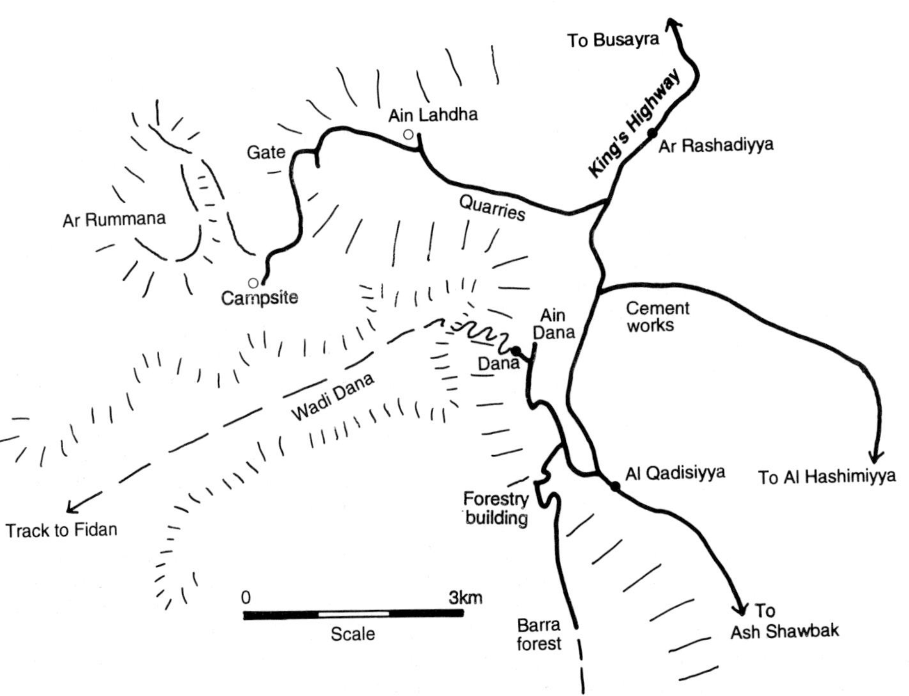

Barra Forest contains a habitat of open oak and juniper woodland on the south side of the wadi. Turn off left 1km down the Al Qadisiyya to Dana village road, and then left again at the Department of Forestry building to reach the forest.

On spring visits, it should be possible to see the local breeding birds, such as Chukar, Cuckoo, Hoopoe, Desert Lark, Rock Martin, Black-eared Wheatear, Orphean Warbler, Orange-tufted Sunbird, Fan-tailed Raven, Tristram's Grackle and Rock Sparrow. Several drinking pools have been provided in the vicinity of the campsite, and in dry periods these prove a great attraction for the local birds, especially Sinai Rosefinch. Tristram's Serins are resident on the wooded slopes of Barra Forest, and also adjacent to the tarmac road down to Dana village; Cretzschmar's Buntings are summer visitors to these same areas, and Pale Rock Sparrow was found breeding in 1994. Woodlarks have been heard singing on the high land to the north. Eagle Owl, Hume's Tawny Owl, and Scops Owls (in summer only) can be heard at night in the vicinity of the camp.

Resident birds of prey include Griffon Vulture, Bonelli's Eagle and Barbary Falcon, with Short-toed Eagle also present in summer. A major raptor migration route passes over Wadi Dana in the spring, with probably hundreds of thousands of birds (mainly Steppe Buzzard) involved. As many as 20 species of raptor (resident and migrant) can be seen on spring days. Passerine migrants also stop off in the wooded areas and wadis.

With a four-wheel-drive vehicle, it is possible to drive from Dana village down a very steep track to the wadi bottom, and then to Feinan, Fidan, and Wadi Araba. In the lower wadi, there are Hooded Wheatear, Blackstart, Cetti's Warbler, Scrub Warbler and Brown Babbler; Hume's Tawny Owl is also present.

Petra

The world-famous antiquities of Petra are a must from an archaeological viewpoint, but the well-used tracks also allow easy access into the mountains of the Southern Rift Margins. Approach is on foot (or horse) from the Resthouse through the Siq to the Amphitheatre. After this, exploration can be made in various directions:

(a) to the High Place and descending via Wadi al Farasa,
(b) to Ad Dayr (the Monastery), with views down to Wadi Araba, and stopping off at the Qattar ad Dayr spring, and
(c) the bushes and spring in Wadi as Siyyagh.

Longer walks for the more adventurous explorer, for which a guide is recommended, are to the spring and oasis at Sabra, and the mountain peak of Jabal al Harun.

The area around Al Bayda (or Little Petra), 9km to the north of the Petra Resthouse, is also worthy of exploration, as is the road north from there to Siq Umm al Hiran. This is signposted to Wadi Araba, but only four-wheel-drive vehicles can go that far at present.

The main attraction at Petra is the resident and fairly common Sinai Rosefinch, which can be most easily seen in the Siq, and en route to Ad Dayr (frequently drinking at the Qattar ad Dayr spring). For a chance of hearing or glimpsing the other Petra speciality – Hume's Tawny Owl – it is necessary to stay at the Corinthian Tomb (one of the Royal Tombs), or try the Siq area as night falls, and then be prepared to walk out with the aid of a torch.

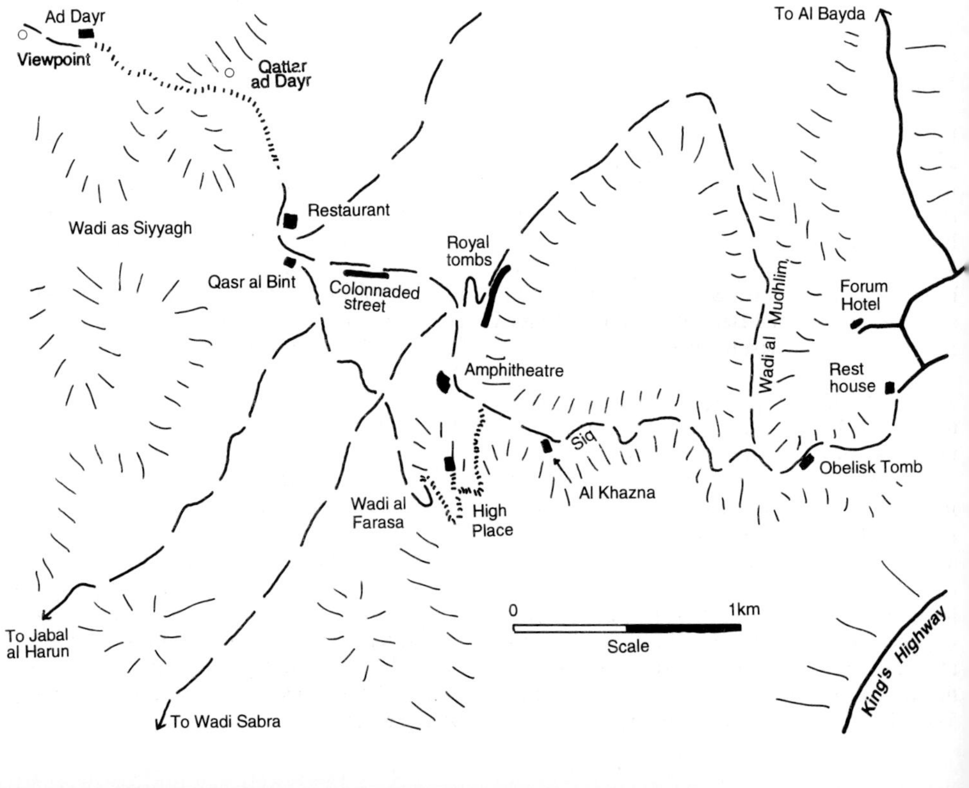

Other typical breeding birds of the Petra area include Bonelli's Eagle, Sooty Falcon, Barbary Falcon, Pallid Swift, Rock Martin, Blackstart, Mourning and White-crowned Black Wheatears, Scrub Warbler, Brown Babbler, Fan-tailed Raven, Tristram's Grackle, Rock Sparrow and House Bunting. The majority of raptors that pass over Eilat and Aqaba subsequently use the thermals along the Rift Margin mountains, and pass over Petra in large numbers. The best observation points are at Ad Dayr, and near the Restaurant area. The list of migrants, seen particularly in spring, is impressive; they can drop in anywhere, but especially in the vegetated wadis and near any trace of water. A few Tristram's Serins have been seen in winter, often accompanying Goldfinch flocks.

Northern Highlands

Wadi as Sir Area

The closest wadis to western Amman are Wadi as Sir and Wadi ash Shita, and both are easily reached from Bayder Wadi as Sir. A road runs down Wadi as Sir to the ruins of Iraq al Amir, whilst an alternative route follows its southern ridge to Abu as Sous and then down into Wadi ash Shita, as far as Al Bahhath if you choose.

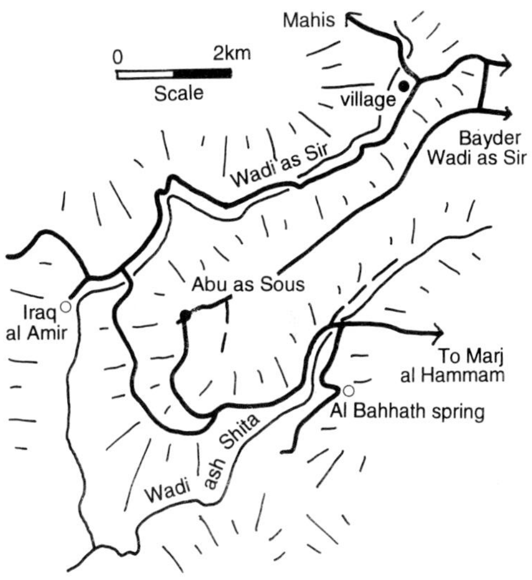

On the ridges, there are remnants of the original oak forests, some pine plantations, and many olive orchards amongst the agricultural areas (for example, either side of Abu as Sous). The following species breed in these more wooded areas: Collared Dove, Palm Dove, Turtle Dove, Hoopoe, Syrian Woodpecker, Olivaceous Warbler, Lesser Whitethroat, Spotted Flycatcher, Blackbird, Great Tit, Woodchat Shrike, Masked Shrike, Jay, Greenfinch, Goldfinch, Cretzschmar's Bunting and Black-headed Bunting.

In the wadi bottoms, pomegranates and vegetables are grown adjacent to the perennial streams. The flowing water and the fringing Oleander scrub attract Smyrna Kingfisher, Yellow-vented Bulbul, Rufous Bush Robin, Cetti's Warbler, Graceful Warbler and, in particular, Orange-tufted Sunbird. There are Spanish Sparrow colonies in the stands of poplars, and Bee-eater and Red-rumped Swallow may also nest in the valleys.

The more rocky slopes with low shrubs above the streams hold breeding Kestrel, Chukar, Little Owl, Crested Lark, Long-billed Pipit, Black-eared Wheatear, Blue Rock Thrush, Sardinian Warbler, Rock Sparrow and Linnet. Desert Lark, Blackstart and Scrub Warbler can be found in the more arid habitat in the lower reaches of both wadis.

Many passerine migrants frequent these rich feeding areas in both spring and autumn. Birds of prey also fly overhead, and some roost overnight in the more wooded areas. Winter visitors include Water Rail, Kingfisher and Hawfinch.

Amman National Park

This is a good place for migrants, breeding, and winter birds close to Amman, and there is plenty of scope for walking and exploration. The so-called National Park, which is actually a recreational park, is situated west of the Desert Highway, some 13km south of Amman's 7th Circle. Pines planted in the 1960s make up the park itself, but more attractive for birdwatchers are the surrounding orchards and extensive rolling hills and wadis to the south and west.

The breeding birds of the pines, orchards, and surrounding rocky, scrubby slopes include Hobby, Chukar, Collared Dove, Turtle Dove, Little Owl, Hoopoe, Calandra Lark, Short-toed Lark, Crested Lark, Yellow-vented Bulbul, Rufous Bush Robin, Black-eared Wheatear, Blackbird, Olivaceous Warbler, Upcher's Warbler, Spectacled Warbler, Sardinian Warbler, Lesser Whitethroat, Spotted Flycatcher, Great Tit, Woodchat Shrike, Masked Shrike, Rock Sparrow, Greenfinch, Goldfinch, Linnet, Black-headed Bunting and Corn Bunting. Bee-eater may breed nearby.

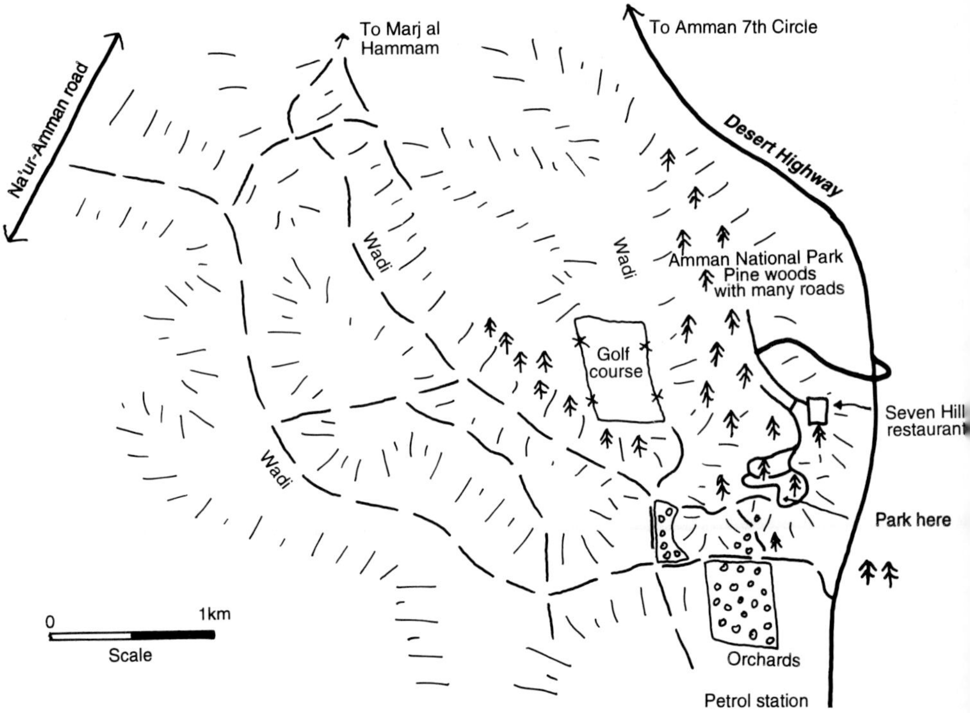

To Marj al Hammam
To Amman 7th Circle
Na'ur-Amman road
Desert Highway
Wadi
Wadi
Amman National Park
Pine woods
with many roads
Golf course
Seven Hill restaurant
Wadi
Park here
0
1km
Scale
Orchards
Petrol station

Many finches roost in the trees in winter, with large numbers of Chaffinch, Greenfinch, Linnet and Serin, and a few Brambling, Hawfinch, Yellowhammer and Rock Bunting. It is these flocks that attract Sparrowhawks and Merlins, with up to 10 of the latter also roosting nearby. Wintering groups of Woodlarks are regular.

Dibbin Forest and Najde

Dibbin Forest is reached via tarmac roads south-west from Jarash or south from Sakib. It is a remnant forest of mature Aleppo Pine *Pinus halepensis* and the evergreen oak *Quercus calliprinus*. The popular parts of the park are busy on Fridays, but it is possible to explore and get away from the people and litter.

The breeding population of Dibbin has a Mediterranean character, with resident Syrian Woodpecker, Wren, Blackbird, Sardinian Warbler, Lesser Whitethroat, Blue Tit, Great Tit, Jay and Hooded Crow. Short-toed Eagle, Sparrowhawk and Hobby possibly nest in the forest, as may Bonelli's Warbler. In the winter months numbers of Sparrowhawk, Robin, Blackbird, Song Thrush, Chiffchaff and Chaffinch arrive, along with rarer Brambling, Siskin, Woodlark, Goldcrest and Hawfinch. At this time of the year, large numbers of finches roost in the pines, and they can be seen arriving at dusk.

A track along the ridge running west from the village of Najde passes through more open habitat, with a range of similar breeding species, including Syrian Woodpecker, Wren and Jay. In winter, Black Redstart, Stonechat, Finsch's Wheatear, Fieldfare, Mistle Thrush, Woodlark, Yellowhammer, and Rock Bunting can be seen on this walk.

Other sites in the Northern Highlands include: the Zarqa River where it is crossed by the Amman to Jarash road, the 'Scandinavian Forest' north-west of the Al Baq'a refugee camp, and the oak woodland around the Qal'at ar Rabad west of Ajlun.

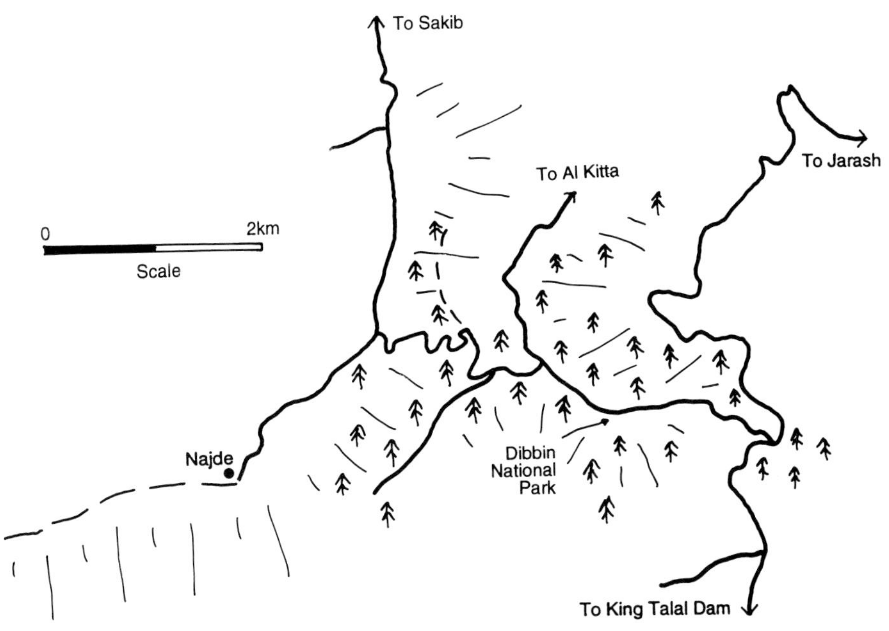

Northern Steppes

South of Queen Alia International Airport

The steppe desert south of the airport has been largely ploughed and partly cultivated. From the Desert Highway, it can be explored from the roads heading off east to Al Qunaytira and Al Amiriyya, and west to the ruins of Umm ar Rasas. The road to Al Amiriyya is 15km south of the airport and signposted to Dubiya and Hammam Shamut. Beyond Al Amiriyya, a track continues to Wadi al Jilat.

Autumn and winter specialities in this area include: Cream-coloured Courser, Dotterel, Desert Finch, Calandra Lark, Bimaculated Lark and Black-bellied Sandgrouse.

Eastern Desert

Qasr al Kharana

Qasr al Kharana is a convenient stop 57km east of Amman on the road to Azraq. The desert south and west of this desert castle contains a variety of habitats dominated by flint hills, broad wadis, and low limestone bluffs. This is an excellent area to look for the typical species of the Eastern Desert such as Temminck's Horned Lark, Desert Lark (dark subspecies on flint hills), Cream-coloured Courser (summer), Red-rumped Wheatear (several pairs in areas of soft white limestone), Hoopoe Lark, Thick-billed Lark (rare on flint), and Trumpeter Finch (occasional).

It is also possible to see a variety of migrants in the area, including raptors, hirundines, chats, wheatears, Spotted Flycatcher, shrikes and buntings. Less expectedly, Common Tern, Snipe, Common Sandpiper, Black-headed Gull, Corncrake and White-throated Robin have been seen here.

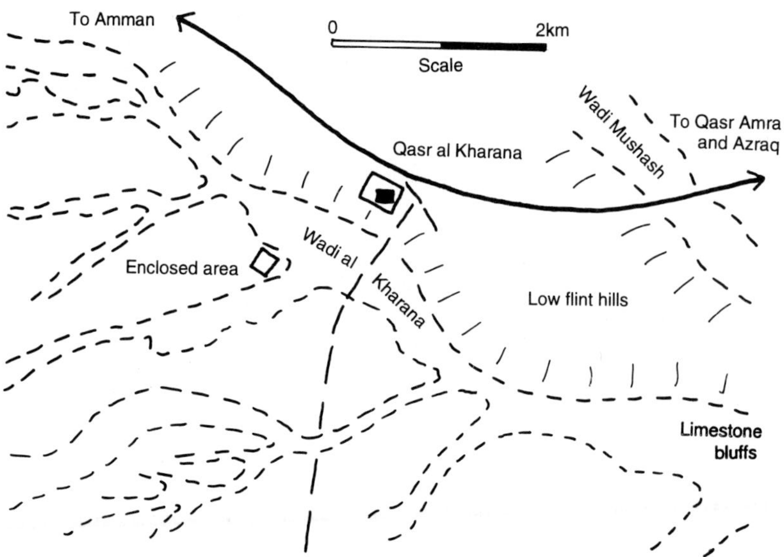

Wadi al Butm

15km east of Qasr al Kharana, further along the road to Azraq, is the Umayyad bath-house of Qasr Amra. It is situated in Wadi al Butm, a broad open wadi lined with old butm or Atlantic Pistachio *Pistacia atlantica* trees and other shrubby vegetation, such as White Broom. This is one of the best migrant traps in the Eastern Desert, and it can be easily explored by walking west from the ruin. A four-wheel-drive track parallels the wadi, giving access to the trees further west.

Breeding birds of the wadi include Little Owl and Great Grey Shrike, but Temminck's Horned Lark and Bar-tailed Desert Lark breed in the surrounding desert. Striated Scops Owls have been reported here. In spring, many migrant passerines stop over in the wadi vegetation. It is a good site for *Ficedula* flycatchers, nightingales, redstarts, wheatears, warblers, shrikes and buntings. Less frequent visitors include Nightjar, Woodlark, White-throated Robin, Rock Thrush, Upcher's Warbler and Desert Finch. Small, transient floodpools can hold a few waders, Greater Sand Plover being the most interesting.

The importance of the site increases in winter, when ten Imperial Eagles and five Steppe Eagles frequent the area, roosting on the pylons and trees. Large flocks of Stock Doves (up to 500) also winter, along with Fieldfare and Corn Bunting.

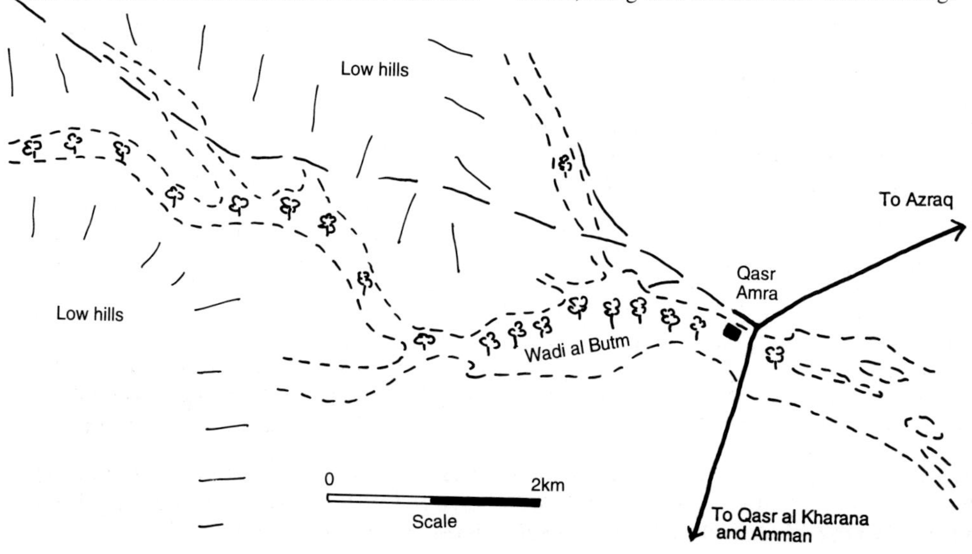

Shaumari

Shaumari is another migrant trap in the Eastern Desert, lying some 11km south of Azraq. (See map on page 44.) Formerly an experimental desert-farming station, it is now the headquarters of the RSCN Wildlife Reserve, which breeds locally extinct or endangered species such as Arabian Oryx, Gazelle, Wild Ass (Onagar) and Ostrich. It is reached by turning west off the road to Al Umari on a signposted road 8km south of Azraq. This approach road crosses 5km of typical degraded desert, holding low densities of typical desert species such as Temminck's Horned Lark, Hoopoe Lark and Desert Wheatear. The fenced-off reserve has much more luxuriant growth – a vivid display of the damage that grazing animals are doing to the desert.

After reaching the car park (there is a small entrance fee), wander round the trees, and view the area from the viewing platform. Mature, irrigated casuarina and eucalyptus dominate the reserve centre. These trees are visible as an 'island' in the distance from as far as 30km away, and they offer extensive cover and shade for migrants.

It is possible to see a wide range of migrants in spring and autumn. Shaumari is a particularly good place for Golden Oriole, Pied Flycatcher, Semi-collared Flycatcher, and even Red-breasted Flycatcher (in late autumn). Scops Owl, Squacco Heron, and Black-headed Bunting have also been seen. Cranes winter in the area, a few Hen Harrier and Merlin hunt over the reserve, while Long-eared Owls roost in the larger trees and Spanish Sparrow, and Corn Bunting occur in flocks. Rarities like Tristram's Serin have turned up.

Local breeding species include Long-legged Buzzard, Barn Owl (one pair), Collared Dove, Great Grey Shrike and Desert Finch.

Basalt Desert

As Safawi to Wadi Rajil

The Basalt Desert would be largely impenetrable but for the main road which joins Azraq with the Iraqi border. Exploration in this terrain is difficult, but east of As Safawi the old road parallels the new highway giving access to the favoured habitat of the Bar-tailed Desert Lark, dark race Desert Lark, Temminck's Horned Lark, dark morph Mourning Wheatear, Thick-billed Lark, Desert Wheatear and Trumpeter Finch. A good area for the dark wheatears lies 9km east of As Safawi (on the old road), in an area of derelict stone buildings. In the next 3-4km are both a range of low hills north of the road and the shallow gorge of Wadi Rajil. Both are worthy of exploration.

The qas between the lava fields may flood in winter, attracting flocks of Cranes and duck, or in spring, attracting White-winged Black Tern. Hen Harrier, Finsch's Wheatear and Stock Dove can also be seen in winter.

Ghadir Burqu'

Ghadir Burqu' (pronounced 'beurka') is situated on the eastern limit of the Basalt Desert. The site consists of a ruined fort on the shore of a permanent pool, that is some 500m wide by 2km long. The shores are sparsely vegetated, and the lake is largely surrounded by basalt boulders. Large amounts of water are pumped by the bedouin, and the lake occasionally dries out. Access, strictly by four-wheel-drive vehicle only, is through 18km of featureless, dusty desert on a NNW bearing from Muqat pumping station (west of Ar Ruwayshid).

The importance of this isolated, permanent pool to migrant birds cannot be overestimated. Unfortunately trapping and shooting of birds is all too commonplace, and can seriously disrupt a visit here.

Large numbers of birds, including ducks, waders and raptors were seen when the site was visited in September 1991. Passerines were also seen in the boulder fields and around the castle, making use of the limited cover provided by the rocks themselves.

Rum Desert

The Rum Desert is an extensive area of dramatic sandstone mesas that rise up to 800m from the surrounding sea of sand. Leave the Desert Highway at Ar Rashidiyya, and take a tarmac road east for 16km; after forking right drive a further 12km to the Resthouse and Rum settlement.

The majority of the local species can be seen from this road, but a particularly productive area lies 3km north of the Wadi Rum village. Here there are cliffs and boulder slopes ① and sandy desert with bushes ②, where it is possible to see Long-legged Buzzard, Sand Partridge, Desert Lark, Rock Martin, Mourning and White-crowned Black Wheatear, Scrub Warbler, Brown-necked Raven, Trumpeter Finch, Sinai Rosefinch and House Bunting. A few Hooded Wheatear are also resident, but they can be very difficult to pin down. The settlement itself is good for Sinai Rosefinch and Tristram's Grackle, and migrants are often concentrated there. There are springs, including Lawrence's 'Well', at the base of the cliffs behind the Resthouse. Some of the more unusual migrants recorded here include River Warbler, Olive-tree Warbler, Semi-collared Flycatcher and Isabelline Shrike.

Migrating raptors pass over the jabals, and are most easily seen in early to mid morning as they rise with the first thermals. The two speciality birds of prey of the Rum Desert are Verreaux's Eagle and Sooty Falcon, and both can be seen in this general area. The Verreaux's Eagle, although common in Africa, is one of the most sought-after of Western Palearctic specialities; the best place to look for it is high over the cliffs behind the settlement. A few pairs of Sooty Falcon breed on the neighbouring cliff faces, but they are only present between May and October.

Wadi Rum is but a small corner of this dramatic landscape, and a useful booklet available in Jordan details *Walks and scrambles in Wadi Rum*. Exploration of the surrounding area requires a four-wheel-drive vehicle, which can be hired with driver from Rum village. A particularly scenic area, with local birds and migrants, is the Rakabat Canyon in Wadi Umm Ishrin.

The large irrigated agricultural complexes of Disi and Sahl as Suwwan lie east of Wadi Rum, and they attract a wider variety of migrants, including wetland birds, to this otherwise desert habitat. There are roads east from Disi village, but entry may have to be negotiated at the barrier, as the farms are private.

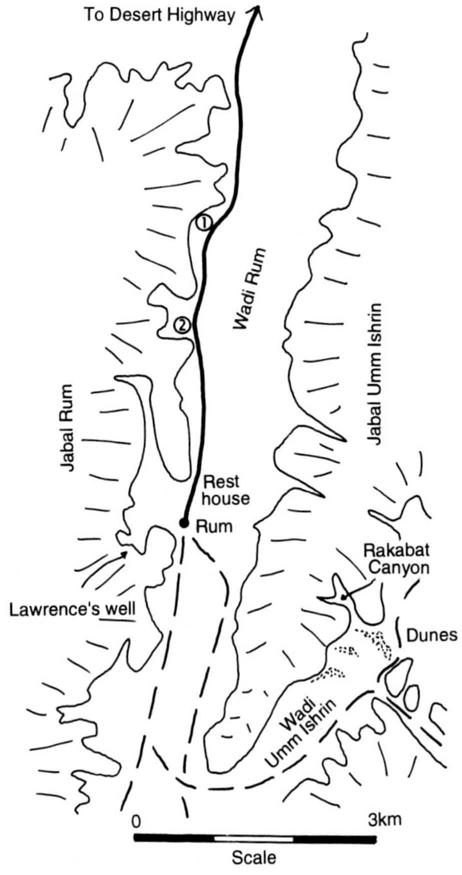

Azraq Oasis

The name Azraq conjures up images of a lush oasis brimming with wildlife, and a magnet for migrant birds in a sea of desert. Nowadays, however, water is hard to find and visitors are often disappointed. Many of the species recorded in the systematic list and illustrated in the plates were seen at sites that no longer exist. The success of a visit depends largely on the amount of run-off water that has accumulated during the previous winter. It is a sad fact that the oasis is on its last legs.

Shishan Pools

Only limited areas of water remain in the vicinity of the Shishan pools, immediately east of South Azraq village, but there is still a large amount of vegetation there. From a vantage point on a small mound to the south-east of the southern Shishan pool, it is also possible to scan the Wetland Reserve area (now dry).

Interesting species seen here include Penduline Tit, Cetti's Warbler, Moustached Warbler, Cyprus Pied Wheatear, singing Reed Warblers, Lesser Grey Shrike, Roller, and Marsh Harrier. It is also a good place to see the large hirundine roost at dusk, and some raptors also drop in to roost in the vegetation here. Migrant passerines can turn up in the village itself.

Fish Pools

A group of small fish pools is located just south of South Azraq village, to the east of the Azraq-Shaumari road. Three small rectangular pools and two larger ones lie adjacent to the Herza-Baker canal. The pools were dug in the 1980s, but water levels are falling, as everywhere in the oasis. Access is by following a track from the southern limit of South Azraq, and permission to enter is easily obtained.

Total numbers of birds rarely exceed 200, but the lack of large numbers is made up for by their variety. The following species have been seen in recent years: Glossy Ibis, Purple Heron, Little Bittern, Little Crake, White-tailed Plover, Black-tailed Godwit, Curlew, Marsh Sandpiper, Broad-billed Sandpiper, Black-winged Pratincole, Little Gull, Lesser Grey Shrike and Citrine Wagtail.

Few birds breed at this site, but locally-fledged Little and Gull-billed Terns visited in 1991. A pair of Marbled Duck bred in 1990, and Black-winged Stilt reared young in 1991.

In autumn, birds of prey drop out of the sky to drink. Fifteen species of raptor have been seen, with records including 66 drinking Montagu's Harriers and 14 Honey Buzzards (both in mid September). Black-necked Grebe, Common Gull, Kingfisher and Pied Kingfisher have been seen in winter. Starling, Corn Bunting and Spanish Sparrow can also be seen at that time of the year.

Qa' al Azraq

The qa' is a flat, crescent-shaped basin surrounding the wetland, which floods in wet winters to a

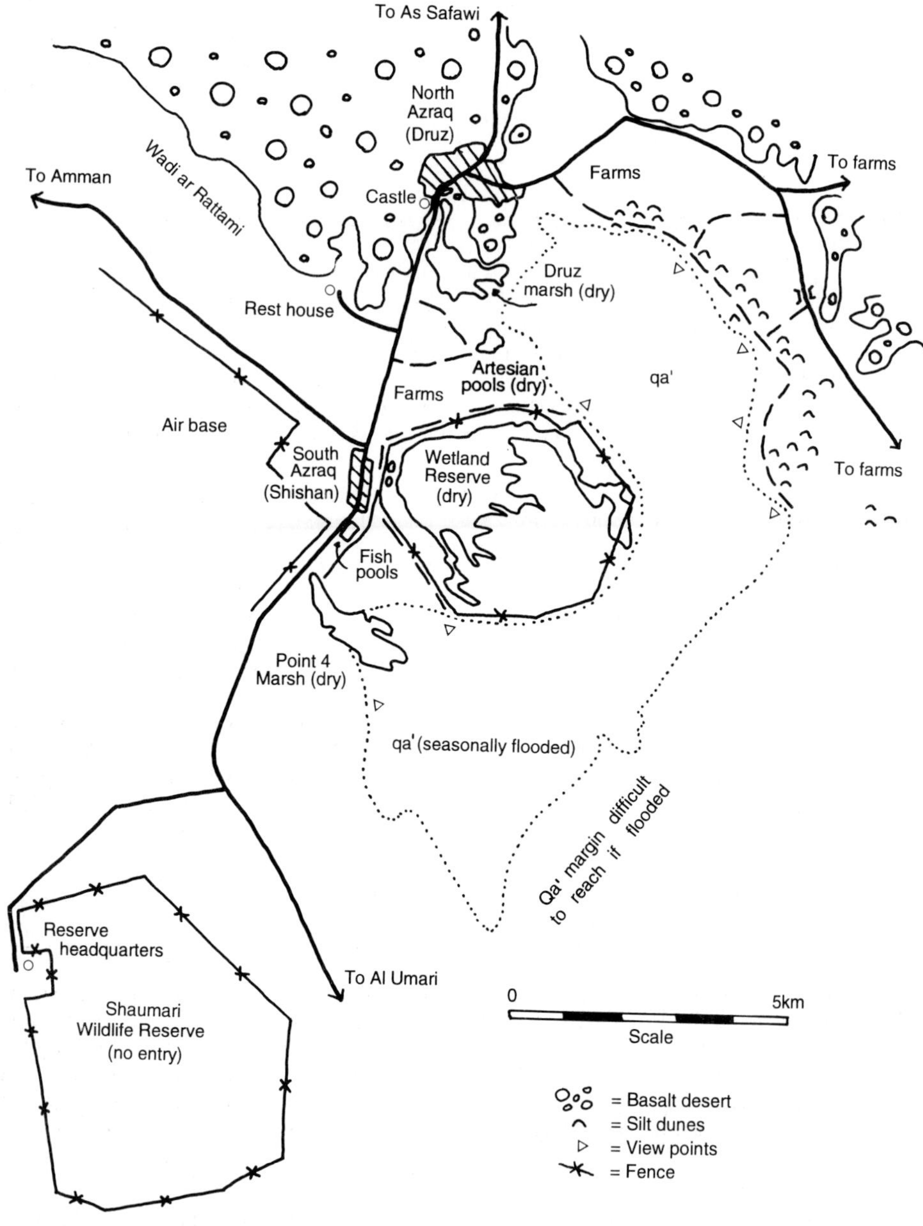

maximum depth of 1.25m. The water evaporates over a period of three months or so, after which time the qa' returns to a dusty mudflat. The circumference of the qa' is about 35km. Access can be made from various points, but even drivers of four-wheel-drive vehicles should remember that wet mud starts way before the water's edge. On no account attempt to drive on even damp mud. The amount of water and location of birds cannot be predicted, so exploration may be necessary.

NW edge: access from the Artesian Pools, or the end of the track running along the northern perimeter fence of the Wetland Reserve.

N edge: access east from North Azraq village and neighbouring farm tracks.

E edge: access from the tarmac road running east from North Azraq village 1km north of the castle. About 11km from North Azraq village, after a small hump-backed bridge, turn right off the tarmac onto a short track through the dunes. On reaching the water's edge (if it is flooded, of course) explore to the north and south.

SE edge: the most difficult area to reach even with a four-wheel-drive vehicle (continue south from the eastern access point).

SW edge: access from the track along the southern fence of the Wetland Reserve, from the Point 4 Marsh or off the road to Shaumari.

If flooded in spring, the qa' is a superb place for migrant waterbirds. Numbers of waders and terns can be well in excess of 5000, the majority being Ruff, Little Stint, and White-winged Black Terns. Amongst the more regular migrant waders are Black-winged Stilt, Avocet, Collared Pratincole, Kentish Plover, Greater Sand Plover, Curlew Sandpiper, Marsh Sandpiper, Greenshank, Wood Sandpiper and Red-necked Phalarope. In total, 27 species of wader, nine of gulls and terns, and seven of ducks, plus Black-necked Grebe and Coot have been seen on the flooded qa'. Migrant pipits, wagtails, wheatears, shrikes and warblers feed in the grasses and scrub around the mudflat.

Scattered islands, formed by mounds of the local salt workings in the dry season, form important refuges for breeding birds. In wet springs, Kentish Plover, Black-winged Stilt (300 pairs) and Avocet (20 pairs) can breed. A few Shelduck, Little Tern and Gull-billed Tern have also bred successfully in recent years. Lesser Short-toed Lark, Rufous Bush Robin and Desert Wheatear breed in the surrounding vegetation.

In 1991/92 the qa' flooded in winter, and a large number of wildfowl were counted: 3490 Shelduck, 100 Wigeon, 6000 Teal, 500 Mallard, 50 Pintail, 1000 Shoveler, 3 Pochard, 60 Tufted Duck, 610 Coot and 2000 Crane. Of particular note were the huge concentrations of Shelduck, Teal and Cranes, but rarities such as Greater Flamingo, White-fronted Goose and Ruddy Shelduck were also significant. Wader numbers in winter are usually not great, but include Lapwing, Dunlin, Little Stint, Kentish Plover and Redshank.

Azraq Resthouse and Wadi ar Rattami

This new government Resthouse is located 2km north of the Azraq T-junction, and then a further 1.5km to the west. It is set in an area of tall eucalyptus and casuarina trees, and a borehole in one corner flows warm, sulphurous water. The Resthouse itself has luxuriant, irrigated gardens which offer cover to migrants. Past sightings include Nightjar, Thrush Nightingale, Rock Thrush, Isabelline Shrike, Barred Warbler and Desert Finch. Wadi ar Rattami, which passes south of the Resthouse, is well-vegetated. Its broom bushes offer further cover to migrants.

Al Khirba as Samra Sewage Works

The Al Khirba as Samra sewage works were completed in 1985, and they are situated north-east of Az Zarqa on the desert fringe, 35km from central Amman. Access is east off the Az Zarqa to Irbid road, at Al Hashimiyya (just north of a petrol station); there is a watchman, but entry should not be a problem if you explain you are birdwatching. The treatment pools are extensive, and habitats range from vegetated, muddy (and smelly) pools at the east end to cleaner, partly-treated water at the west end. There are also some small pools near the office buildings.

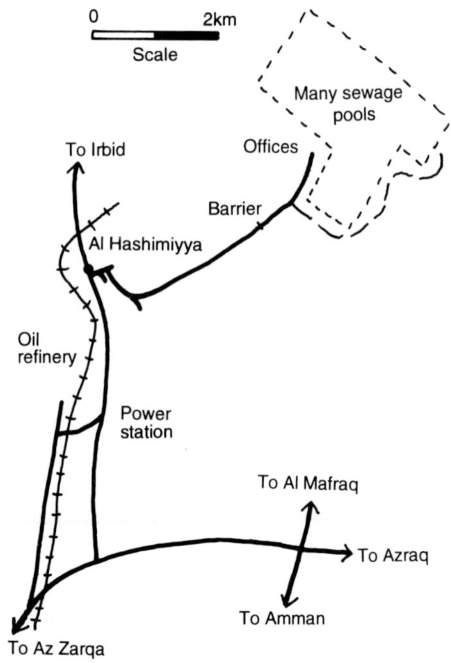

The site holds numerous birds in spring and autumn. When there is no water in the desert, the sewage lagoons provide a valuable alternative to birds that may have used the Azraq staging post in the past. The main species involved are passage storks, herons, ducks, waders, gulls and terns, as well as a small number of passerines. Most notable are the White Storks, which roost at the site in their thousands in late August and early September.

A selection of the common regular waders (with maximum counts) include: Black-winged Stilt (25), Avocet (4), Collared Pratincole (6), Little Ringed Plover (25), Ringed Plover (30), Kentish Plover (25), Little Stint (500), Temminck's Stint (3), Curlew Sandpiper (15), Ruff (150), Snipe (40), Green Sandpiper (110), and Wood Sandpiper (100).

Rarities for Jordan seen at Samra include: White Pelican, Ferruginous Duck, Pacific Golden Plover, Grey Plover, Turnstone and Curlew. Breeding birds are few, but they include Spur-winged Plover, and possibly Citrine Wagtail and Desert Finch.

CHECKLIST OF THE BIRDS OF JORDAN

The status of each species on the Jordan List is summarised by means of a code. Lower case is used to denote the less common and rarer species; a question mark indicates an unproven or possible status and an 'f' a former status which is no longer valid. If more than one abbreviation is used, such are listed in order of importance.

RB/rb – resident breeding species
MB/mb – migrant breeding species
PM/pm – passage migrant
r – non-breeding resident
WV/wv – winter visitor
V – vagrant or accidental

	Species	Status
☐	Ostrich *Struthio camelus*	fb
☐	Little Grebe *Tachybaptus ruficollis*	WV/?fb
☐	Great Crested Grebe *Podiceps cristatus*	wv/pm
☐	Black-necked Grebe *Podiceps nigricollis*	wv/pm
☐	Cory's Shearwater *Calonectris diomedea*	PM
☐	Sooty Shearwater *Puffinus griseus*	V
☐	Brown Booby *Sula leucogaster*	pm or r
☐	Cormorant *Phalacrocorax carbo*	wv/pm
☐	Pygmy Cormorant *Phalacrocorax pygmeus*	fwv
☐	Darter *Anhinga melanogaster*	fwv
☐	White Pelican *Pelecanus onocrotalus*	pm
☐	Bittern *Botaurus stellaris*	wv
☐	Little Bittern *Ixobrychus minutus*	PM/fb
☐	Night Heron *Nycticorax nycticorax*	PM
☐	Green-backed Heron *Butorides striatus*	V
☐	Squacco Heron *Ardeola ralloides*	PM/fb
☐	Cattle Egret *Bubulcus ibis*	PM/r
☐	Western Reef Heron *Egretta gularis*	r
☐	Little Egret *Egretta garzetta*	PM/r
☐	Yellow-billed Egret *Egretta intermedia*	V
☐	Great White Egret *Egretta alba*	wv/pm
☐	Grey Heron *Ardea cinerea*	PM/r
☐	Purple Heron *Ardea purpurea*	PM/fb
☐	Black Stork *Ciconia nigra*	PM/wv
☐	White Stork *Ciconia ciconia*	PM
☐	Glossy Ibis *Plegadis falcinellus*	pm
☐	Spoonbill *Platalea leucorodia*	V
☐	Greater Flamingo *Phoenicopterus ruber*	wv
☐	White-fronted Goose *Anser albifrons*	V
☐	Greylag Goose *Anser anser*	wv
☐	Ruddy Shelduck *Tadorna ferruginea*	V
☐	Shelduck *Tadorna tadorna*	WV/pm/mb
☐	Wigeon *Anas penelope*	WV/pm
☐	Falcated Duck *Anas falcata*	V
☐	Gadwall *Anas strepera*	wv
☐	Teal *Anas crecca*	WV/pm
☐	Mallard *Anas platyrhynchos*	WV/fb
☐	Pintail *Anas acuta*	WV/pm
☐	Garganey *Anas querquedula*	PM/?fb
☐	Shoveler *Anas clypeata*	WV/pm
☐	Marbled Duck *Marmaronetta angustirostris*	pm/mb
☐	Red-crested Pochard *Netta rufina*	wv/pm
☐	Pochard *Aythya ferina*	wv/pm
☐	Ferruginous Duck *Aythya nyroca*	pm
☐	Tufted Duck *Aythya fuligula*	WV/PM
☐	Honey Buzzard *Pernis apivorus*	PM
☐	Black Kite *Milvus migrans*	PM
☐	Red Kite *Milvus milvus*	V
☐	Lammergeier *Gypaetus barbatus*	fb
☐	Egyptian Vulture *Neophron percnopterus*	PM/mb
☐	Griffon Vulture *Gyps fulvus*	RB
☐	Lappet-faced Vulture *Torgos tracheliotus*	V
☐	Black Vulture *Aegypius monachus*	V
☐	Short-toed Eagle *Circaetus gallicus*	PM/MB
☐	Marsh Harrier *Circus aeruginosus*	PM/wv/?fb
☐	Hen Harrier *Circus cyaneus*	wv/pm
☐	Pallid Harrier *Circus macrourus*	PM/wv
☐	Montagu's Harrier *Circus pygargus*	PM
☐	Goshawk *Accipiter gentilis*	pm
☐	Sparrowhawk *Accipiter nisus*	WV/pm/?mb
☐	Levant Sparrowhawk *Accipiter brevipes*	PM
☐	Steppe Buzzard *Buteo buteo vulpinus*	PM
☐	Long-legged Buzzard *Buteo rufinus*	RB
☐	Rough-legged Buzzard *Buteo lagopus*	V
☐	Lesser Spotted Eagle *Aquila pomarina*	pm
☐	Spotted Eagle *Aquila clanga*	V
☐	Steppe Eagle *Aquila nipalensis*	PM
☐	Imperial Eagle *Aquila heliaca*	WV/pm
☐	Golden Eagle *Aquila chrysaetos*	RB
☐	Verreaux's Eagle *Aquila verreauxii*	RB
☐	Booted Eagle *Hieraaetus pennatus*	PM
☐	Bonelli's Eagle *Hieraaetus fasciatus*	RB
☐	Osprey *Pandion haliaetus*	PM
☐	Lesser Kestrel *Falco naumanni*	PM/MB
☐	Kestrel *Falco tinnunculus*	RB/pm
☐	Red-footed Falcon *Falco vespertinus*	pm
☐	Merlin *Falco columbarius*	WV
☐	Hobby *Falco subbuteo*	PM/mb
☐	Eleonora's Falcon *Falco eleonorae*	V
☐	Sooty Falcon *Falco concolor*	MB
☐	Lanner *Falco biarmicus*	RB
☐	Saker *Falco cherrug*	wv/pm

Species	Status
Peregrine *Falco peregrinus*	wv/pm
Barbary Falcon *Falco pelegrinoides*	RB
Chukar *Alectoris chukar*	RB
Sand Partridge *Ammoperdix heyi*	RB
Black Francolin *Francolinus francolinus*	RB
Quail *Coturnix coturnix*	PM
Water Rail *Rallus aquaticus*	wv/pm/fb
Spotted Crake *Porzana porzana*	pm
Little Crake *Porzana parva*	pm
Baillon's Crake *Porzana pusilla*	pm/mb
Corncrake *Crex crex*	pm
Moorhen *Gallinula chloropus*	wv/pm/fb
Coot *Fulica atra*	WV/pm/fb
Crane *Grus grus*	WV/pm
Houbara Bustard *Chlamydotis undulata*	RB
Oystercatcher *Haematopus ostralegus*	pm
Black-winged Stilt *Himantopus himantopus*	PM/MB
Avocet *Recurvirostra avosetta*	PM/MB
Stone-curlew *Burhinus oedicnemus*	pm/mb
Egyptian Plover *Pluvianus aegyptius*	V
Cream-coloured Courser *Cursorius cursor*	PM/MB
Collared Pratincole *Glareola pratincola*	PM/MB
Black-winged Pratincole *Glareola nordmanni*	V
Little Ringed Plover *Charadrius dubius*	PM/mb
Ringed Plover *Charadrius hiaticula*	PM
Kentish Plover *Charadrius alexandrinus*	PM/WV/MB
Greater Sand Plover *Charadrius leschenaultii*	PM/MB
Caspian Plover *Charadrius asiaticus*	pm
Dotterel *Charadrius morinellus*	wv
Pacific Golden Plover *Pluvialis fulva*	V
Grey Plover *Pluvialis squatarola*	pm
Spur-winged Plover *Hoplopterus spinosus*	RB
Blackhead Plover *Hoplopterus tectus*	V
Sociable Plover *Chettusia gregaria*	V
White-tailed Plover *Chettusia leucura*	pm/mb
Lapwing *Vanellus vanellus*	WV/pm
Knot *Calidris canutus*	V
Sanderling *Calidris alba*	V
Little Stint *Calidris minuta*	PM/wv
Temminck's Stint *Calidris temminckii*	PM
Curlew Sandpiper *Calidris ferruginea*	PM
Dunlin *Calidris alpina*	PM/WV
Broad-billed Sandpiper *Limicola falcinellus*	pm
Ruff *Philomachus pugnax*	PM/wv
Jack Snipe *Lymnocryptes minimus*	wv/pm
Snipe *Gallinago gallinago*	WV/PM
Great Snipe *Gallinago media*	V
Woodcock *Scolopax rusticola*	V
Black-tailed Godwit *Limosa limosa*	pm
Bar-tailed Godwit *Limosa lapponica*	pm
Whimbrel *Numenius phaeopus*	V
Slender-billed Curlew *Numenius tenuirostris*	V
Curlew *Numenius arquata*	pm
Spotted Redshank *Tringa erythropus*	pm
Redshank *Tringa totanus*	WV/PM
Marsh Sandpiper *Tringa stagnatilis*	PM
Greenshank *Tringa nebularia*	PM
Green Sandpiper *Tringa ochropus*	WV/PM
Wood Sandpiper *Tringa glareola*	PM
Terek Sandpiper *Xenus cinereus*	V
Common Sandpiper *Actitis hypoleucos*	PM
Turnstone *Arenaria interpres*	pm
Red-necked Phalarope *Phalaropus lobatus*	pm
Pomarine Skua *Stercorarius pomarinus*	V
Arctic Skua *Stercorarius parasiticus*	pm
Long-tailed Skua *Stercorarius longicaudus*	V
White-eyed Gull *Larus leucophthalmus*	r
Great Black-headed Gull *Larus ichthyaetus*	wv/pm
Little Gull *Larus minutus*	V
Black-headed Gull *Larus ridibundus*	WV/PM
Grey-headed Gull *Larus cirrocephalus*	V
Slender-billed Gull *Larus genei*	PM
Audouin's Gull *Larus audouinii*	V
Common Gull *Larus canus*	wv
Lesser Black-backed Gull *Larus fuscus*	PM
Yellow-legged Gull *Larus (argentatus) cachinnans*	WV/PM
Armenian Gull *Larus (argentatus) armenicus*	wv/pm
Glaucous Gull *Larus hyperboreus*	V
Gull-billed Tern *Gelochelidon nilotica*	PM/mb
Caspian Tern *Sterna caspia*	r
Crested Tern *Sterna bergii*	V
Lesser Crested Tern *Sterna bengalensis*	V
Sandwich Tern *Sterna sandvicensis*	pm
Common Tern *Sterna hirundo*	PM
White-cheeked Tern *Sterna repressa*	pm
Bridled Tern *Sterna anaethetus*	pm
Little Tern *Sterna albifrons*	PM/mb
Whiskered Tern *Chlidonias hybridus*	PM
Black Tern *Chlidonias niger*	pm
White-winged Black Tern *Chlidonias leucopterus*	PM
Crowned Sandgrouse *Pterocles coronatus*	?rb
Spotted Sandgrouse *Pterocles senegallus*	?rb
Chestnut-bellied Sandgrouse *Pterocles exustus*	V
Black-bellied Sandgrouse *Pterocles orientalis*	wv
Pin-tailed Sandgrouse *Pterocles alchata*	?rb
Rock Dove *Columba livia*	RB
Stock Dove *Columba oenas*	wv
Woodpigeon *Columba palumbus*	V
Collared Dove *Streptopelia decaocto*	RB
Turtle Dove *Streptopelia turtur*	PM/MB
Palm Dove *Streptopelia senegalensis*	RB
Namaqua Dove *Oena capensis*	pm

- [ ] Ring-necked Parakeet *Psittacula krameri* RB
- [ ] Great Spotted Cuckoo *Clamator glandarius* pm/?mb
- [ ] Cuckoo *Cuculus canorus* pm/?mb
- [ ] Barn Owl *Tyto alba* rb
- [ ] Striated Scops Owl *Otus brucei* ?rb
- [ ] Scops Owl *Otus scops* pm/MB
- [ ] Eagle Owl *Bubo bubo* rb
- [ ] Brown Fish Owl *Ketupa zeylonensis* ?rb
- [ ] Little Owl *Athene noctua* RB
- [ ] Tawny Owl *Strix aluco* rb
- [ ] Hume's Tawny Owl *Strix butleri* RB
- [ ] Long-eared Owl *Asio otus* wv/pm
- [ ] Short-eared Owl *Asio flammeus* pm
- [ ] Nubian Nightjar *Caprimulgus nubicus* ?rb
- [ ] Nightjar *Caprimulgus europaeus* pm
- [ ] Egyptian Nightjar *Caprimulgus aegyptius* mb/?pm
- [ ] Swift *Apus apus* PM/?mb
- [ ] Pallid Swift *Apus pallidus* PM/MB
- [ ] Alpine Swift *Apus melba* PM/MB
- [ ] Little Swift *Apus affinis* PM/MB
- [ ] Smyrna Kingfisher *Halcyon smyrnensis* RB
- [ ] Kingfisher *Alcedo atthis* WV/PM/?mb
- [ ] Pied Kingfisher *Ceryle rudis* RB/wv
- [ ] Little Green Bee-eater *Merops orientalis* RB
- [ ] Blue-cheeked Bee-eater *Merops superciliosus* pm/fb
- [ ] Bee-eater *Merops apiaster* PM/MB
- [ ] Roller *Coracias garrulus* PM/?mb
- [ ] Hoopoe *Upupa epops* PM/rb
- [ ] Wryneck *Jynx torquilla* PM
- [ ] Syrian Woodpecker *Dendrocopos syriacus* RB
- [ ] Dunn's Lark *Eremalauda dunni* rb
- [ ] Bar-tailed Desert Lark *Ammomanes cincturus* RB
- [ ] Desert Lark *Ammomanes deserti* RB
- [ ] Hoopoe Lark *Alaemon alaudipes* RB
- [ ] Thick-billed Lark *Rhamphocoris clotbey* rb
- [ ] Calandra Lark *Melanocorypha calandra* WV/rb
- [ ] Bimaculated Lark *Melanocorypha bimaculata* pm
- [ ] Short-toed Lark *Calandrella brachydactyla* PM/mb
- [ ] Lesser Short-toed Lark *Calandrella rufescens* MB/pm
- [ ] Crested Lark *Galerida cristata* RB
- [ ] Woodlark *Lullula arborea* WV/?mb
- [ ] Skylark *Alauda arvensis* WV
- [ ] Temminck's Horned Lark *Eremophila bilopha* RB
- [ ] Sand Martin *Riparia riparia* PM
- [ ] Rock Martin *Ptyonoprogne fuligula* RB
- [ ] Crag Martin *Ptyonoprogne rupestris* wv/pm
- [ ] Swallow *Hirundo rustica* PM/RB
- [ ] Red-rumped Swallow *Hirundo daurica* PM/mb
- [ ] House Martin *Delichon urbica* PM
- [ ] Richard's Pipit *Anthus novaeseelandiae* pm
- [ ] Tawny Pipit *Anthus campestris* PM
- [ ] Long-billed Pipit *Anthus similis* RB
- [ ] Tree Pipit *Anthus trivialis* PM
- [ ] Meadow Pipit *Anthus pratensis* WV/pm
- [ ] Red-throated Pipit *Anthus cervinus* wv/PM
- [ ] Water Pipit *Anthus spinoletta* WV
- [ ] Yellow Wagtail *Motacilla flava* PM/mb
- [ ] Citrine Wagtail *Motacilla citreola* pm
- [ ] Grey Wagtail *Motacilla cinerea* wv/pm
- [ ] White Wagtail *Motacilla alba alba* WV/PM
- [ ] White-cheeked Bulbul *Pycnonotus leucogenys* V
- [ ] Yellow-vented Bulbul *Pycnonotus xanthopygos* RB
- [ ] Wren *Troglodytes troglodytes* RB
- [ ] Dunnock *Prunella modularis* wv
- [ ] Rufous Bush Robin *Cercotrichas galactotes* PM/MB
- [ ] Robin *Erithacus rubecula* WV
- [ ] Thrush Nightingale *Luscinia luscinia* PM
- [ ] Nightingale *Luscinia megarhynchos* PM/?mb
- [ ] Bluethroat *Luscinia svecica* WV/PM
- [ ] White-throated Robin *Irania gutturalis* pm
- [ ] Black Redstart *Phoenicurus ochruros* WV/PM
- [ ] Redstart *Phoenicurus phoenicurus* PM
- [ ] Blackstart *Cercomela melanura* RB
- [ ] Whinchat *Saxicola rubetra* PM
- [ ] Stonechat *Saxicola torquata* WV/PM
- [ ] Isabelline Wheatear *Oenanthe isabellina* MB/pm/wv
- [ ] Wheatear *Oenanthe oenanthe* PM
- [ ] Cyprus Pied Wheatear *Oenanthe (pleschanka) cypriaca* pm
- [ ] Black-eared Wheatear *Oenanthe hispanica* PM/MB
- [ ] Desert Wheatear *Oenanthe deserti* RB
- [ ] Finsch's Wheatear *Oenanthe finschii* WV
- [ ] Red-rumped Wheatear *Oenanthe moesta* RB
- [ ] Red-tailed Wheatear *Oenanthe xanthoprymna* V
- [ ] Mourning Wheatear *Oenanthe lugens* RB
- [ ] Hooded Wheatear *Oenanthe monacha* RB
- [ ] White-crowned Black Wheatear *Oenanthe leucopyga* RB
- [ ] Rock Thrush *Monticola saxatilis* PM
- [ ] Blue Rock Thrush *Monticola solitarius* RB/pm
- [ ] Ring Ouzel *Turdus torquatus* V
- [ ] Blackbird *Turdus merula* RB/wv
- [ ] Fieldfare *Turdus pilaris* wv
- [ ] Song Thrush *Turdus philomelos* wv
- [ ] Redwing *Turdus iliacus* V
- [ ] Mistle Thrush *Turdus viscivorus* wv
- [ ] Cetti's Warbler *Cettia cetti* RB
- [ ] Fan-tailed Warbler *Cisticola juncidis* pm/fb
- [ ] Graceful Warbler *Prinia gracilis* RB
- [ ] Scrub Warbler *Scotocerca inquieta* RB
- [ ] Grasshopper Warbler *Locustella naevia* V
- [ ] River Warbler *Locustella fluviatilis* pm
- [ ] Savi's Warbler *Locustella luscinioides* pm/fb
- [ ] Moustached Warbler *Acrocephalus melanopogon* wv/fb

- [ ] Aquatic Warbler *Acrocephalus paludicola* V
- [ ] Sedge Warbler *Acrocephalus schoenobaenus* PM
- [ ] Marsh Warbler *Acrocephalus palustris* V
- [ ] Reed Warbler *Acrocephalus scirpaceus* MB/PM
- [ ] Clamorous Reed Warbler *Acrocephalus stentoreus* fb
- [ ] Great Reed Warbler *Acrocephalus arundinaceus* pm/fb
- [ ] Olivaceous Warbler *Hippolais pallida* MB/PM
- [ ] Booted Warbler *Hippolais caligata* pm
- [ ] Upcher's Warbler *Hippolais languida* MB/pm
- [ ] Olive-tree Warbler *Hippolais olivetorum* pm
- [ ] Icterine Warbler *Hippolais icterina* pm
- [ ] Spectacled Warbler *Sylvia conspicillata* RB/wv
- [ ] Subalpine Warbler *Sylvia cantillans* pm
- [ ] Ménétries's Warbler *Sylvia mystacea* V
- [ ] Sardinian Warbler *Sylvia melanocephalus* RB/wv
- [ ] Cyprus Warbler *Sylvia melanothorax* wv
- [ ] Rüppell's Warbler *Sylvia rueppelli* pm
- [ ] Desert Warbler *Sylvia nana* wv/pm
- [ ] Arabian Warbler *Sylvia leucomelaena* RB
- [ ] Orphean Warbler *Sylvia hortensis* PM/?mb
- [ ] Barred Warbler *Sylvia nisoria* PM
- [ ] Lesser Whitethroat *Sylvia curruca* PM/mb
- [ ] Whitethroat *Sylvia communis* PM
- [ ] Garden Warbler *Sylvia borin* PM
- [ ] Blackcap *Sylvia atricapilla* PM/wv
- [ ] Bonelli's Warbler *Phylloscopus bonelli* PM/mb
- [ ] Wood Warbler *Phylloscopus sibilatrix* PM
- [ ] Plain Willow Warbler *Phylloscopus neglectus* V
- [ ] Chiffchaff *Phylloscopus collybita* PM/WV
- [ ] Willow Warbler *Phylloscopus trochilus* PM
- [ ] Goldcrest *Regulus regulus* V
- [ ] Spotted Flycatcher *Muscicapa striata* PM/MB
- [ ] Red-breasted Flycatcher *Ficedula parva* pm
- [ ] Semi-collared Flycatcher *Ficedula semitorquata* PM
- [ ] Collared Flycatcher *Ficedula albicollis* PM
- [ ] Pied Flycatcher *Ficedula hypoleuca* PM
- [ ] Brown Babbler *Turdoides squamiceps* RB
- [ ] Blue Tit *Parus caeruleus* RB
- [ ] Great Tit *Parus major* RB
- [ ] Wallcreeper *Tichodroma muraria* V
- [ ] Penduline Tit *Remiz pendulinus* wv/pm
- [ ] Orange-tufted Sunbird *Nectarinia osea* RB
- [ ] Golden Oriole *Oriolus oriolus* PM
- [ ] Isabelline Shrike *Lanius isabellinus* pm
- [ ] Red-backed Shrike *Lanius collurio* PM
- [ ] Lesser Grey Shrike *Lanius minor* PM
- [ ] Great Grey Shrike *Lanius excubitor* RB
- [ ] Woodchat Shrike *Lanius senator* MB/PM
- [ ] Masked Shrike *Lanius nubicus* MB/PM
- [ ] Jay *Garrulus glandarius* RB
- [ ] Jackdaw *Corvus monedula* wv/mb
- [ ] Indian House Crow *Corvus splendens* RB
- [ ] Rook *Corvus frugilegus* V
- [ ] Hooded Crow *Corvus corone cornix* RB
- [ ] Brown-necked Raven *Corvus ruficollis* RB
- [ ] Raven *Corvus corax* fb
- [ ] Fan-tailed Raven *Corvus rhipidurus* RB
- [ ] Tristram's Grackle *Onychognathus tristramii* RB
- [ ] Starling *Sturnus vulgaris* WV
- [ ] Rose-coloured Starling *Sturnus roseus* pm
- [ ] House Sparrow *Passer domesticus* RB
- [ ] Spanish Sparrow *Passer hispaniolensis* RB/WV
- [ ] Dead Sea Sparrow *Passer moabiticus* RB
- [ ] Pale Rock Sparrow *Petronia brachydactyla* mb/pm
- [ ] Rock Sparrow *Petronia petronia* RB
- [ ] Chaffinch *Fringilla coelebs* WV
- [ ] Brambling *Fringilla montifringilla* wv
- [ ] Serin *Serinus serinus* WV/mb
- [ ] Tristram's Serin *Serinus syriacus* wv/pm/?mb
- [ ] Greenfinch *Carduelis chloris* RB/wv
- [ ] Goldfinch *Carduelis carduelis* RB/wv
- [ ] Siskin *Carduelis spinus* wv
- [ ] Linnet *Carduelis cannabina* RB/wv
- [ ] Desert Finch *Rhodospiza obsoleta* RB
- [ ] Trumpeter Finch *Bucanetes githagineus* RB
- [ ] Scarlet Rosefinch *Carpodacus erythrinus* V
- [ ] Sinai Rosefinch *Carpodacus synoicus* RB
- [ ] Hawfinch *Coccothraustes coccothraustes* wv
- [ ] Yellowhammer *Emberiza citrinella* wv
- [ ] Rock Bunting *Emberiza cia* wv
- [ ] House Bunting *Emberiza striolata* RB
- [ ] Cinereous Bunting *Emberiza cineracea* pm
- [ ] Ortolan Bunting *Emberiza hortulana* PM
- [ ] Cretzschmar's Bunting *Emberiza caesia* PM/MB
- [ ] Little Bunting *Emberiza pusilla* V
- [ ] Reed Bunting *Emberiza schoeniclus* wv
- [ ] Black-headed Bunting *Emberiza melanocephala* PM/MB
- [ ] Corn Bunting *Miliaria calandra* WV/mb
- [ ]
- [ ]
- [ ]
- [ ]
- [ ]
- [ ]
- [ ]
- [ ]
- [ ]
- [ ]
- [ ]
- [ ]
- [ ]
- [ ]
- [ ]

SYSTEMATIC LIST

Struthio camelus
Ostrich

AR: Na'ām
GE: Strauß

The Arabian Ostrich *S. c. syriacus* is the only bird species known to have become extinct recently in Jordan, as it has throughout the Middle East. It formerly ranged widely across the Jordanian desert, as testified by its frequent appearance in bedouin rock drawings. This Safaitic and Thamudic rock art is thought to date from the Nabatean and Roman periods (312 B.C. to 324 A.D.).

Although still fairly common in 1914, the Ostrich was exterminated in the 1920s and 1930s following the increased availability of firearms and motor transport. The last birds had, by this time, retreated to the eastern and southern extremities of Jordan adjacent to Saudi Arabia. By 1939 the subspecies was extinct across the whole of its former range.

There are two recent, but unfortunately unproven Jordanian records: two birds said to have been shot near the Jordan-Iraq-Saudi border in 1948, and a dying bird found in Wadi al Hasa in February 1966, brought down by floods from higher ground.

Birds of one of the larger African races form part of the planned reintroduction programme at Shaumari.

Tachybaptus ruficollis
Little Grebe

AR: Ghawass sagheer
GE: Zwergtaucher

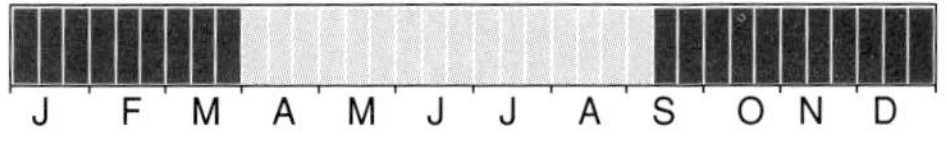

The record of three or four pairs trilling at Azraq oasis in the 1960s and again in 1983 suggests that there has been a small breeding population in the past. There is no recent evidence of breeding, but one or two Little Grebes have summered at Shuna Reservoir and on the Zarqa River, and one was seen at Azraq on 25 May 1991.

It is generally an uncommon winter visitor to the reservoirs and pools in the Jordan Valley (for example Kafrayn, Shuna, Al Arab and Birket al Rais), also at Aqaba and formerly at Azraq. It is recorded mainly between mid September and late March, with some birds lingering to late April.

Podiceps cristatus
Great Crested Grebe

AR: Ghawass mutawaj
GE: Haubentaucher

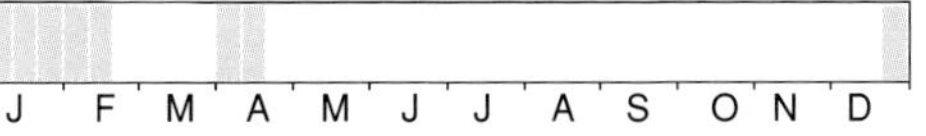

A scarce winter visitor with records of ones and twos from Aqaba, Shuna Reservoir and Azraq.

Most sightings are during late December to February, but there are two records from the Gulf of Aqaba during the period 10-19 April.

Podiceps nigricollis
Black-necked Grebe

AR: Ghatāss aswad er-raqbah
GE: Schwarzhalstaucher

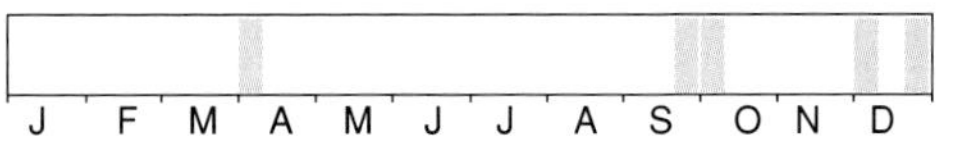

A scarce migrant and winterer recorded at Azraq, Al Khirba as Samra, Ghadir Burqu' and Aqaba in April, September-October and December. It usually occurs as singles, but 13 were counted on Qa' al Azraq on 5 April 1991.

Calonectris diomedea
Cory's Shearwater

AR: Hayem al-mā'a al-kouri
GE: Gelbschnabel-Sturmtaucher

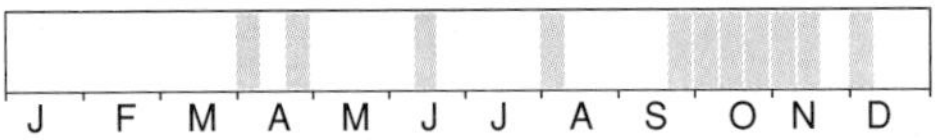

J F M A M J J A S O N D

Uncommon in the Gulf of Aqaba, mainly in summer and autumn, but with records in most months. Peak counts are of six in April, six in August, and five in October, so 50+ on 20 June 1992 was an unusually high number.

Puffinus griseus
Sooty Shearwater

AR: Hayem al-mā'a al-ramadi
GE: Dunkler Sturmtaucher

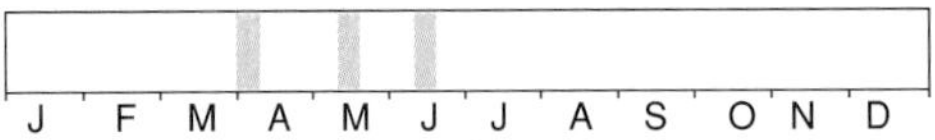

J F M A M J J A S O N D

Vagrant: one off Aqaba on 13-14 May 1991, at least two on 20 June 1992 and one on the early date of 7 April 1994.

Sula leucogaster
Brown Booby

AR: Ateesh
GE: Weißbauchtölpel

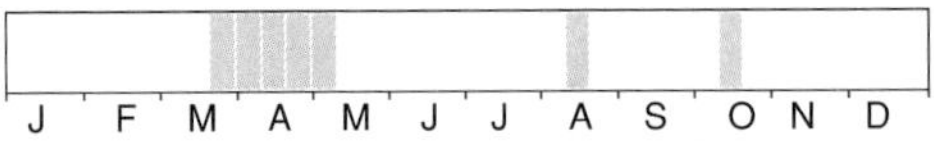

J F M A M J J A S O N D

A rare visitor to the head of the Gulf of Aqaba, with up to three seen in March to May, August, and October. Based on evidence elsewhere in the Gulf of Aqaba, however, it could be observed in any month. It is most likely to be seen patrolling up and down the coast, or resting on the buoys and rafts off the harbour.

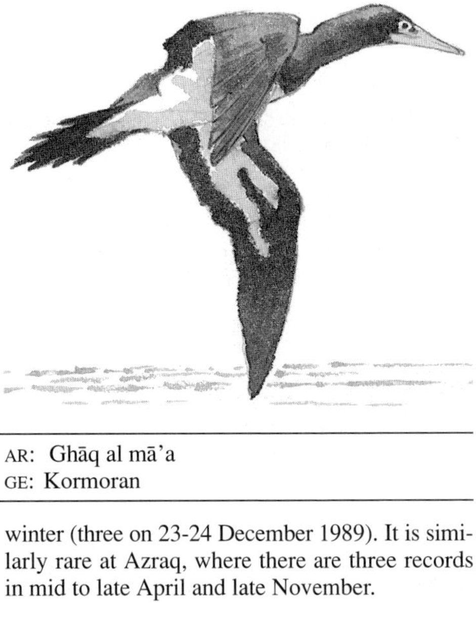

Phalacrocorax carbo
Cormorant

AR: Ghāq al mā'a
GE: Kormoran

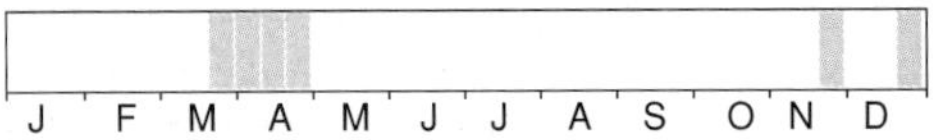

J F M A M J J A S O N D

A scarce bird, found in small numbers in the Gulf of Aqaba in late March to late April and rarely in winter (three on 23-24 December 1989). It is similarly rare at Azraq, where there are three records in mid to late April and late November.

Phalacrocorax pygmeus
Pygmy Cormorant

GE: Zwergscharbe

Regular winter parties were recorded at the Yarmuk estuary reservoir prior to 1946, but it has not been recorded subsequently as a result of loss of breeding habitat in neighbouring countries.

Anhinga melanogaster
Darter

AR: Zuqq
GE: Schlangenhalsvogel

In 1946 this African species was described as a common winter visitor to the Yarmuk estuary reservoir (September to March). In about 1955 its breeding grounds in the swamps of Lake Antioch (Turkey) were drained, and it subsequently became extinct throughout this part of its range.

Pelecanus onocrotalus
White Pelican

AR: Baja'a abiad
GE: Rosapelikan

J F M A M J J A S O N D

Possibly a regular winter visitor in small numbers to Azraq in the past, but definite records are few, and all are before 1970. There are only four recent sightings: 40 at Aqaba on 25 April 1984, two at Al Khirba as Samra on 31 August 1990, a flock of 350 over Al Manshiyya on 8 November 1991, and 130 flying south over Azraq on 9 November 1994. The latter were probably passing through to winter further south, since there are no suitable sites in Jordan.

Botaurus stellaris
Bittern

AR: Al-wāq
GE: Rohrdommel

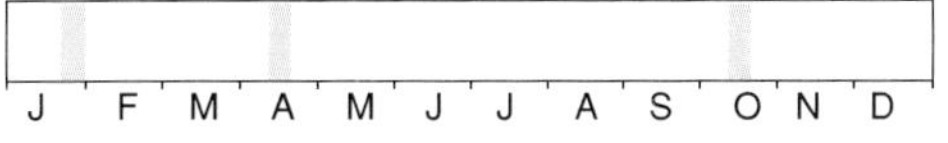

A rare winter visitor to Azraq and the northern Jordan Valley, but unfortunately most records refer to birds being shot for 'sport' or are in museum collections. Singles seen at Azraq on 13 April 1985 and 12 October 1989 are the only sight records.

Ixobrychus minutus
Little Bittern

AR: Al wāq es-sagheer
GE: Zwergdommel

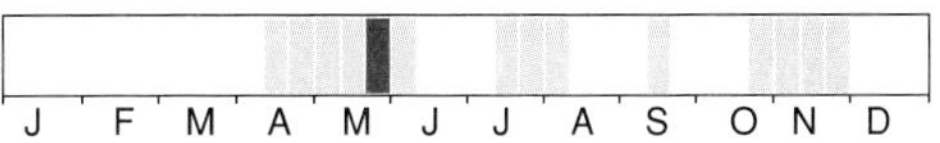

When Azraq was at its best, this was a fairly common resident breeding bird in rushy areas. It is now mainly restricted to passage times, with a few possibly summering and breeding. It is uncommon during mid April to early June, with a peak in late May. In autumn it occurs in smaller numbers from late October to end November.

It is very rare away from Azraq, with singles at Wadi al Hasa on 24 April 1986 and 1 May 1990 and at Aqaba on 14 May 1991.

Nycticorax nycticorax
Night Heron

AR: Ghurāb al-layl
GE: Nachtreiher

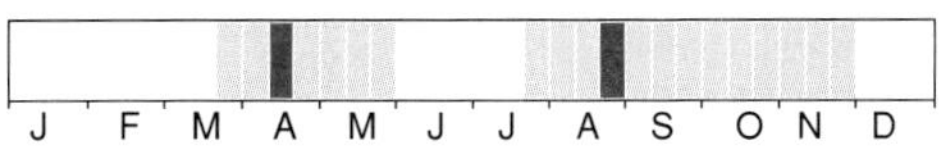

An uncommon passage bird, most frequently seen at Azraq. It occurs in the wetlands in small numbers from late March to late May and late July to late November. Up to 30 were recorded at a daytime roost in Shishan village during April-May 1980 and in April 1985. Previously it was also considered to be a winter visitor to Azraq. At Aqaba small flocks can be seen arriving from the south in spring, and elsewhere there are scattered records from the Jordan Valley, the Rift Margin rivers, Al Khirba as Samra, Shaumari and Ghadir Burqu'. Twenty-seven were recorded at King Talal Dam on 28 March 1994.

Butorides striatus
Green-backed Heron
(Green or Striated Heron)

AR: Balshon akhdar ath-thahr
GE: Mangrovereiher

J F M A M J J A S O N D

A vagrant to the head of the Gulf of Aqaba with an adult, probably the same individual, on 13 May and 5 August 1991 and 14 April 1992.

Ardeola ralloides
Squacco Heron

AR: Wāq abiad sagheer
GE: Rallenreiher

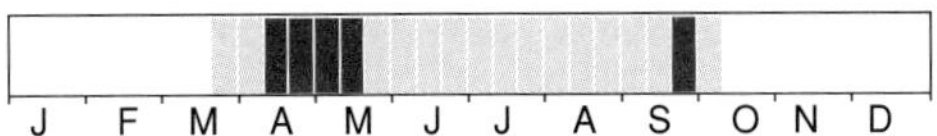

In the late 1960s there were several small breeding colonies in the heart of the Azraq marsh, with 14 pairs in one clump of mature *Arundo donax*; however, there has been no suggestion of breeding in recent years.

A fairly common migrant to Azraq during early April to mid June. Up to 80 were recorded in the 1960s, but recent counts are all under 20. Return passage is evident in autumn from mid July, with a minor peak in late August to early October.

At Aqaba, passage is evident during early April to mid May with small flocks heading north up the gulf. Birds have also been seen there in early August. Mainly singles are recorded elsewhere at the pools, reservoirs and streams of the lower Jordan Valley, Petra and Shaumari.

Bubulcus ibis
Cattle Egret

AR: Abu qardān
GE: Kuhreiher

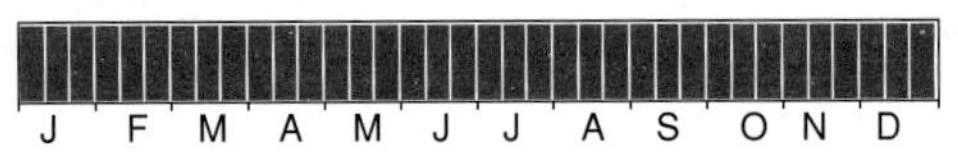

A fairly common non-breeding resident of the Jordan Valley, where it is found on agricultural land, near rivers, and at reservoirs. It is most common in winter when groups of up to 10 are widespread. A maximum of 43 have been counted by the Jordan River.

Elsewhere it is only recorded on passage in small numbers between mid April to early June and mid September to October. At these times birds have been recorded at Azraq, Shaumari, Ar Ruwayshid, Al Khirba as Samra and Aqaba.

Egretta gularis
Western Reef Heron

AR: Balshon as-sakhr
GE: Küstenreiher

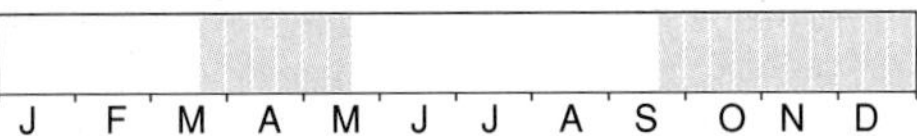

A few wandering individuals can usually be found at the head of the Gulf of Aqaba in at least March-May and September-December. It is most often seen on the beaches south towards the Saudi border, and white phase or slightly pied birds typically outnumber dark phase birds.

Egretta garzetta
Little Egret

AR: Ibn al-mā'a as-sagheer
GE: Seidenreiher

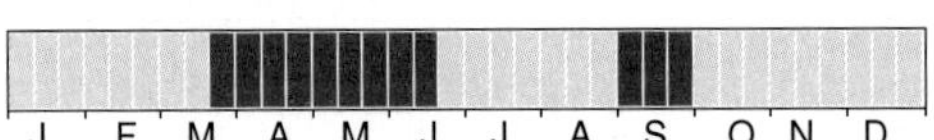

A common non-breeding bird seen at wetland sites throughout the year, with the largest numbers in spring. Passage begins in late March, but mid April to late May sees the largest number of migrants, with 41 at Azraq on 3 May 1991. Northerly passage can be observed at Aqaba, and the reservoirs on the edge of the Jordan Valley are also visited by migrants. Less expectedly, birds have stopped off at Wadi al Butm and irrigated fields at Disi. Small summering flocks of 12-15 have remained at Azraq and Shuna Reservoir through to the end of July, a time when autumn passage begins. Numbers in autumn are much less than in spring with up to 11 at Azraq and Al Khirba as Samra, mainly in September.

A number of this common migrant remain through the winter in the Jordan Valley and Southern Ghor. At this season there are records at Kafrayn Reservoir (45), Al Manshiyya (6), the Dead Sea, and As Safi. At Azraq very few have been seen in winter.

Egretta intermedia
Yellow-billed Egret (Intermediate Egret)

AR: Wāq asfar al-menqār
GE: Mittelreiher

Vagrant: one near As Safi on 23 April 1963.

Egretta alba
Great White Egret

AR: Ibn al-mā'a
GE: Silberreiher

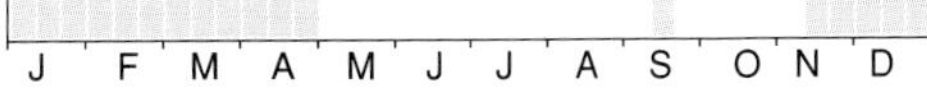

A scarce winter visitor and spring migrant; numbers are restricted by the lack of suitable habitat, though hundreds are present in neighbouring countries. Small numbers (up to 11) formerly wintered at Azraq, but it is now very rare there and mostly seen on spring migration. A few also winter in the Jordan Valley at sites such as Al Manshiyya and Kafrayn Reservoir. At Aqaba a few occur in April, and there are also a few spring records from the Zarqa River and the King Talal Dam. It has been recorded from mid November to late April, but from as early as September in the past.

Ardea cinerea
Grey Heron

AR: Balshon (ramādi) senjābi
GE: Graureiher

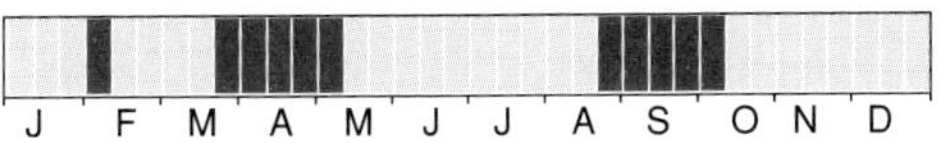

A common migrant occurring in all months, but never recorded breeding. The main passage periods occur from late March to early May and from late August to late September. Peak counts include 28 at Aqaba on 9 April 1990, 30 on 8 October 1994, 24 at Al Khirba as Samra on 31 August 1990, 20 at Azraq on 15 September 1989 and 10 by the Dead Sea on 4 May 1990.

Only small numbers remain through the winter at wetland sites in the Jordan Valley, Dead Sea, Al Khirba as Samra, Azraq and Aqaba. A roost of 72 counted on the shore of King Talal Dam on 3 February 1990 is therefore exceptional.

Ardea purpurea
Purple Heron

AR: Balshon urjouāni
GE: Purpurreiher

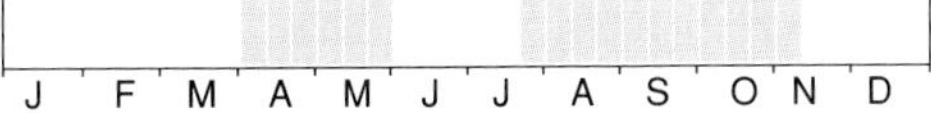

In the 1960s three or four pairs bred at Azraq in tall dense reeds, but this population appears to have died out due to habitat loss.

At that time there was also a large spring passage through Azraq with up to 40, possibly 50-100 on peak days. Numbers are now much reduced with only one to three in mid April to late May and between late July and early October.

Elsewhere it has been recorded between Qasr Amra and Shaumari, at King Talal Dam, Al Khirba as Samra, Wadi al Mujib, Suwayma and Aqaba, and on the Jordan River.

Ciconia nigra
Black Stork

AR: Al laq laq al-aswad
GE: Schwarzstorch

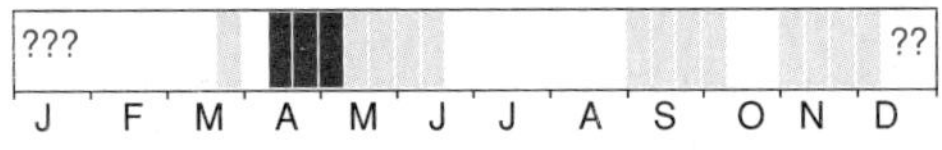

Last century there were reports that Black Storks bred on oak trees in the Northern Highlands (then known as Bashan), but Canon Tristram failed to see any.

An uncommon passage bird during mid April to late June, and rare in early September to early October. The earliest sighting comes from Petra on 30 March. It is most frequent at Azraq, where small numbers occur annually, and on passage along the Rift Margins. Sixteen were observed flying NE over Shuna Reservoir on 27 April 1990, and up to seven have been seen on autumn passage

over Wadi Rum and Dana. A small number can be seen in the Jordan Valley in winter with birds presumably wandering from the fish pools to the west of the river.

Ciconia ciconia
White Stork

AR: Al laq laq al-abiad
GE: Weißstorch

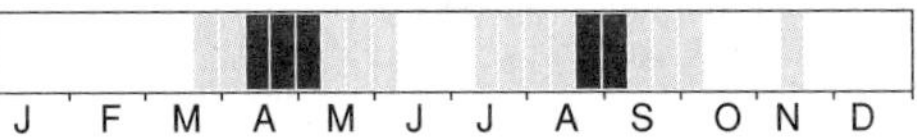

An abundant migrant through Jordan, especially in autumn when the main migration path is apparently further east than in the spring. At all seasons, however, Azraq appears to be off the main route.

It occurs in rather small numbers (rarely over 50) in the spring, from late March to mid May, a few tail-enders still passing into early June. Umm Qays, in the far north-west, appears to be the only locality where good numbers pass at this season. Autumn passage extends from mid July to early October, but the majority are consistently seen around 30 August to 1 September. Based on rather limited data, it appears that the birds enter Jordan near Ar Ramtha, stop off to roost at Al Khirba as Samra, then use the Zarqa River valley as a route westwards to the rift valley which they then follow south. Flocks of one or more thousands have been seen between Ar Ramtha and Amman, at Al Khirba as Samra, over the Zarqa River, over Zai, and north of the Dead Sea. Only occasionally do significant numbers appear at Azraq.

Plegadis falcinellus
Glossy Ibis

AR: Abu minjall
GE: Sichler

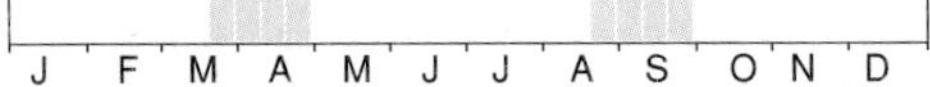

A rare passage bird at Azraq during late March to late April (rarely early June), and late August to late September. Usually only small numbers are involved, but one group of 11 was seen in mid April 1969. It is a rarity at Aqaba, with three records of singles in April, but 11 were seen on 7 April 1994.

Platalea leucorodia
Spoonbill

AR: Abu mila'qa
GE: Löffler

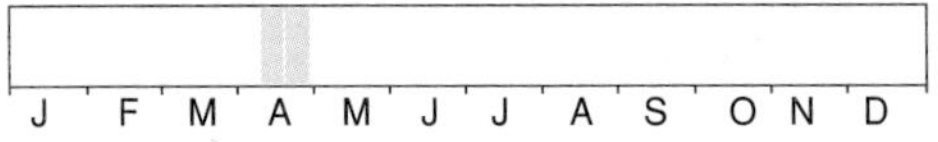

A vagrant at Azraq, with ten on 26 April 1983, three on 15 April 1989, and a single on 19 April 1991.

Phoenicopterus ruber
Greater Flamingo

AR: An-nehām
GE: Rosaflamingo

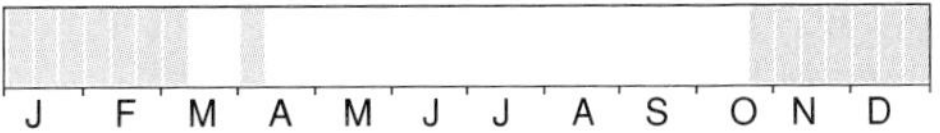

Although small numbers may have regularly wintered at Azraq in the past, there are few published records: an immature in late October 1922, a record in January 1967, an immature shot on 18 December 1968, three adults seen on 14 December 1991 and an immature present during 10 January to 14 February 1992. Elsewhere, an adult was seen at Suwayma (Dead Sea) during 5-10 March 1992, and 14 flew past Aqaba on 10 April 1994.

Anser albifrons
White-fronted Goose

AR: Ewazzā gharrā'a
GE: Bläßgans

A winter vagrant at Azraq, with two on 13-18 January 1979 and eight on 14 December 1991.

Anser anser
Greylag Goose

AR: Ewazzā rabdā'a
GE: Graugans

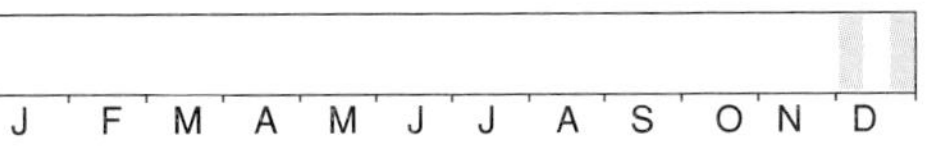

Geese (maybe Greylags) were reported as 'common in winter' at Azraq in the 1920s at a time when many were apparently shot by the Royal Air Force. Greylag Geese were reported in small numbers in the 1960s, between one and four each year (for example singles were seen on 1st and 10 December and four were reported on 22 December).

Tadorna ferruginea
Ruddy Shelduck

AR: Abu furwah
GE: Rostgans

J F M A M J J A S O N D

A vagrant: two at Azraq in April 1955, three on 13-30 January 1979, one on 13th and on 29-30 April 1985, and five on 7 February 1992.

Last century, Canon Tristram reported that Ruddy Shelduck were found in the As Safi area at the south end of the Dead Sea, and probably bred in the cliffs of the Rift Margin. He also reported that in the north they bred among the Griffon Vulture colonies.

Tadorna tadorna
Shelduck

AR: Shahraman
GE: Brandgans

J F M A M J J A S O N D

A pair bred at Azraq in 1990, when a brood of 15 chicks was seen on the flooded qa' on 24 May. It was previously suspected of breeding at this site, with four or five pairs courting in the 1960s.

As with all duck species (see below), the status of the Shelduck in Jordan is constrained by the availability of wetland habitat at Azraq (nowadays mainly the flooded qa'). In wet winters it can be an abundant winter and spring visitor, but in dry years it can go unrecorded. Peaks for recent winters are: 1982/83 (150 on 26-29 April), 1988/89 (120 on 21 March), 1989/90 (13 on 10 February), 1990/91 (2 on 3 May) and 1991/92 (first two on 30 November, then record numbers with a peak of 3490 during January and February 1992).

In addition, up to 40 were seen at Suwayma (Dead Sea) in March-April 1992, having apparently wintered there. Two recorded at Shaumari on 4 June 1976 were at a strange place on an unusual date for Shelduck.

Anas penelope
Wigeon

AR: Suwāee
GE: Pfeifente

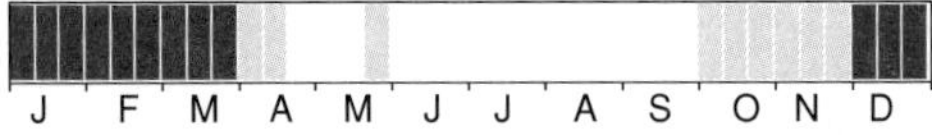

Recorded at Azraq as an abundant winter resident when conditions permit. Some 5000 were recorded around the limits of the marsh on 15 January 1969, but only 40-60 were counted in February 1979. With the recent drying of the marshland, numbers in 1989/90 and 1990/91 were extremely low, but in 1991/92 100 were estimated among the duck flocks on the flooded qa'. The main winter influx occurs between December and March, but Wigeon have been recorded from early October to late May.

Large numbers can occur at the head of the Gulf of Aqaba in spring (for example, 100 on 28 March 1994), but it is only rarely seen elsewhere. Up to ten have been recorded at the Dead Sea, Shuna Reservoir and Al Khirba as Samra.

Anas falcata
Falcated Duck

AR: Hathaf menjali
GE: Sichelente

A winter vagrant: a female was shot at Azraq on 10 January 1969.

Anas strepera
Gadwall

AR: Samāri al-muhājira
GE: Schnatterente

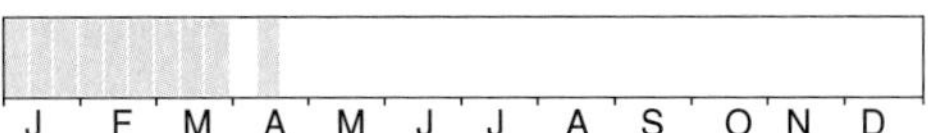

A scarce winter visitor to Azraq, with small numbers frequenting the marsh and flooded qa' from early January to mid April. The maximum number recorded was 25 in January-February 1979. There are no records from elsewhere.

Anas crecca
Teal

AR: Hathaf shatawi
GE: Krickente

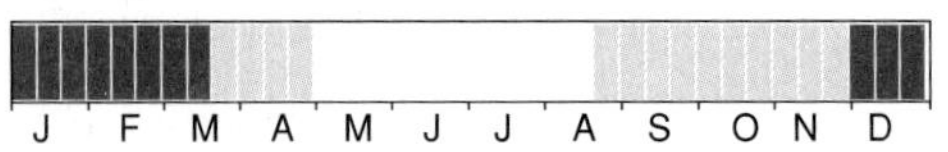

The commonest winter duck at Azraq, with large numbers wintering in the past, but now only present when the qa' is flooded. About 15,000 were present in January 1969; but there were only 1520 on 18 February 1979. The recent maximum after the marshes had dried was 300 on 26 December 1989, but on some occasions none were seen. However, in 1991/92 over 6000 were seen on the flooded qa', appearing only days after the rains.

The first arrivals of the autumn appear in late August, although the winter influx is not until December. Most have left by mid March, but considerable numbers remain into April in some years.

Elsewhere in Jordan, it occurs less frequently and in smaller numbers as a passage migrant. There are records of 300 on the Dead Sea at Suwayma on 10-13 March 1992, 40 on a sandpit east of Al Mafraq on 16 December 1989, 20 at Al Khirba as Samra on 18 October 1990, and 10 at Ghadir Burqu' on 21-22 September 1991. Reservoirs and desert flood pools are also potential sites for this species.

Anas platyrhynchos
Mallard

AR: Al-birkeh
GE: Stockente

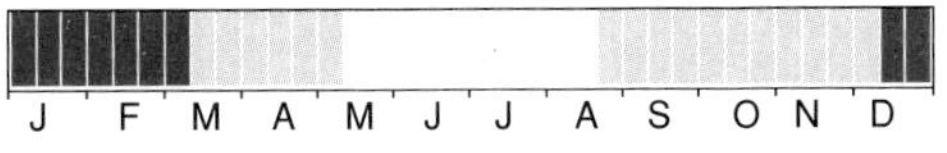

In the 1960s it was estimated that probably nine to 15, but possibly 30, pairs bred in the freshwater marshes at Azraq. It is now presumably extinct there, but it may also breed on the Jordan River.

A few are present at Azraq throughout the year, but there is a large influx in winter (mid December to early March) if conditions are suitable. Up to 500 have been counted deep in the marsh or on the flooded qa'. Up to 40 have also occurred in winter at Shuna Reservoir, with smaller numbers at Kafrayn Reservoir, Mafraq, Jordan River, King Talal Dam, Zarqa River and Al Khirba as Samra.

Anas acuta
Pintail

AR: Balbool
GE: Spießente

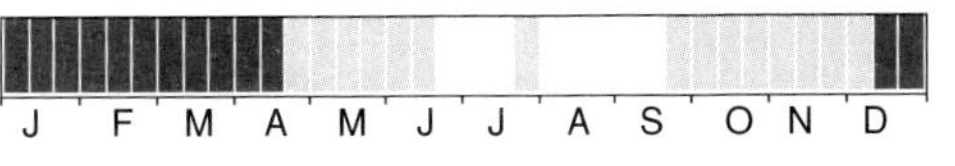

Formerly the second most common duck wintering at Azraq but now, even when conditions are suitable, the numbers are much reduced: 2000 in early December 1968, 400 on 20 February 1979 and 70 on 18 April 1992.

In dry years and at other sites, it occurs principally as an uncommon spring migrant from mid March to late May: for example at King Talal Dam (60 on 20 March 1992) and the Dead Sea (50 on 13 March 1992). Significant numbers also occur on spring passage in the Gulf of Aqaba, before heading off north. After a few mid-summer appearances, it also occurs in autumn from late September, for example 30 at Azraq on 25 October 1990, and 50 at Aqaba on 8-9 October 1994.

Anas querquedula
Garganey

AR: Hathaf saifi
GE: Knäkente

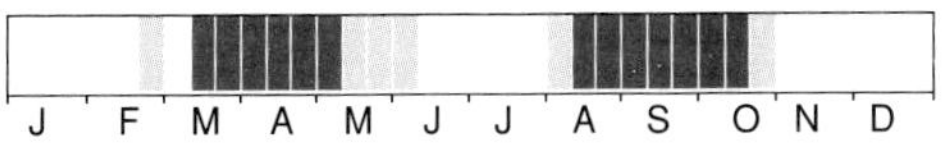

In the 1960s up to ten pairs, some in courtship flight, were seen at Azraq oasis during May. Displaying birds were last recorded in 1985. However, breeding has never been proven.

A very common migrant duck, recorded on spring and autumn passage (mid March to early June and early August to late October). Twelve seen at Azraq on 22 February constitute the earliest record. It is most common at Azraq in spring (up to 300) and at Al Khirba as Samra and Ghadir Burqu' in autumn (230 on 7 September 1990 and 250 on 22 September 1991 respectively). It also occurs in moderate numbers at King Talal Dam, Qa' Khanna, and in the Gulf of Aqaba, but it can turn up on any wetland site. Over 500 were seen at Aqaba sewage works on 8-9 October 1994. It was formerly reported as a rare winter bird at Azraq – one of few sites north of the Sahara.

Anas clypeata
Shoveler

AR: Al-keesh
GE: Löffelente

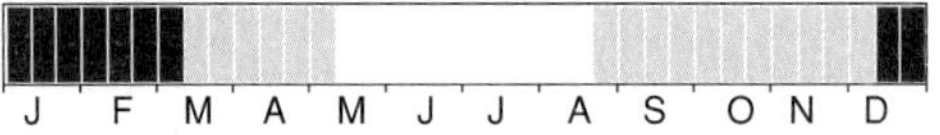

A very common winter visitor to Azraq from October to mid April when conditions are suitable. Up to 2000 were present in 1968/69 and, more recently, 1000 were estimated on the flooded qa' in February 1992.

Elsewhere, and at Azraq in dry years, it is rare in winter and occurs mainly as an uncommon spring and autumn migrant with counts of 75 at the Dead Sea on 10 March 1992, 70 at Shuna Reservoir on 12 April and 53 at Azraq on 26 April 1990. Significant numbers can also be found in the Gulf of Aqaba in spring, and 100 were counted on 8-9 October 1994. Smaller numbers, up to 15, have been seen at Al Khirba as Samra and Ghadir Burqu'. The species can be seen in Jordan from late August to early May.

Marmaronetta angustirostris
Marbled Duck (Marbled Teal)

AR: Hathaf mu'araq
GE: Marmelente

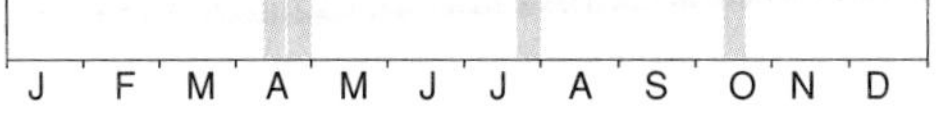

A rare spring migrant to Azraq which has bred on one occasion. It was first recorded at Azraq in October 1922, but not again until 27 April 1983. There have been some five mid to late April records at this site, with a maximum count of 12 birds. Although the 1983 record involved paired birds, the breeding record at Azraq fish pools in 1990 was unexpected in that no migrants were seen that spring, and there were no previous records from the fish pools site. The brood of seven large young was seen on 23 July, but not subsequently.

Birds have also been reported by locals along the Jordan River (for example, near Damiya and Al Adasiyya), and it is thought that a small number of pairs breed in the riverside reedbeds, and also spend the winter there.

Netta rufina
Red-crested Pochard

AR: Wanās
GE: Kolbenente

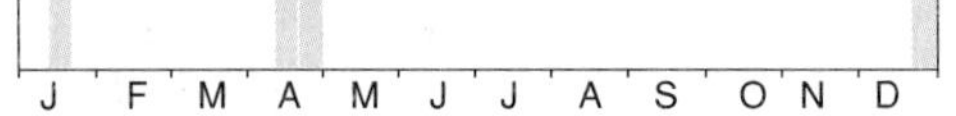

A very rare visitor to Azraq: one shot on 29 December 1969, two shot on 12 January 1979, one seen 20 April 1984 and two seen 15 April 1988.

Aythya ferina
Pochard

AR: Butt ahmar
GE: Tafelente

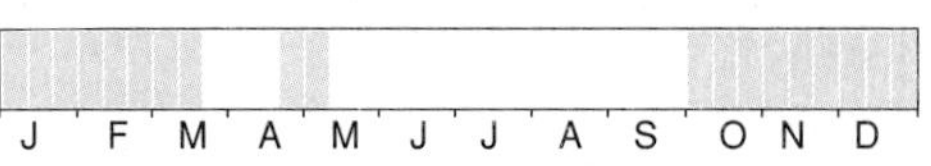

An uncommon winter visitor and passage bird to Azraq (the largest count being of only six), Al Khirba as Samra (three), Shuna Reservoir, and Aqaba. Most occur from early October to mid March, but a few linger as late as early May.

Aythya nyroca
Ferruginous Duck

AR: Az-zarqāwi al-ahmar
GE: Moorente

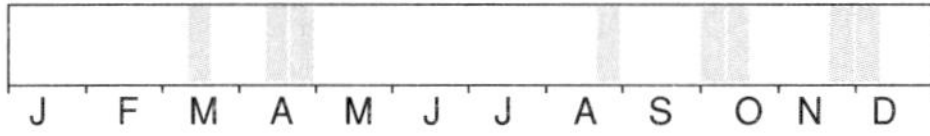

Although it was reported as the commonest duck at Azraq in October 1922, it has proved to be a rather scarce passage migrant subsequently. Singles were shot at Azraq on 29 November and 6 December 1969, followed by four sight records during 14-29 April in the 1980s. One was seen at Aqaba on 29 April 1985, two at Al Khirba as Samra on 31 August 1990, nine at King Talal Dam on 20 March 1992, and three at Aqaba on 9 October 1994.

Aythya fuligula
Tufted Duck

AR: Butt Abu Khasseh
GE: Reiherente

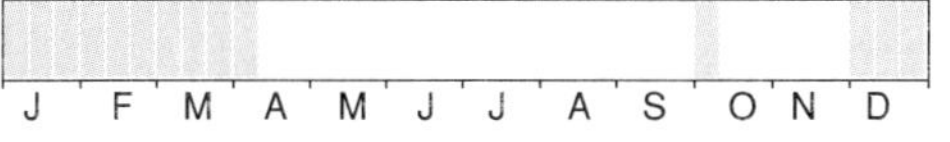

An uncommon winter and spring migrant to wetland sites. Flocks are occasionally seen on the flooded Azraq qa': 80 on 21 March 1989, 50 on 10 April 1990, and 60 on 14 December 1991. It can also occur in fairly large numbers in the Gulf of Aqaba on spring passage, for example 30 on 28 March 1994. Otherwise, it is a rare winter visitor (early December to early April) in very small numbers to reservoirs in the southern Jordan Valley and even to desert flood pools.

Pernis apivorus
Honey Buzzard

AR: Hawām an-nahel
GE: Wespenbussard

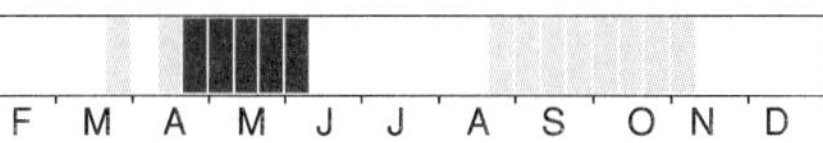

A fairly common passage migrant, recorded mainly between late April and early June and late August to early November. Although the earliest arrival on record is on 29 March, the vast majority pass through during early May. Most are involved in a northerly passage along the Rift Margin highlands, with huge numbers on some days: for example 650 over Petra on 10 May 1983, 750 on 2 May 1990, and 1000 between Petra and Aqaba on 3 May 1990. Smaller numbers can also be seen at Aqaba, in the Jordan Valley and Northern Highlands, and at Azraq. Away from the Rift Margin, the largest recorded passage was 100 over Qa' al Hibabiya on 1 May 1991, in poor weather.

It is considerably less numerous in autumn, when the majority of records are from Azraq and other Eastern Desert watering sites, mainly in mid September.

Milvus migrans
Black Kite

AR: Al-hudāt as-sawda'a
GE: Schwarzmilan

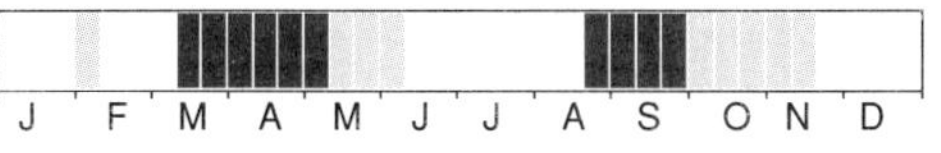

Black Kites do not breed in Jordan, but the record of a pair of yellow-billed birds (probably *M. m. aegyptius*) seen at Petra on 13 March 1923 has been quoted as a case of probable breeding.

A fairly common spring and autumn passage migrant, recorded mainly in mid March to early May and late August to the end of September. In spring it is about three times more common than in autumn, and it is most often recorded on passage along the Rift Margins, with a peak of 200 NE at Petra on 5 April 1988. It is also recorded elsewhere in Jordan in smaller numbers, with up to 76 birds roosting in the marsh at Azraq. As with many other raptors, autumn sees a concentration at Eastern Desert watering sites, with 30 at Azraq on 22 September 1989.

It is absent in winter, but has been recorded at Aqaba as late as 15 November and at Wadi al Mujib as early as 9 February.

Milvus milvus
Red Kite

AR: Hada'a hamra'a
GE: Rotmilan

There are three old records: one shot near Aqaba in March 1946, several seen at the King Hussein Bridge on 17 March 1946 and two seen flying north at Wadi Dana on 29 April 1955. There are also a few more recent, but unsubstantiated records, which are not included here.

Gypaetus barbatus
Lammergeier

AR: Kāsirat al-ithām
GE: Bartgeier

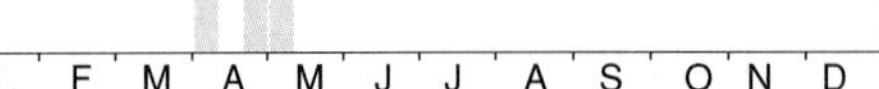

Last century this species frequented the gorges opening onto the Dead Sea and the Jordan Valley, notably the ravines of Wadis al Mujib and Zerqa Ma'in. The last recorded nests were in 1963 and 1966, when at least one pair still bred on Jabal Umm Ishrin (in Wadi Rum). Although absent from here in the late 1970s, occasional sightings in the 1980s suggest that individuals may still be present in the Rum Desert and Aqaba Mountains. Local observers have also reported birds at Wadi al Mujib and Al Fajij (east of Ash Shawbak) in recent years.

Neophron percnopterus
Egyptian Vulture

AR: Ar-rakha'meh (Ash-shooheh)
GE: Schmutzgeier

J F M A M J J A S O N D

A pair may have bred at Petra in 1935, and it definitely bred in the Zarqa River valley in the 1960s. It may also nest at other sites in the Rift Margins, since a few summering birds have been observed at Zerqa Ma'in, Umm ar Rasas, Wadi al Mujib and Disi, as well as in Wadi Araba.

The Egyptian Vulture occurs in rather small numbers on passage with other raptors from early March to early June, peaking in early April. It occurs widely in the Central and Southern Rift Margins, and Eastern Desert. It often roosts on pylons, with 11 counted east of Al Muwaqqar on 6 April 1990. It is far from common in autumn, with a few records at Dana, Azraq and Tulul al Wisad between late August and early October.

Little Bittern, Azraq, May 1991

White Storks, Al Khirba as Samra, August 1990

Squacco Heron, Azraq, May 1992

White Stork, Aqaba, October 1994 (Tim Loseby)

Western Reef Heron, Aqaba, November 1990

Honey Buzzard, adult, Azraq, September 1989

Honey Buzzard, juvenile, Azraq, September 1989

Egyptian Vulture, adult, near Zerqa Ma'in, May 1991

Egyptian Vulture, immature, Wadi al Mujib, June 1991

Griffon Vulture, adult, Fidan, April 1992

Griffon Vulture, immature, Fidan, April 1992

Short-toed Eagle, Azraq, September 1989

Long-legged Buzzard, dark-phase, Shaumari, September 1990

Pallid Harrier, male, Azraq, March 1990

Buzzard, adult, vulpinus *subspecies, Dana, April 1990*

Montagu's Harrier, female, Ghadir Burqu', September 1991

Montagu's Harrier, male, Qasr al Kharana, April 1990

Steppe Eagle, Shaumari, April 1983 (Peter Boye)

Bonelli's Eagle, Nepal, December 1984 (Tim Loseby)

Verreaux's Eagle, adult, South Africa (Roger Tidman)

Steppe Eagle, immature, Azraq, September 1990

Imperial Eagle, adult, Wadi al Butm, November 1990

Golden Eagle, pair, Wadi as Sarhan region, May 1990

Osprey, Azraq, September 1989

Chukar, Dana, October 1994 (Tim Loseby)

Sooty Falcon, Bahrain
(Dr Mike Hill/Nature Photographers)

Hobby, Al Khirba as Samra, October 1990

Corncrake, Azraq, May 1991

Baillon's Crake, juvenile, Azraq, July 1990

Black-winged Stilts, Al Khirba as Samra, May 1990

Black-winged Stilt, immature, Azraq, August 1989

Cream-coloured Courser, Qasr al Kharana, June 1990

Cream-coloured Courser, Qasr al Kharana, June 1990

Collared Pratincole, Al Khirba as Samra, May 1990

Kentish Plover, Azraq, May 1990

Caspian Plover, Azraq, April 1990

White-tailed Plover, Azraq, April 1992

Spur-winged Plover, Aqaba, October 1994 (Tim Loseby)

Marsh Sandpiper, Azraq, July 1991

Temminck's Stint, Azraq, September 1990

Common Sandpiper, Qa Hibabiya, May 1991

Curlew Sandpiper, adult, Al Khirba as Samra, May 1990

Gyps fulvus
Griffon Vulture

AR: An-nisr
GE: Gänsegeier

J F M A M J J A S O N D

Last century there were many breeding colonies in the Rift Margin ravines, for example the Zarqa River valley, Wadi Zerqa Ma'in and Wadi al Mujib, some of them containing over 100 nests. There was even a colony in a gorge near Amman. A dramatic decline is evident, however. In recent years Griffon Vultures have been recorded in the spring and summer at only four sites with suitable breeding cliffs: Yarmuk River, Wadi al Mujib, Wadi Dana, and Jabal Umm Ishrin. Although no active nests have been located, many well-used roosting sites can be seen on the cliffs of Wadi Dana.

Away from the Rift Margins, where wandering birds can be seen from Ar Ramtha south to Ma'an, a few also venture to the Azraq area, Wadi al Butm, and southern Wadi as Sarhan in March-April and October-December.

Torgos tracheliotus
Lappet-faced Vulture

AR: Nisr thu al-uthun
GE: Ohrengeier

Vagrant: one roosted with two Griffon Vultures, then flew away north-west at Wadi al Butm on 16 April 1963.

Although there are no published records from elsewhere, locals have reported birds from Wadi Araba and Wadi Dahil (Fidan area). These will have undoubtedly been wanderers from the remnant population which still bred until recently on the Israeli side of Wadi Araba. Interestingly, some ten pairs still breed only 50km away from Jordan in the Tubayq mountains of Saudi Arabia.

Aegypius monachus
Black Vulture (Monk Vulture)

AR: An-nisr al-aswad
GE: Mönchsgeier

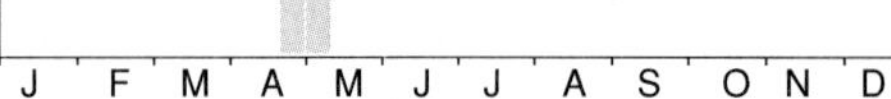

J F M A M J J A S O N D

In 1888 Canon Tristram reported that the Black Vulture occurred sparingly on the plains of Moab, but with seldom more than two seen together. At that time a small breeding population may have existed in Jordan. More recently it has only been recorded as a vagrant, with singles at Busayra in spring 1955, Qal'at al Hasa on 24 April 1963 and near Ma'an on 4 May 1963. Locals also report it as a scarce winter visitor to the Hisban-Madaba Plains.

In the early 1990s, breeding was suspected at Harrat al Harrah (Saudi Arabia) near the border with Jordan. One was also seen from Israel on 8 December 1990 landing in acacias north of Aqaba.

Circaetus gallicus
Short-toed Eagle

AR: Eqāb al-hayāt
GE: Schlangenadler

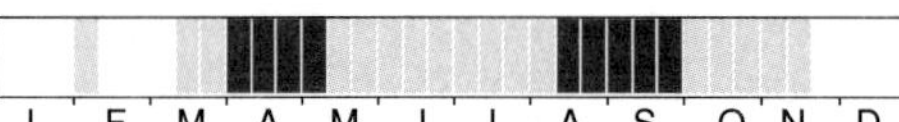

J F M A M J J A S O N D

A tree nest found in the Rum Desert in 1992 is the first proof of breeding in Jordan since it bred at Hisban about 1865. However, the species may breed more widely in the Northern Highlands and Rift Margins, as hunting birds and displaying pairs have been observed in potential breeding areas there.

A rather uncommon but widely distributed summer migrant, recorded between 6 February and 17 November, with passage most evident from mid March to mid May and again from late July to late September. Migrants are most often seen along the Rift Margins, and less frequently in the Eastern Desert and Azraq areas.

Circus aeruginosus
Marsh Harrier

AR: Marazat al-batā'eh
GE: Rohrweihe

J F M A M J J A S O N D

Formerly a resident at Azraq, with three or four pairs almost certainly breeding in the 1960s (although nesting was never proven). However, since 1985 there have been very few summer records, suggesting that the local breeding population may now be extinct.

Otherwise it is a fairly common passage migrant in spring and autumn, recorded between mid March and mid May, and from late August to mid October. It occurs along the Rift Margins as a scarce addition to the mixed flocks of passage raptors, as well as in the desert. A total of 14 flew south at Dana on 7 October 1994.

A small population of up to eight birds still winters at Azraq, and there is some evidence that a few also winter in the Rift Valley and Southern Ghor.

Circus cyaneus
Hen Harrier

AR: Marazat ad-dajaj
GE: Kornweihe

J F M A M J J A S O N D

A scarce winter visitor, recorded mainly in the open country of the Eastern and Basalt Deserts between late September and early April, with a few lingering to early May. The ungrazed, and hence more vegetated desert at Shaumari is a favoured site. A migrant was seen at Aqaba on 7 April 1994.

Circus macrourus
Pallid Harrier

AR: Marazah baghtha'a
GE: Steppenweihe

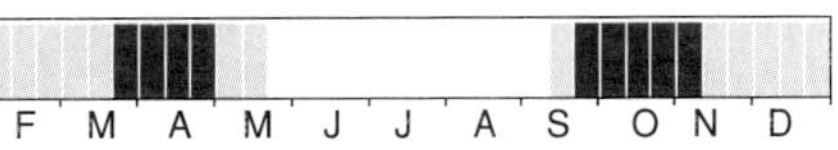

An uncommon passage raptor, to be seen from late March to mid May and from mid September to late November along the Rift Margin migration path and in the Eastern and Basalt Deserts. It can be seen with other raptors spiralling high in the sky, but at dawn and dusk it descends to search for roost sites. It can interrupt its migration to hunt at sites like Azraq.

A small number also winter in the desert and open agricultural areas of the Eastern Desert and Steppes, notably at Azraq and Shaumari.

Circus pygargus
Montagu's Harrier

AR: Marazat muntājou (Abu shooda)
GE: Wiesenweihe

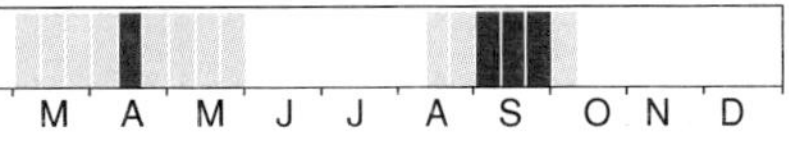

A rare spring, and fairly common autumn passage migrant, recorded early March to late May and mid August to early October. The majority of records come from Azraq and other desert watering-holes in September, but it occurs widely along the Rift Margins as well as in desert areas during both seasons.

Accipiter gentilis
Goshawk

AR: Al bāz
GE: Habicht

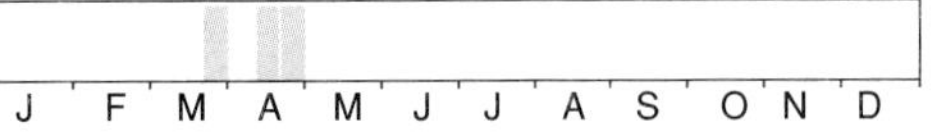

This species has been recorded only rarely on spring passage, with singles at Azraq, Shaumari, Wadi al Butm, Zarqa River, At Tafila, Petra, and Aqaba between late March and late April. In Jordan, as elsewhere, care should be taken with *Accipiter* identification.

Accipiter nisus
Sparrowhawk

AR: Bāsheq
GE: Sperber

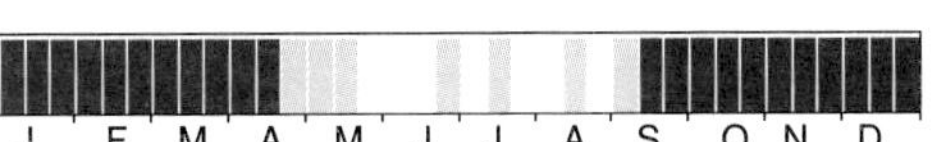

Infrequent sightings around the pine woods of Dibbin and the Amman National Park during the summer months could conceivably involve local breeding birds.

A fairly common winter visitor, spring and autumn migrant, recorded mainly from mid September to mid April, with a few as late as 12 May. It is a winter bird of the Highlands from Umm Qays south to Aqaba, although it is most frequently seen in ones and twos in the wooded parts of the Northern Highlands and at Azraq. Spring passage is light, and peaks in early to mid April.

Accipiter brevipes
Levant Sparrowhawk

AR: Al baidaq
GE: Kurzfangsperber

J F M A M J J A S O N D

An abundant spring migrant recorded along the Rift Margins in late April and early May; the earliest date being 12 April. Passage is restricted to about ten days each year, and the birds pass through in huge flocks, which roost over-night. Examples of this spectacular passage include: 1680 west of Na'ur on 1 May 1990, 2000 over Wadi al Mujib on 30 April 1990 and 8000 spiralling north there on 24 April 1992.

Further east, it is an uncommon migrant at Azraq and Wadi al Butm, but 200 roosted at Shaumari on 15-16 April 1977. It is less common in autumn: 75 roosted at Aqaba on 30 September-1 October 1990.

Buteo buteo vulpinus
Steppe Buzzard

AR: Saqr hawām
GE: Falkenbussard

J F M A M J J A S O N D

By far the most frequently seen passage raptor in Jordan, with huge numbers passing through in spring and autumn. From late March to mid April large numbers use the Rift Margin flyway from Aqaba to the Dead Sea, but at various points the birds then veer off to the east and north-east up tributary wadis to continue their flight to the breeding grounds in Russia. Birds also migrate over the Rum Desert peaks and cross the Ras an Naqab escarpment on their way north. Smaller numbers pass over Azraq and some roost in the marsh there. The spring passage period extends from early March to early May.

No extended counts have yet been made in Jordan, but an estimate of a million passage birds each spring would not be unreasonable. Large counts made over periods of only an hour or two include: 1450 over Aqaba on 28 March 1994, 2000 north-east at Petra on 5 April 1988, 1700 north there on 27 March 1992, 800 north at Fidan on 24 March 1989, 700 north over Wadi Dana on 13 April 1990, and 900 east over As Suwayfiyya (Amman) on 12 April 1990.

Autumn migration, from late September to the end of October, is less dramatic and likely to be more dispersed across the country. Example counts include: 2000 south at Ghadir Burqu' on 29 September 1994, 500 south at Wadi al Butm on 30 September 1994, 250 over the Amman National Park on 22 October 1990, 300 there on 30 September 1991, and 300 at Azraq on 22 September 1989. A total of 5800 were counted passing over Dana between 5-22 October 1994.

There are a few records in November and December, which may be late migrants, so the only mid winter records are: one at Pella on 19 January, and three at Wadi al Mujib on 9 February.

Three main plumage types have been recognised amongst the birds passing through Eilat in spring, and these also occur in Jordan: fox-red morph (60%), grey-brown morph (30%) and dark morph (3-5%), although many intermediates also occur. The grey-brown morph predominated in a late October passage near Amman in 1990.

Buteo rufinus
Long-legged Buzzard

AR: Al-humaimeq at-taweel as-sāqeen
GE: Adlerbussard

J F M A M J J A S O N D

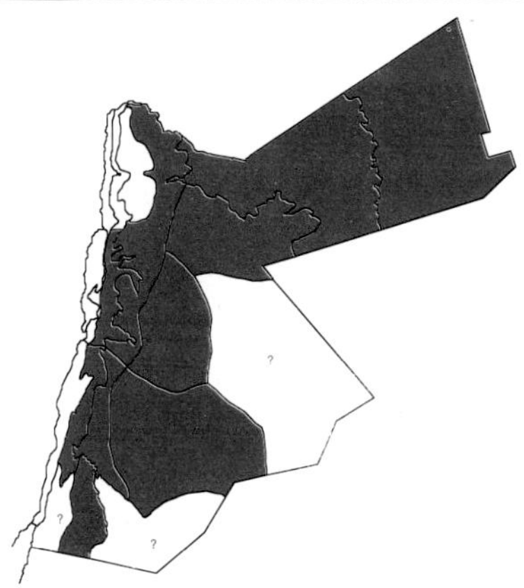

A widespread, but thinly distributed, resident breeding bird found in the arid country of the Rift Margins (from the Zarqa River south to Petra), and the Rum Desert. Cliff nesting has been recorded at Wadi al Hasa, Wadi Rum and Petra. It also occurs, and presumably breeds, in the Eastern, Basalt, and Ar Ruwayshid deserts.

Both normal (pale) and dark phase birds occur, and in 1963 a pair at Wadi Rum was thought to belong to the small North African race *B. r. cirtensis*.

Buteo lagopus
Rough-legged Buzzard

AR: Al-humaimeq al-musarwal
GE: Rauhfußbussard

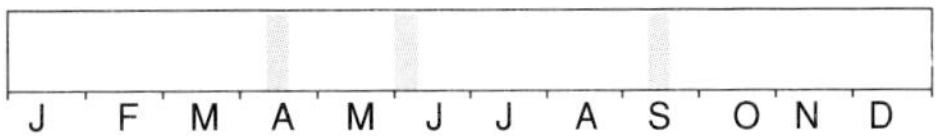

An unexpected vagrant to Azraq with singles on 11 September 1963, 16 April 1965 and 4 June 1969.

Aquila pomarina
Lesser Spotted Eagle

AR: Eqāb saqa'a sughra
GE: Schreiadler

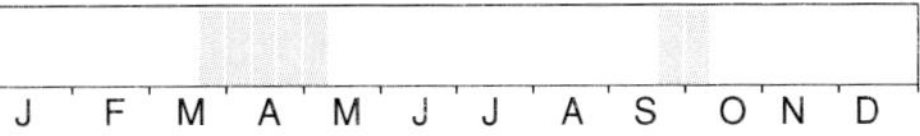

A rather scarce migrant, passing through Jordan in late March to early May and less commonly in late September and October. In spring, most use a route along the Rift Margins, although four were seen heading NW over Wadi al Butm. A count of ten over Aqaba on 28 March 1994 is significant. In autumn, a higher percentage occur in the Eastern and Basalt Deserts, but systematic counts have not been carried out. A total of 18 flew south over Wadi Dana during 7-10 October 1994.

Aquila clanga
Spotted Eagle

AR: Eqāb saqa'a kobra
GE: Schelladler

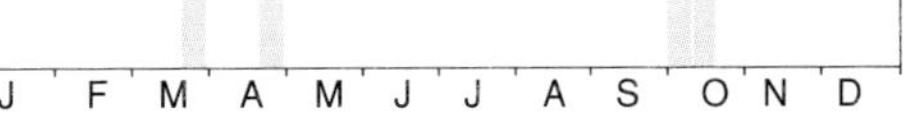

A vagrant: one at Azraq on 18 October 1968, one north over Petra on 21 April 1983, an adult at Aqaba on 26 March 1985, and one south at Wadi Dana on 5 October 1994.

Tristram reported a pair nesting in Wadi Zerqa Ma'in in 1872, but it has long since abandoned any breeding sites it once had in Jordan. A number of these eagles winter around the fish pools immediately to the west and north-west of Jordan. Although there are as yet no sightings on this side of the Jordan Valley birds could well wander across in winter.

Aquila nipalensis
Steppe Eagle

AR: Eqāb al-bādiah
GE: Steppenadler

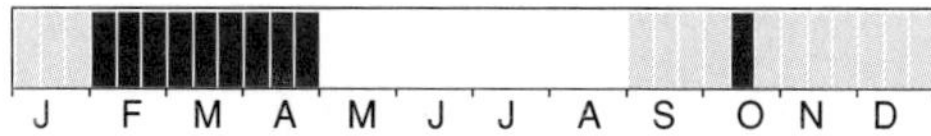

A fairly common passage migrant, mainly in spring but also in autumn. Spring passage starts early with the first adults moving north in early February. Peak passage is not until early to mid April, when most birds passing are immatures. Return autumn passage begins in early September, with a concentration in October, but a few linger into December and January. Since passage in the region starts so early and finishes so late, it is difficult to know if birds are actually wintering in Jordan. Two adults at Aqaba on 23 December, and one at Wadi al Butm on 27 January are the most likely candidates.

Birds are most likely to be seen along the raptor migration routes of the Rift Margins, but Azraq and the Rum Desert are frequently overflown, as are many other desert areas. Peak counts include: 90 over Aqaba on 28 March 1994, 60 above Wadi as Sir on 14 April 1990, 35 at Wadi Dana on 13 April 1990, and a total of 69 migrating south there during 7-22 October 1994. Systematic counting could produce much larger totals.

Aquila heliaca
Imperial Eagle

AR: Malik al eqbān
GE: Kaiseradler

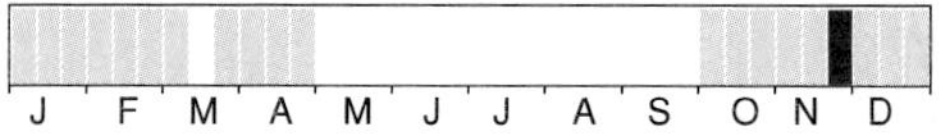

A regular winter visitor in small numbers to a wide area of desert around Azraq during mid November to early March. In the evening of 29 November 1990, up to five adults and three immatures were seen at one site, presumably going to roost, and the whole area may hold up to 20 birds. Locals have also reported wintering/passage birds on the Irbid-Mafraq and Hisban-Madaba Plains (Northern Steppes), and at Dibbin and Burqu'. As a globally threatened species, this winter population is highly significant and needs to be surveyed in detail.

Light spring passage has been noted at Azraq, Wadi Dana and Aqaba during late March to mid April. A small number of autumn migrants have also been seen at Dana, Wadi al Mujib and Disi in October-November.

Aquila chrysaetos
Golden Eagle

AR: Al-eqāb ad-dahabiah
GE: Steinadler

A rare breeding species of the Desert, and possibly also the Rift Margin mountains. Two cliff nests and a further displaying pair have recently been found in the Eastern, Basalt, and Wadi as Sarhan Deserts, with other records in the same general area during early March to late April, late August, and early September.

The Rift Margin records come from Wadi as Sir south to Petra in spring and late autumn, suggesting either a light passage or a very small resident population.

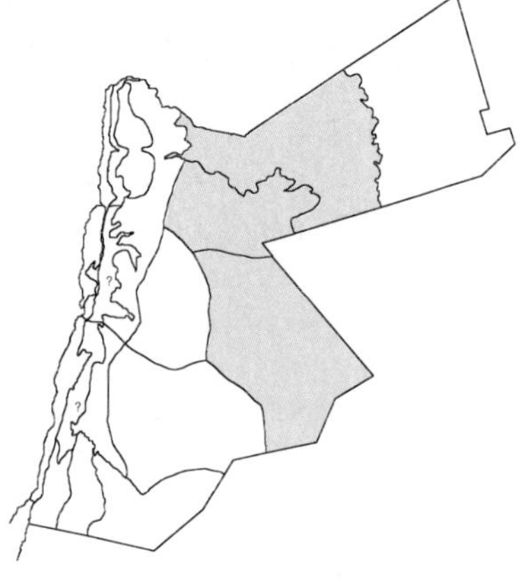

Aquila verreauxii
Verreaux's Eagle

AR: Al-eqāb al-aswad
GE: Kaffernadler

J F M A M J J A S O N D

A single pair of this African eagle has been resident in the Rum Desert since at least 1981. The birds usually keep to the highest mountain tops and cliffs, where they presumably have a traditional nest site. Fledged immature birds were seen with the adults on 14-16 April 1990, and on 19 June 1992. An adult was also seen 15km north-east of Aqaba on 30 April 1993, a juvenile was observed at Fidan on 22 October 1994, and an adult 7km to the north on 14 November 1994.

Hieraaetus pennatus
Booted Eagle

AR: Eqāb musayara sagheereh
GE: Zwergadler

J F M A M J J A S O N D

A scarce passage migrant during late March to mid May, mainly in the western and central parts of the country (Pella south to Aqaba), and only rarely at Azraq. In autumn, it is a rare migrant at Azraq and Shaumari (mid September to early October), and there is a late record at the latter site on 2 November.

Hieraaetus fasciatus
Bonelli's Eagle

AR: Eqāb benli
GE: Habichtsadler

J F M A M J J A S O N D

A small number, maybe ten breeding pairs are resident in the Rift Margins from the Dead Sea south to Petra. They nest at traditional locations on cliff sites mainly in remote wadis and gorges. Last century Canon Tristram noted two nests in the neighbourhood of Jarash, but there have been no breeding records in the Northern Highlands since a pair was seen near Ajlun in April 1955.

A few occur on passage away from these breeding areas: two at Azraq on 30 April-1 May 1980, one over Wadi as Sir on 25 December 1989, three flying south-west over the Amman National Park on 15 April 1991, and one at Wadi Rabigh on 17 April 1991.

Pandion haliaetus
Osprey

AR: Eqāb nasāriyya
GE: Fischadler

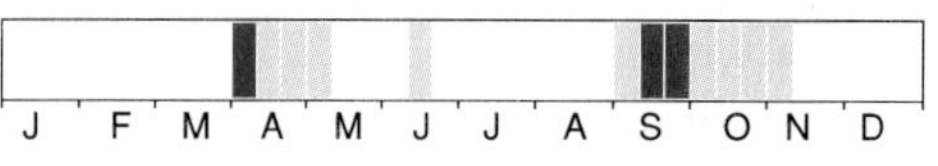

A scarce spring and autumn passage migrant during early April to early May, and again early September to early November. It is most likely to be seen near pools, rivers or reservoirs. On migration it also crosses expanses of desert, where it has been seen roosting overnight on electricity pylons. It is normally seen in ones and twos, but small gatherings occasionally interrupt their migration at good fishing sites.

Falco tinnunculus
Kestrel

AR: Al-'awsaq
GE: Turmfalke

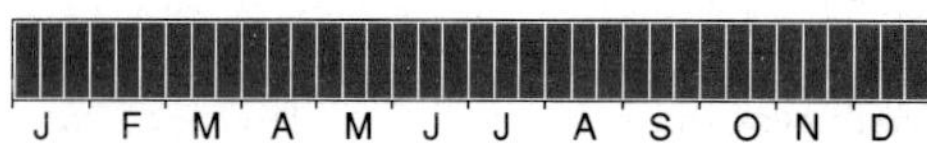

A widespread and fairly numerous resident breeding species, occurring in all desert and highland areas where there are suitable nest sites. It nests in trees, on cliffs, and in abandoned buildings. There is also evidence of a small passage in spring and autumn, and it is a winter visitor to some non-breeding areas.

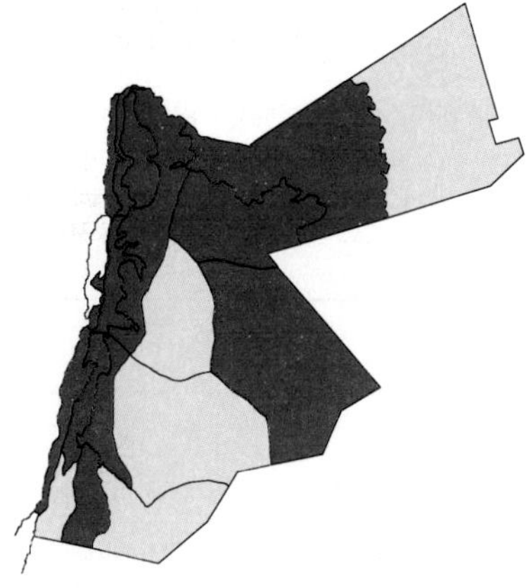

Falco naumanni
Lesser Kestrel

AR: Al-owaiseq
GE: Rötelfalke

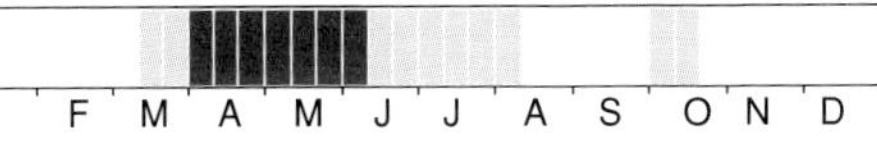

An uncommon summer visitor, a local breeding species in the Rift Margins, and also a spring passage migrant. It nests in small colonies on natural cliffs, quarries and ruins in several of the wadis flowing into the rift, from As Salt south to Wadi Dana. This globally threatened species may therefore have a significant population in Jordan, and a survey is urgently needed.

It also occurs as a spring migrant in the Azraq area from mid March to late April, occasionally in flocks of up to 50 birds, with some roosting. Migrants also occur in desert areas, for example in the Sharra Highlands and Rum Desert.

Autumn passage has been observed in the Southern Rift Margins and Rum Desert in early and mid October. Possibly as many as 80 were seen over this period at Wadi Dana in 1994. It is rare in the east in autumn: two at Shaumari on 5 October and 7 on 10 October 1976.

Falco vespertinus
Red-footed Falcon

AR: Al-lazaiq
GE: Rotfußfalke

J F M A M J J A S O N D

A rare spring migrant in the latter half of April with up to nine (18 total) at Azraq during 15-21 April 1963 and singles at Wadi al Butm on 19 April 1963, Azraq on 27 April 1980, and Petra on 24 April 1984. In autumn three females were seen at Petra on 16 October 1993, and a male at Wadi Dana on 11 October 1994. However, based on the pattern of occurrences in Egypt and Israel, it is probable that it is a more numerous passage migrant in autumn than the two records suggests.

Falco columbarius
Merlin

AR: Al-jolmm
GE: Merlin

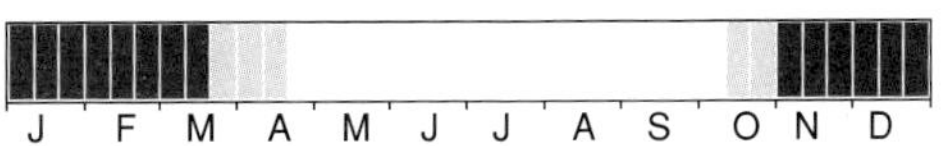

An uncommon autumn migrant and winter visitor to the Northern Highlands and Steppes and the Eastern Desert. A roost of up to nine birds was found south-west of Amman in 1989/90, and up to six were seen in 1990/91. These birds, mainly males, congregated in hawthorn bushes at dusk adjacent to a pine wood; it is assumed they roosted there after harrying the roosting finch flocks. Recorded mid October to mid March, with stragglers as late as 16 April.

Most birds are of the race *F. c. aesalon*, but a few males are paler and may be of the Siberian *pallidus* race.

Falco subbuteo
Hobby

AR: Al-kunj
GE: Baumfalke

Probably breeds rather uncommonly in native pine forests and plantations in the Northern Highlands. Birds have been observed in the breeding season at Dibbin Forest, King Talal Dam, and the Amman National Park. Adult and immature birds were seen in pine woods near Ajlun on 21 September 1990.

It is also an uncommon passage migrant through desert areas from early April to late May, and early September to mid October. The earliest recorded arrival is on 5 April. Eight observed at Aqaba at dusk on 9 October 1994 is a large concentration.

Falco eleonorae
Eleanora's Falcon

AR: Saqr al-yonorā
GE: Eleonorenfalke

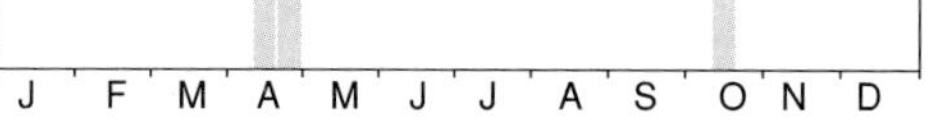

A very rare spring migrant, with singles at Aqaba or Wadi Rum on 24 April 1987, Dibbin Forest on 11 April 1988, Azraq on 14 April 1989 and Qasr al Kharana on 17 April 1992. In autumn two migrating birds were seen south of Aqaba on 15 October 1993.

Falco concolor
Sooty Falcon

AR: As-saqr ar-ramādi
GE: Schieferfalke

J F M A M J J A S O N D

This Middle Eastern speciality breeds locally in the sandstone mountains of the Rum Desert and Southern Rift Margins. It was first recorded in Jordan as recently as 1979, but since then it has been seen regularly at Petra, Wadi Dana, and the Wadi Rum area. There is at least one breeding pair at each of these sites and a pair nested on the same cliff in the Rum Desert during the 1989 to 1991 breeding seasons. It is probably more widespread in areas with sandstone cliffs, especially those facing north and offering that little extra shade. There are two undocumented reports of birds in the Dead Sea Rift Margins.

It is a late arrival on its breeding grounds, having a similar breeding strategy to the closely-related Eleanora's Falcon. Both species co-ordinate the chicks' greater demand for food with the availability of autumn migrants. It has been seen with certainty between late May and mid October, but possibly arrives as early as mid April.

Falco biarmicus
Lanner

AR: Saqr hor
GE: Lannerfalke

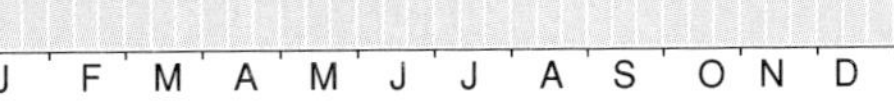

A bird of the mountainous Southern Rift Margins, Aqaba Mountains, and Rum Desert, where it is probably a thinly distributed resident breeding species. However, confusion can arise between this species and Barbary Falcon, which occurs in similar habitats. The Lanner is longer-winged and tailed, normally rufous crowned, and has a less well-marked moustachial stripe and darker central band to the underwing.

In the Rift Margins, Lanners have been recorded from Wadi Dana, Ash Shawbak, and Petra. It has also occurred at Azraq in April, June and September, at Al Muwaqqar on 13 December 1990, and Al Khirba as Samra on 30 August 1991 – indicating that at least a few birds wander into the interior deserts.

Falco cherrug
Saker

AR: As-saqr (ash-sharq)
GE: Würgfalke

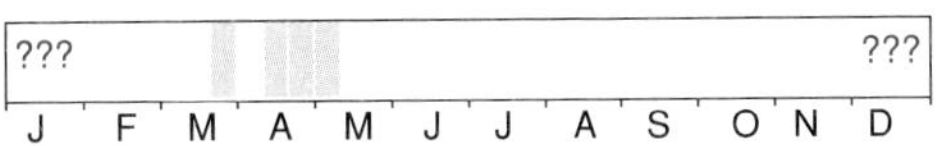

The small number of published records refer to birds on spring passage from late March to early May at Azraq, Shaumari, Qa' Khanna, Wadi al Mujib and Wadi Rum. However, at least one of these records, at Azraq, referred to an escaped falconer's bird. Locals have reported a few passage or wintering birds in the Burqu' area of the Basalt Desert, and also in the Rum Desert. Look out for them perched on pylons in the interior deserts.

Falco peregrinus
Peregrine

AR: Ash-shāheen
GE: Wanderfalke

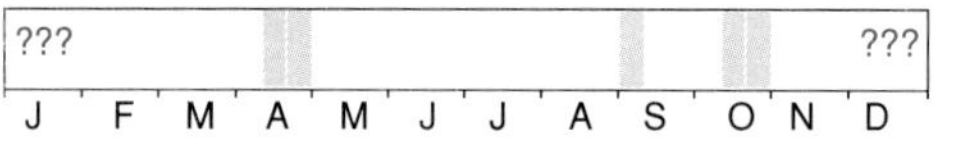

A few Peregrines have been recorded wintering at Azraq, with further reports suggesting a limited spring and autumn passage through the desert at Ar Ruwayshid and Al Jafr. The Peregrine is the most highly sought-after falcon by trappers at these sites.

Identification is least controversial in winter, when birds are likely to be of the northern races *F. p. peregrinus* or *calidus*. There could be confusion at other times between Mediterranean and Middle Eastern Peregrines *F. p. brookei* and the closely-related, resident Barbary Falcon; these are sometimes treated as conspecific.

Falco pelegrinoides
Barbary Falcon

AR: Shaheen al-maghreb
GE: Wüstenfalke

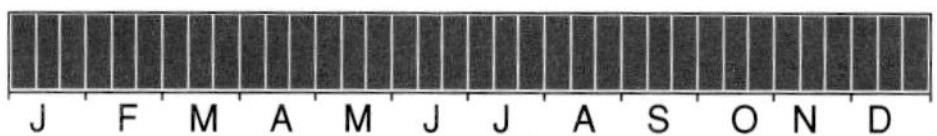

Small numbers of this desert relative of the Peregrine breed in the arid Rift Margin highlands from the Dead Sea south to Aqaba, as well as in the Rum Desert. A pair regularly breeds on the cliffs at Petra, which has become one of the best places to see this species. A wanderer was seen between Wadi al Butm and Azraq on 27-28 April 1965.

Alectoris chukar
Chukar

AR: Al-hajal er-roomi
GE: Chukarhuhn

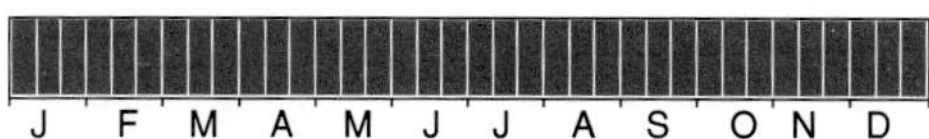

This fairly common, resident game bird is found in open country in the Rift Margins from the Zarqa River south to Petra. It also occurs less commonly in the Northern Highlands, including western Amman. It is rather local and nowhere abundant in these areas, however, probably due to hunting.

Small groups have been recorded from a few sites in the Eastern Desert (Wadi al Jilat and Wadi al Butm) and Basalt Desert (Jawa, and on the basalt edge near Azraq). Six birds were introduced at Shaumari in October 1976 but were not seen after a few months. A small number occur in the Rum Desert, on Jabals Rum and Umm Ishrin, and perhaps elsewhere.

Ammoperdix heyi
Sand Partridge

AR: Qahbby
GE: Arabisches Wüstenhuhn

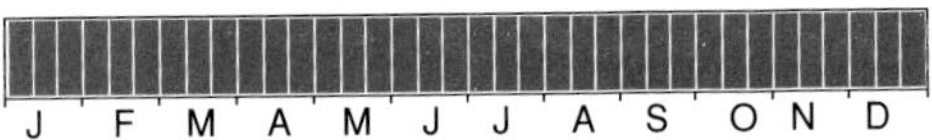

A fairly common resident, recorded in the arid mountains of the Rift Margins and Rum Desert, and sparsely in the Azraq and Shaumari areas. It occurs as far north as the Yarmuk River, but is most numerous on the mountain slopes abutting the Dead Sea. It occurs on the eastern margins of

the Jordan Valley and Wadi Araba, but is typically never far from rocky hills. It is therefore surprising that an isolated population also exists along the basalt edge near Azraq.

Francolinus francolinus
Black Francolin

AR: Hajal aswad
GE: Halsbandfrankolin

J F M A M J J A S O N D

A localised, but probably not uncommon resident of the Jordan Valley, especially adjacent to the Jordan River and near Suwayma (Dead Sea). It is a bird of dense vegetation, in which it typically skulks, so is most easily located by the male's strident, harsh, seven-syllabic call in early morning and evening.

Coturnix coturnix
Quail

AR: As-selwa
GE: Wachte

J F M A M J J A S O N D

A rather scarce migrant in late February to mid May, and even less common in early September to late October. It occurs in open country or in wadis, and has been recorded in the Jordan Valley (including As Safi), Northern Highlands, desert fringe, Eastern Desert (including Azraq) and Wadi as Sarhan. One was even flushed from barren mountains near Wadi Rum.

Quail have not been recorded breeding in Jordan, but could conceivably do so in the northern agricultural areas.

Rallus aquaticus
Water Rail

AR: At-tafāloq
GE: Wasserralle

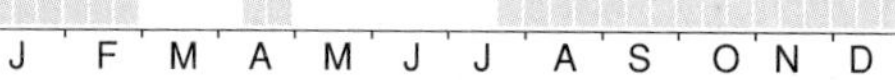

A small resident breeding population of 9-12 (possibly 20) pairs was found in the Azraq marshes during 1963-66. A local reed cutter is reported to have found several nests with eggs in May. However breeding no longer occurs at Azraq.

When the marshes were more extensive than at present, this small number of resident birds was augmented by a large winter influx, such that the marshes may have held 100-500 birds. Now that the Azraq oasis is all but dry, Water Rail numbers have crashed, and it is mainly recorded as an uncommon autumn and winter visitor (late July to late December) and rarely in April.

A few also occur on migration and winter on streams in the major vegetated wadis of the northern Rift Margins (for example Wadi as Sir and the Zarqa River).

Porzana porzana
Spotted Crake

AR: Al-mer'a al-monaqata
GE: Tüpfelsumpfhuhn

J F M A M J J A S O N D

There are as few as six records of this migrant at Azraq: singles on 17th and 19 April 1963, 30 April-2 May 1966, 12 October 1990, 3 May 1991 and 19 April 1992. It has also been recorded in the desert at Tell Qorma on 2 and 6 May 1966, between Azraq and Al Karak on 21 April 1986, and in the lower Zarqa River on 8 November 1991.

Porzana parva
Little Crake

AR: Al-mer'a al-monaqata as-sagheereh
GE: Kleines Sumpfhuhn

J F M A M J J A S O N D

A rather rare, or just elusive migrant at the Azraq oasis, and there are surprisingly two records at nearby Shaumari. Ones and twos are typically recorded in overgrown, damp marshy areas during March and April, but it has been seen in late August, late October, and late November.

Porzana pusilla
Baillon's Crake

AR: Mar'at bilown as-sagheereh
GE: Zwergsumpfhuhn

J F M A M J J A S O N D

In the 1960s there was a breeding population of five to ten pairs in the Azraq marshes, and a nest with a clutch of five eggs was found on 17 April 1963. It seems to still nest occasionally, as calling males were heard in 1980 and 1985, and a juvenile was seen on 23 July 1990.

A few migrants pass through Azraq in mid April and October, but their significance was masked, at least in the past, by the presence of the breeding population.

Crex crex
Corncrake

AR: As-sforrd
GE: Wachtelkönig

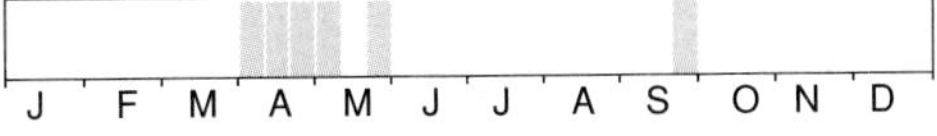

A rare spring migrant at Azraq and the surrounding desert, recorded during early April to late May. Away from the oasis itself birds can turn up in any habitat, for example one was seen wandering across the desert at Qasr al Kharana. Unfortunately, tired migrants are liable to be caught, killed, or just succumb to the elements. One was killed by a cat at Aqaba on 9 April 1990, and a captive bird was seen at Wadi Rum on 5 May 1963. Elsewhere, there is a record from the vicinity of the Dead Sea.

It is rare in autumn: one was seen flying around buildings and gardens in Amman on 28 September 1994.

Gallinula chloropus
Moorhen

AR: Dajajat al-ma'a
GE: Teichhuhn

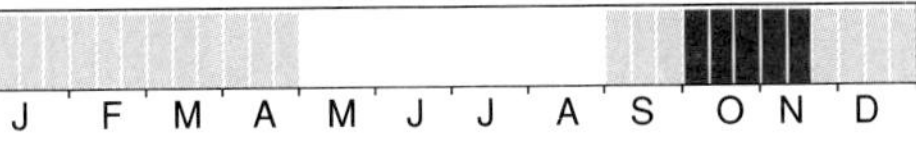

A small breeding population was discovered in the Azraq marshes in the 1960s, and in winter up to 100-500 birds were estimated there. A few may breed on the Zarqa River, and it has also been reported as a possible breeder in Wadi as Siyyagh, Petra, and Wadi Dana.

Due to habitat loss, however, it is now recorded at Azraq only rarely, with a maximum of seven between early September and late April. It has also been recorded as an uncommon winter visitor on rivers, reservoirs, and pools at other sites in the north and west of the country. One found dead on the Amman to Azraq road 5km east of Qasr Amra on 5 April 1991 is evidence of cross-desert passage.

Fulica atra
Coot

AR: Ghara
GE: Bläßhuhn

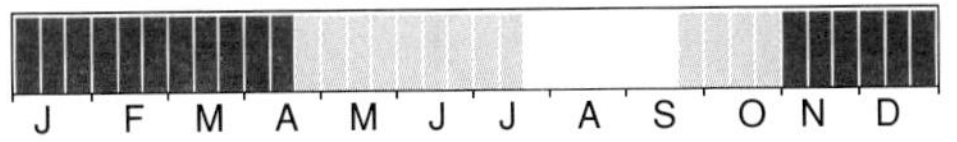

Small numbers were seen regularly at Azraq oasis in the springs of 1963-66, and it was suspected that a few pairs bred there. Recently, up to three have remained at Shuna Reservoir and Azraq through the summer, and it may well have bred at the latter site in recent years.

The Coot is otherwise a very common winter visitor to suitable wetland sites mainly during mid September to late April. Numbers at Azraq were presumably more stable in the past, as birds fed on the permanent marsh outflows, and an incredible 40,000 were estimated in February 1967. Winter peaks at Azraq now vary considerably with up to 610 wintering when the qa' is flooded (1991/92), to less than 10 when it is not.

Moderate numbers, up to 100, regularly winter on the Jordan Valley tributary reservoirs and pools, from Birket al Rais in the north, to the King Talal Dam and the Kafrayn Reservoir in the south. Aqaba sewage works may also hold significant numbers.

Grus grus
Crane

AR: Kirki
GE: Kranich

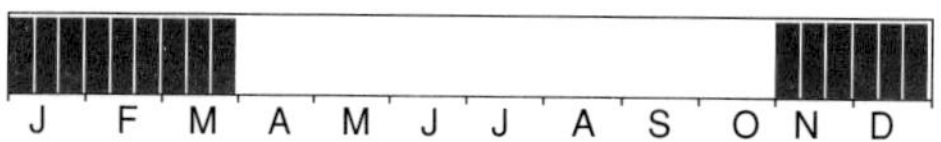

A locally abundant winter visitor to several areas in the Eastern Desert, possibly other temporarily flooded areas and around the cultivated fringes of the desert. Recorded during late October to late March.

The main wintering flock frequents the desert between Azraq and Shaumari, feeding in the desert and roosting on the qa' if it is flooded. Peak numbers in recent years have been 250 in 1989/90, 170 in 1990/91 and 2500 in 1991/92. A regular flock has also been recorded between Qasr al Hallabat and Qa' Khanna. Flocks of up to 100 birds winter within the Basalt Desert around As Safawi and Ghadir Burqu', and in the Northern Steppes.

Small numbers can be seen on passage along the Rift Valley and its margins. A few fly north in mid March (35 past Sirfa, north of Wadi al Karak, and 80 over Dibbin), and south in November (five at Aqaba on 16 November 1990, and 17 over Al Manshiyya on 8 November 1990).

Chlamydotis undulata
Houbara Bustard

AR: Habari
GE: Kragentrappe

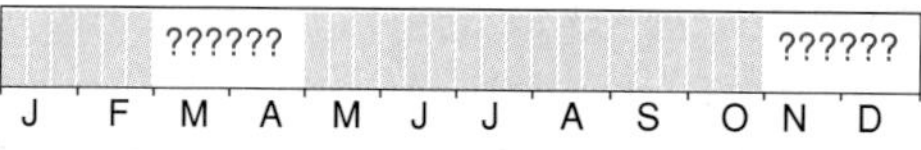

There was a time when Houbara Bustards were distributed widely across the Jordanian desert, and occurred locally in considerable numbers. However, it has long been the target for bedouin hunters, for whom falconry has a long tradition. Numbers were probably not affected too greatly in the past, but indiscriminate shooting since the 1930s, together with falconry by more than just the local peoples, have seen a drastic decline in numbers.

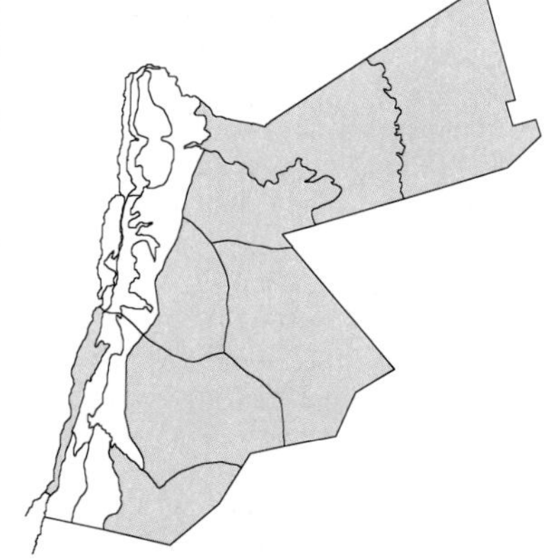

Today, reports of Houbara Bustards in Jordan are easier to find than the birds themselves. Locals are keen to tell where Houbaras are present, but memories are long! Remote areas undoubtedly still hold birds, perhaps more often in winter. Two of the most likely areas for Houbara are in Wadi Araba, and the Basalt Desert. The enormous Harrat al Harrah basalt desert reserve, the last remaining stronghold for the Houbara in the region, lies over the border in Saudi Arabia.

In the 1950s and 1960s, there were scattered, mainly second-hand records from near Wadi al Butm, and east and north of Azraq. It was also reported to be still numerous in the more fertile rolling country south of Amman. A nest was found at Al Jafr in May 1963, but this was later robbed.

During 1975-79, there were 21 sightings of a total of 48 birds in the vicinity of Shaumari. Most of these were during the summer (May to October), but no breeding behaviour was noted. It was also stated at this time that a recovery was evident, especially in the south, with a published map showing birds in the Basalt Desert and around Bayir and Ma'an.

Haematopus ostralegus
Oystercatcher

AR: Akel al-mahār
GE: Austernfischer

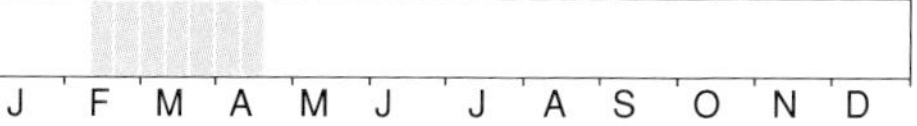

A rare spring migrant to the Aqaba beaches, with a maximum of five seen on 29 March 1992. There are also two spring records of singles inland at Azraq.

Himantopus himantopus
Black-winged Stilt

AR: Abu al-maghāzel
GE: Stelzenläufer

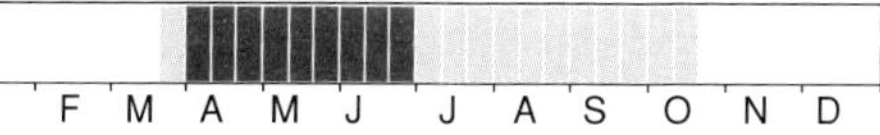

A population of 20-90, or occasionally more breeds at Azraq in wet years, but breeding is frustrated in dry years or due to low water levels. The favoured habitat is along the drying edges and islands in Qa' al Azraq, and it must breed in the short time before the water evaporates. The largest count involved 700 adults and 500 young on 28 June 1991, when some 300 pairs may have bred. A small number of paired birds has occurred in mid summer at Al Khirba as Samra and Shuna Reservoir, but no proof of breeding has yet been observed away from Azraq.

It is also a common spring migrant to Azraq, with obvious passage flocks of up to 160 recorded. It occurs in smaller numbers at Qa' Khanna, Ghadir Burqu', Shuna Reservoir, and Kafrayn Reservoir. Migrant flocks can be seen at Aqaba, where they may rest briefly if they find an undisturbed beach.

It is uncommon in autumn (late July to early October) at Azraq, Aqaba and Al Khirba as Samra, with largest flocks of only 35. It is generally absent during the winter, but there have been a few singles at Azraq in recent years.

Recurvirostra avosetta
Avocet

AR: An-nakāt
GE: Säbelschnäbler

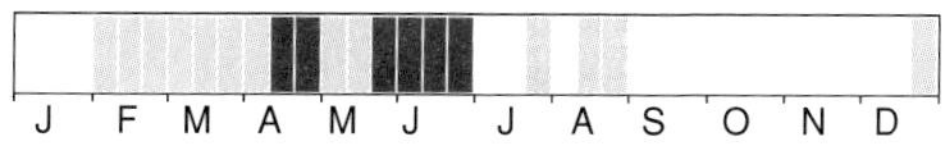

Avocets breed at Azraq in the same habitat as Black-winged Stilts, but in smaller numbers. Again breeding is frustrated in dry years, but a population of 11-50 pairs has been estimated during wet springs. The largest recorded gatherings are 275 adults and 25 young on 24 May 1990, and 38 adults and 80 young on 19 June 1991, both following good breeding seasons.

At Azraq the earliest arrivals of the spring are in mid February, but some are probably still on the move in late April. The only obvious passage record there is of 100 on 23 April 1955. It is rarely reported away from Azraq, with seven at Aqaba on 25 April 1985, two at Qa' al Hibabiya on 24 April 1991, and one on a pool at Ghor Khabid (Jordan Valley) on 25 April 1992.

It is rare in autumn (due to a lack of wetland areas), with one at Azraq on 23 July 1990, four at Al Khirba as Samra on 17 August, and one there on 31 August. The odd bird also turns up occasionally at Azraq in winter.

Burhinus oedicnemus
Stone-curlew

AR: Al-karawān al-jabali (As-smug)
GE: Triel

J F M A M J J A S O N D

A scarce migrant breeding species, that was doubtless more common in the past. It is found mainly in the Eastern Desert from Az Zarqa to Azraq, but now at a very low density. A nest was found at Azraq in the 1960s, and two broods were recorded in Wadi Rajil, where it was then fairly common. It can also be found occasionally in the Northern Steppes, and could occur in other desert regions. Last century it was plentiful in the Jordan

Valley at the north end of the Dead Sea, where it remained throughout the year. Modern records are restricted to the period from 8 March to 9 August, with a late record on 26 October.

A bird, considered to be a migrant, was seen flying NNW at Azraq on 16 April 1965; a flock of 20 was seen on 19 March 1947, and one was recorded at Aqaba on 7 April 1986.

Pluvianus aegyptius
Egyptian Plover

AR: Al qatqāt al-masri
GE: Krokodilwächter

According to Canon Tristram, one was shot on the Jordan River at the end of the 19th century.

Cursorius cursor
Cream-coloured Courser

AR: Al-jaleel
GE: Rennvogel

J F M A M J J A S O N D

A common summer visitor to Jordan's flat deserts. Despite what other texts suggest, the local birds arrive in early March and leave in late June, soon after breeding. Sightings are then rare until late autumn when a small number of apparent migrants turns up at non-breeding sites.

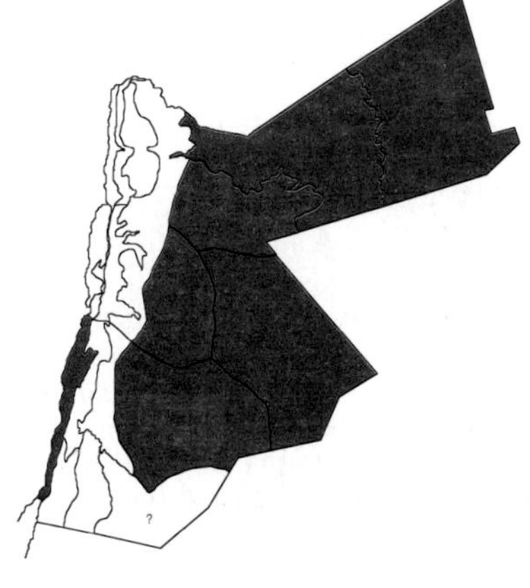

A widespread and not uncommon bird of the low-relief Eastern Desert, especially between Al Muwaqqar, Az Zarqa and Azraq, where many hundred pairs may be scattered throughout the area. Birds have been seen in the western Basalt Desert, and other less well explored areas of the 'badia' presumably also hold good numbers. Its favoured habitat extends over the barest parts of open stony hammada, as well as on desert soils with sparse low vegetation, and tracks left by vehicles. It avoids steeper and rockier slopes, damp depressions or any kind of wetland, or tall dense stands of plants.

Elsewhere, birds frequent the gravel plains west of Al Hashimiyya, Wadi Araba, and the Southern Ghor. It is absent from the sandy Rum Desert.

Glareola pratincola
Collared Pratincole

AR: Abu al-yousor
GE: Rotflügel-Brachschwalbe

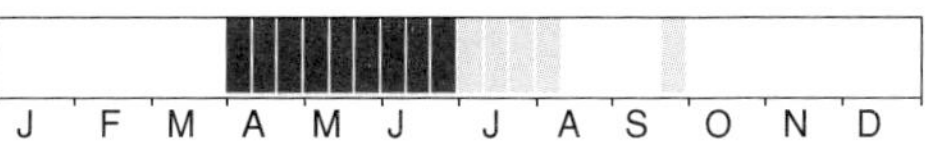

In the 1960s, up to 250 pairs bred at Azraq on the drier areas of the outfalls and adjacent qa'. By 1991, this population had reduced to only 10 pairs.

The earliest birds are seen in early April. Migrants commonly pass through Azraq, and to a lesser extent, other wetland sites and Aqaba up to mid May at least. It is rather scarce away from Azraq, but on migration has occurred in the Jordan Valley, at Al Khirba as Samra, and at Ghadir Burqu'.

A rarity in autumn, recorded only at Azraq up to the end of September.

Glareola nordmanni
Black-winged Pratincole

AR: Abu al-yousor aswad al-janah
GE: Schwarzflügel-Brachschwalbe

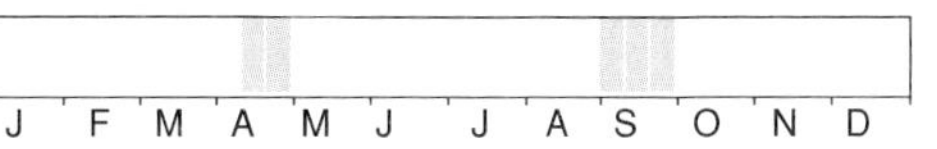

A rare passage migrant at Azraq in April and September (four records). A migrant was also seen at Aqaba on 15 April 1993.

Charadrius dubius
Little Ringed Plover

AR: Abu er-roos as-sagheer
GE: Flußregenpfeifer

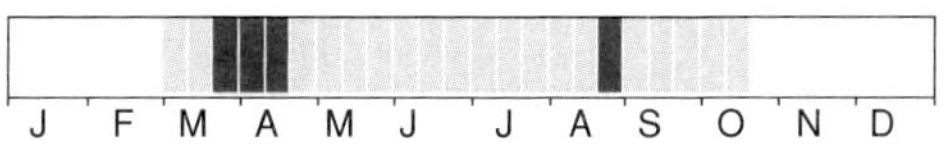

Although only recently proved to breed at Azraq (a few pairs since 1991), it is also suspected to breed at Shuna Reservoir, on gravel banks in the Zarqa River, and possibly along the Jordan River.

It is a common spring migrant at Azraq, especially during late March to mid April when counts reach a peak of 50 birds. Other records come from rain-water pools, such as one east of Al Muwaqqar, and others at Ar Rashadiyya, Al Husayniyya and As Safi. In autumn, when wetland sites are at a premium, it has only been recorded at Azraq, Aqaba, Al Khirba as Samra, and Ghadir Burqu' from mid July to mid October, and with a maximum count of 25. It was described as a common winter visitor at Azraq in the late 1960s, but it is now absent from November to the end of February.

Charadrius hiaticula
Ringed Plover

AR: Abu er-roos al-maqtooq
GE: Sandregenpfeifer

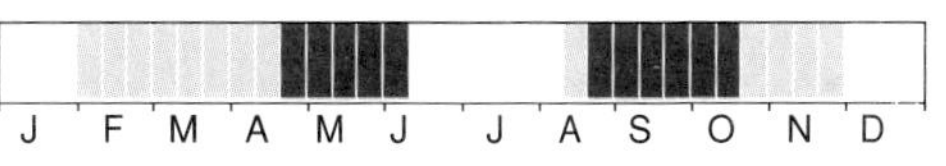

A fairly common migrant to wetlands, especially in autumn. Spring passage is light (up to ten birds) and generally quite late, peaking in late May and extending into early June. It has been recorded at Azraq, Qa' al Hibabiya, the lower Jordan Valley (Shuna Reservoir and Suwayma), and Aqaba.

It is more numerous in autumn with passage peaking in early September. Maximum counts include up to 12 at Azraq, 25 at Ghadir Burqu', and 30 at Al Khirba as Samra. There is also an isolated record from a flood pool at Wadi al Butm on 29 November 1990. Small numbers wintered at Azraq in the late 1960s, but have not done so in recent years.

Charadrius alexandrinus
Kentish Plover

AR: Az-zaqzāq al-iskanderāni
GE: Seeregenpfeifer

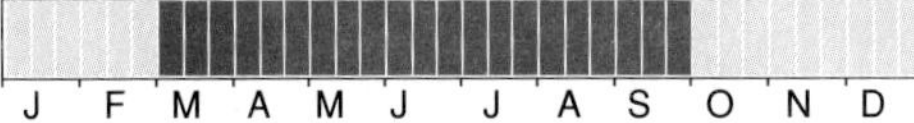

Breeds commonly at Azraq on the edges of the qa', with maybe as many as 200-500 breeding pairs or more. It is also presumed to nest in small numbers at other desert wetlands, such as Ghadir Burqu', Qa' Khanna, and Suwayma (Dead Sea). It is less dependent on wet conditions than other breeding waders.

It is an abundant wader at Azraq, with evidence of spring and autumn passage and a winter influx. Spring passage is particularly obvious, and up to 1500 can be seen on the flooded qa' from late March to mid April. A maximum of 350 has been counted at the restricted number of wetland sites in autumn, reaching a peak in early August. It also occurs in small numbers at Kafrayn Reservoir, Al Khirba as Samra, Qa' Khanna, Aqaba, and doubtless elsewhere.

It used to be most numerous at Azraq in winter (up to 2000), but only a small number (up to 60) now remain at Azraq even when the qa' is flooded. Small numbers have also been recorded in winter at Al Mafraq, Al Khirba as Samra, As Safi and Aqaba.

Charadrius leschenaultii
Greater Sand Plover

AR: Qatqāt er-ramil al-kabeer
GE: Wüstenregenpfeifer

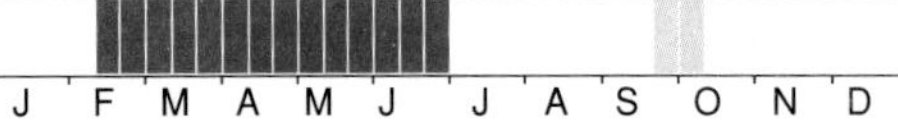

A small number breed at Qa' al Azraq, Qa' Khanna, and possibly other nearby flooded qa's, favouring the carpets of short grass and succulents that grow around the qa' edges. Breeding was first proven in 1963.

A common summer migrant, with birds returning as early as February. Moderately large numbers occur at Azraq on spring passage (up to 75 on the flooded qa' in mid April), and also when breeding birds gather in early June (300 on 4 June 1970). These birds leave by the end of the month. There are other spring records from Aqaba beaches, Suwayma, and flood pools at Qasr Amra and Thulaythuwat during mid March to mid April.

It is very rare in autumn, with one at Azraq on 22-29 September 1989, and two at Aqaba on 9 October 1994.

Charadrius asiaticus
Caspian Plover

AR: Ziqzāq kazwini
GE: Wermutregenpfeifer

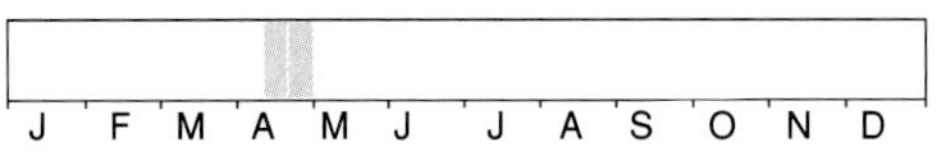

A scarce spring migrant, most likely to turn up at Azraq during mid to late April, and preferring the drier habitats of the qa' edge. It usually occurs in small groups of up to six. Two were seen on Aqaba south beach on 15 April 1993.

Charadrius morinellus
Dotterel

AR: Al-qatqāt al-āghbar
GE: Mornellregenpfeifer

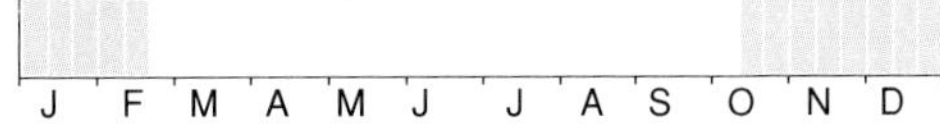

Last century Canon Tristram reported that 'clouds of Dotterel got up every now and then' between Al Jiza and Hisban, and he saw 'plenty' near Faqu. In recent winters, flocks of 2-12 have been rediscovered in the semi-desert south of Queen Alia Airport, and at Azraq and Shaumari between mid October and mid February. Although the natural steppe habitat is now much restricted, Dotterel may turn out to be most numerous and widely distibuted in cultivated land on the Northern Steppes in winter. Local Jordanians have also reported daily maxima of up to 50 in the Jordan Valley in winter.

Pluvialis fulva
Pacific Golden Plover

GE: Pazifischer Goldregenpfeifer

A vagrant, with two adults at Al Khirba as Samra sewage works on 17 August 1990, and one on 24 August.

Pluvialis squatarola
Grey Plover

AR: Al-qatqāt ar-ramādi al-gharbi
GE: Kiebitzregenpfeifer

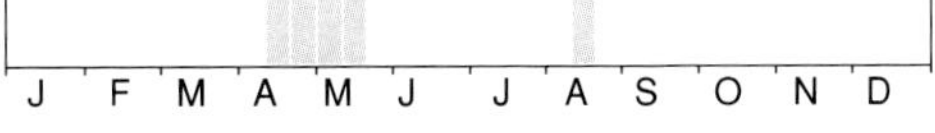

A scarce passage migrant, recorded mainly as singles inland at Azraq, Al Khirba as Samra and Shuna Reservoir, and on the coast at Aqaba. It has occurred between 18 April and 16 May and was reported on 17 August.

Hoplopterus spinosus
Spur-winged Plover

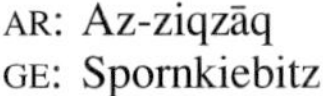

AR: Az-ziqzāq
GE: Spornkiebitz

J F M A M J J A S O N D

A fairly common resident breeding wader, to be found at wetland sites in the Jordan Valley and Dead Sea area (for example Shuna Reservoir, Ghor Khabid, Suwayma and As Safi), at Al Khirba as Samra, Qa' al Hibabiya, Azraq, and Aqaba. Some eight pairs were found at Azraq in 1963, but numbers are now reduced. There are few records from the south and east of Jordan, though one was seen at Disi in 1994.

Hoplopterus tectus
Blackhead Plover

AR: Al-qatqāt aswad ar-rā's
GE: Schwarzkopfkiebitz

One shot in Wadi Araba, south of the Dead Sea in 1869, is the sole Western Palaearctic record of this eastern and central African species. This site is now crossed by the Israel-Jordan border, and its exact location relative to this is not known.

Chettusia gregaria
Sociable Plover

AR: At-taqtaqeeyeh
GE: Steppenkiebitz

In February 1872 Canon Tristram reported plentiful Sociable Plovers on the steppe country near Faqu, north of Ar Rabba. Nowadays, it is a winter vagrant, but with potential for small flocks to winter in unexplored areas around the desert fringe, perhaps most likely in the Irbid-Al Mafraq area. The only recent published record is of seven birds at Azraq on 21 February 1969.

Chettusia leucura
White-tailed Plover

AR: Zaqzāq abiad ith-thanab
GE: Weißschwanzkiebitz

J F M A M J J A S O N D

Most frequent at Azraq in April, with up to eight birds recorded. A small number of pairs probably breed there in most years, although a nest has yet to be found. Birds were seen performing distraction displays in April 1983, and in 1989 and 1990 family parties were seen in autumn. The nearest regular breeding occurs in Iraq, although it nests sporadically in Turkey. There is a single winter record at Al Khirba as Samra, and a migrant turned up at Aqaba on 15 April 1993.

Vanellus vanellus
Lapwing

AR: Az-zaqzāq ash-shami
GE: Kiebitz

J F M A M J J A S O N D

A common winter visitor to agricultural land in the Jordan Valley, with flocks of 50-100 frequenting the irrigated arable fields. Smaller numbers winter in the agricultural fringes of the Northern Highlands, and at Azraq. Spring and autumn passage is also evident. Most records are between October and March, with an isolated record at Azraq on 3 May.

Calidris canutus
Knot

AR: Draijet ash-shamāl
GE: Knutt

A vagrant, with one seen at a desert qa' near Azraq on 25 April 1967.

Calidris alba
Sanderling

AR: Al-mederwān
GE: Sanderling

An unexpected vagrant at the desert oasis of Azraq in November 1964, and at Ghadir Burqu' on 22 September 1991.

Calidris minuta
Little Stint

AR: Ad-draijeh as-sagheereh
GE: Zwergstrandläufer

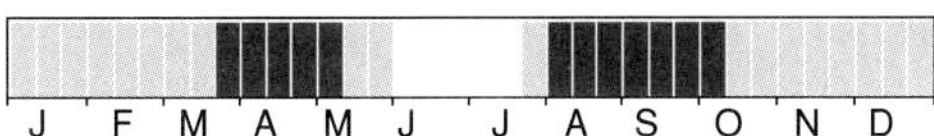

This is an abundant spring, and less common autumn migrant at Azraq and Al Khirba as Samra. Up to 1000 have been estimated on the flooded qa' at Azraq in mid April, with 500 at Al Khirba as Samra in late August. Up to 200 were counted at Aqaba sewage works on 8-9 October 1994. Small numbers are also found on passage at Shuna Reservoir, and they could appear on any reservoir or flood pool. A small number remain in winter at Azraq, but fewer now than formerly since the demise of marsh-edge habitat.

Calidris temminckii
Temminck's Stint

AR: Fateerat tmanek
GE: Temminckstrandläufer

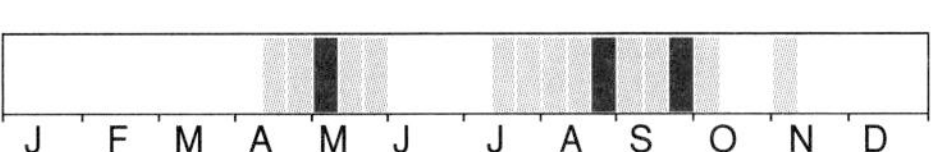

A passage migrant in small numbers in spring (peak early May) and autumn (peaks late August and late September). It prefers mud-edged pools, with Azraq, Al Khirba as Samra and Shuna Reservoir being the main sites. It was much more common than the Little Stint in the 1960s, with up to 1580 recorded (compared with 750 Little Stints). The Little Stint is far more common now, mainly due to the Temminck's preference for wet grassland and marshes, rather than the bare qa' edge.

Calidris ferruginea
Curlew Sandpiper

AR: Karawān al-mā'a
GE: Sichelstrandläufer

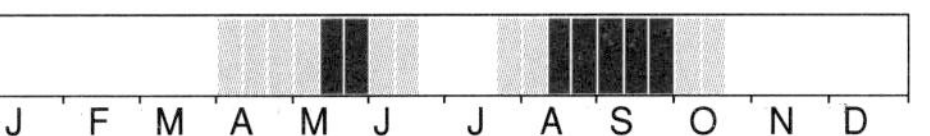

A fairly common passage migrant, mainly at Azraq in late spring, but also to a lesser extent in autumn when adults arrive before immatures. Spring peaks of adults in brick-red, summer plumage are 15 at Al Khirba as Samra, and 40 at Qa' al Azraq both in late May. The only records in the Jordan Valley are one at Shuna Reservoir on 27 April 1990, and four at Suwayma on 25 April 1992.

In autumn up to 12 have been seen at Al Khirba as Samra, 10 at Ghadir Burqu', and 10 at Azraq in late July to mid October.

Calidris alpina
Dunlin

AR: Draijeh
GE: Alpenstrandläufer

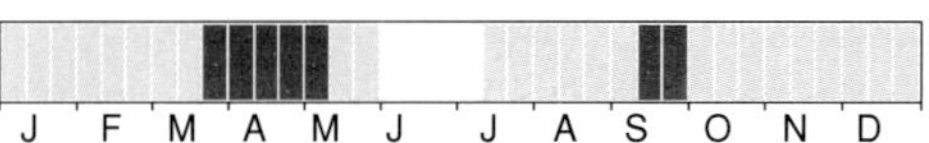

Mainly a passage bird (early February to late May and late August into November), with a very few remaining through the winter. It is most likely to be seen in good numbers at Azraq or Al Khirba as Samra, with up to 500 at the former site in April, although no more than 40 have occurred in recent years.

It was once an abundant winter visitor to Azraq; in the 1960s several thousand were recorded in mid November, and 500-1000 seen in mid January. Recent counts show a drastic decline, even when the qa' is flooded, with no counts greater than ten.

Limicola falcinellus
Broad-billed Sandpiper

AR: Taytawi manjali
GE: Sumpfläufer

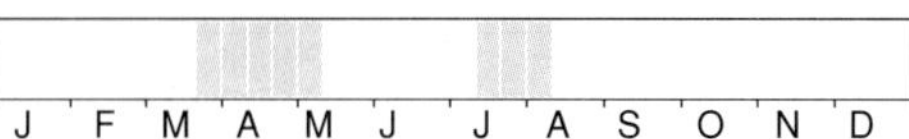

A scarce migrant recorded, mainly at Azraq in spring and early autumn. Ones and twos have been seen on the qa' edge or on nearby marshes. Three were seen at Suwayma, by the Dead Sea on 30 March 1989.

Philomachus pugnax
Ruff

AR: Al-hajoaleh
GE: Kampfläufer

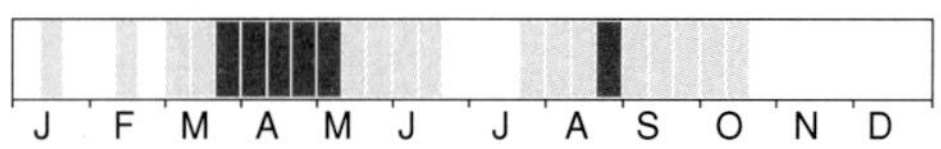

An abundant migrant at Azraq, and also at Al Khirba as Samra. Up to 3000-5000 have been counted in spring at Azraq, and it has been classed as the commonest wader using the oasis. The peak is usually reached in mid April, but a few (by now in summer plumage) continue passing through May until mid June. It has also been recorded at Qa' Khanna, Ghadir Burqu', and Wadi Sultan.

Autumn passage peaks in late August, but it is less numerous then than in spring. It is most common in autumn at Al Khirba as Samra, where up to 150 have been counted. A few are known to linger at Azraq through the winter.

Lymnocryptes minimus
Jack Snipe

AR: Shunqub as-sagheer
GE: Zwergschnepfe

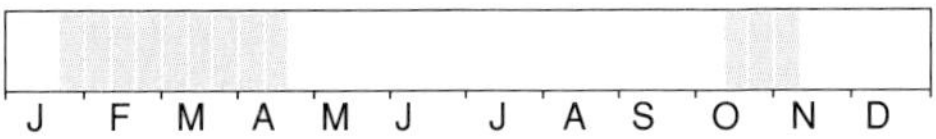

J F M A M J J A S O N D

A winter visitor to Azraq, and possibly fairly numerous in the past when the marshes were more extensive. The only recent records are: singles at Azraq on 2 and 7 April 1985, two at Azraq on 25 October and 1 November 1990, and one by the Dead Sea at Suwayma on 10 March 1992.

Gallinago gallinago
Snipe

AR: Shunqub a'atiyādee
GE: Bekassine

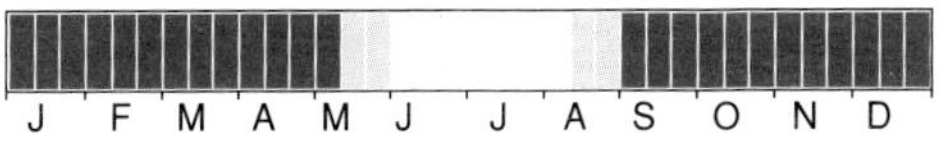

J F M A M J J A S O N D

A fairly common passage migrant and winter visitor at wetland sites from early August through to the end of May. Passage peaks in mid April and early November. Azraq and Al Khirba as Samra are the main sites, but other migrants have been seen at Al Manshiyya, west of Na'ur, Shuna Reservoir, Zarqa River, and Wadi al Wala. One seen by the roadside near Qasr al Kharana alludes to cross-desert passage; this bird possibly mistook the shiny road for water.

In the 1960s there were thought to be thousands of wintering Snipe in the Azraq marshes, with concentrations of 200-370 birds in suitable areas. With the limited amount of marsh habitat remaining now, recent counts have never exceeded 15 birds there. However, there was a late autumn count of 40 at Al Khirba as Samra on 18 October 1990.

Gallinago media
Great Snipe

AR: Shunqub kabeer
GE: Doppelschnepfe

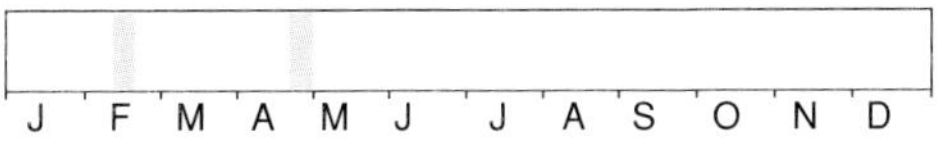

J F M A M J J A S O N D

A very rare spring migrant, with singles at Azraq in February 1967, Shaumari on 30 April 1976, Azraq on 28 April 1980, and Azraq Resthouse on 27-28 April 1990.

Scolopax rusticola
Woodcock

AR: Dajajat al-ard
GE: Waldschnepfe

An autumn and winter vagrant, with singles at Azraq in October 1968 and 31 January 1979 being the only Jordanian records.

Limosa limosa
Black-tailed Godwit

AR: Buqwaiqa sowda'a ith-thanab
GE: Uferschnepfe

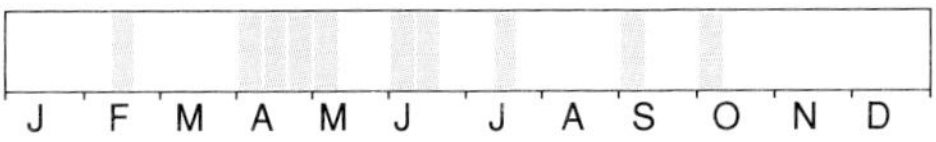

J F M A M J J A S O N D

Small flocks occasionally turn up at Azraq in the late winter, spring, and rarely in autumn. Numbers are small, usually one to 15, but an exceptional count of 210 was made during 16-18 April 1965. Up to three were seen at Aqaba on 8-9 October 1994.

Limosa lapponica
Bar-tailed Godwit

AR: Buqwaiqa mukhattat ith-thanab
GE: Pfuhlschnepfe

A very rare migrant, mainly represented by singles at Azraq in the spring. There are records from Azraq in 1967, 1968 or 1969, and 1987. There is also a record from the lower Jordan Valley in spring 1965.

Numenius phaeopus
Whimbrel

AR: Karawān ghaiti sagheer
GE: Regenbrachvogel

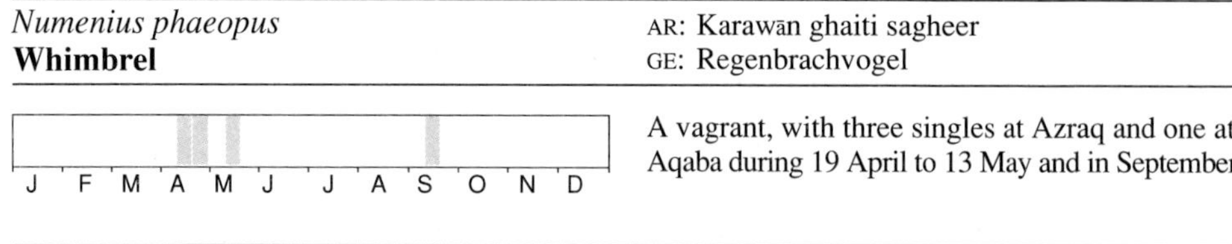

A vagrant, with three singles at Azraq and one at Aqaba during 19 April to 13 May and in September.

Numenius tenuirostris
Slender-billed Curlew

AR: Karawān ghaity mustadaq al-menqar
GE: Dünnschnabel-Brachvogel

Vagrant: one at Azraq on 4 May 1965.

Numenius arquata
Curlew

AR: Al-karawān
GE: Großer Brachvogel

A rare bird in Jordan. A few stragglers have been seen at Azraq in March to April and September to October, with other singles at Aqaba on 19 April, Al Khirba as Samra on 17 August, and Ghor Khabid in the Jordan Valley on 25 April.

Tringa erythropus
Spotted Redshank

AR: Taytawi addkan
GE: Dunkler Wasserläufer

J F M A M J J A S O N D

A scarce passage bird recorded from mid April, practically through the summer, to early October. It has been recorded at Azraq, Qa' Khanna, Shuna Reservoir, Al Khirba as Samra, and Ghadir Burqu', but now only in small numbers – far less numerous than the peak of 40 recorded in the mid 1960s. Hundreds were reported at Azraq in late March 1968, and there are also two winter records from there.

Tringa totanus
Redshank

AR: At-taytawi ahmar as-sāq
GE: Rotschenkel

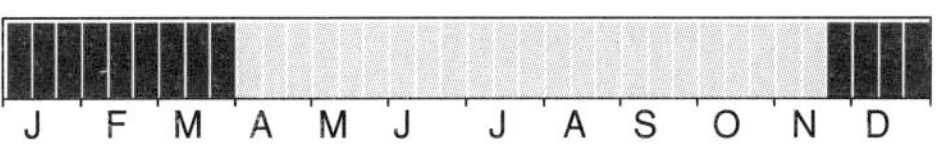

At Azraq and Al Khirba as Samra it is primarily a winter visitor from late November to late March; but small numbers can be seen at other times, and slight passage is evident in autumn. In the 1960s, hundreds were recorded at Azraq in early November and late February, with 250 on 3 February 1979; numbers are now much reduced due to habitat loss. In recent years there, its peak has been 120 in early February. The largest count at Al Khirba as Samra is 45 in early December.

It is scarce away from these two sites, with small numbers at Shaumari, Qa' Khanna, Shuna Reservoir, Ghadir Burqu', Suwayma, Wadi an Numira, As Safi and Aqaba.

Tringa stagnatilis
Marsh Sandpiper

AR: Taytawi al-batā'eh
GE: Teichwasserläufer

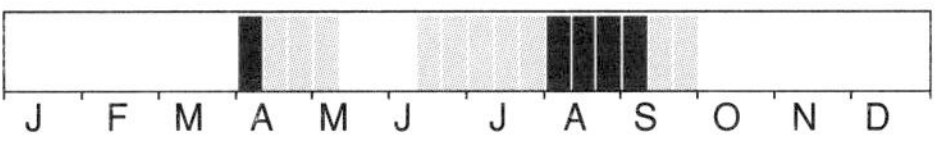

A fairly common spring and autumn migrant to wetland sites. Up to 40 have been recorded at Azraq qa' and pools in spring, and a few have turned up at Qa' Khanna, Shuna Reservoir, and Aqaba. In autumn it occurs from mid June to late September, with peaks of six at Azraq, three at Al Khirba as Samra, and singles at Ghadir Burqu' and Shuna Reservoir.

Tringa nebularia
Greenshank

AR: Al-taytawi al-akhdar as-sāq
GE: Grünschenkel

A common spring and, to a lesser extent, autumn migrant, with singles remaining in winter. Spring passage extends from early March to late May. It peaks in mid April, with 52 at Azraq on 12 April 1991. Away from Azraq, small numbers occur at Aqaba, the Jordan Valley reservoirs, and one has even been seen on a flood pool in Wadi Araba. During autumn migration (mid June to early October), maxima are 17 at Azraq on 20 July and eight at Al Khirba as Samra on 24 August. Others have been recorded at Shuna Reservoir, Ghadir Burqu', and Aqaba. A few stragglers have remained at Azraq in winter.

Tringa ochropus
Green Sandpiper

AR: At-taytawi al-akhdar
GE: Waldwasserläufer

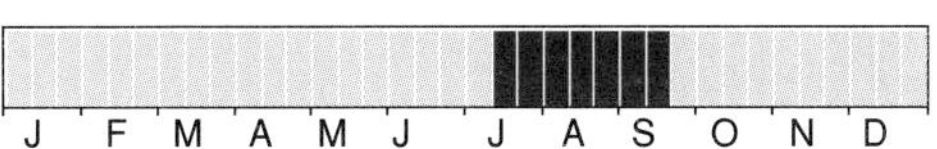

A very common passage migrant and winter visitor, recorded in every month, but generally absent in May and June. Peak numbers occur in late March, mid July, and late August with counts of 25 at Azraq on 31 March, and 110 at Al Khirba as Samra on 13 July (although 'hundreds' were reported at Azraq on 12 March). This species is more likely to turn up on rivers and small rainwater pools than Wood Sandpiper, so it has been recorded at many other sites in the Jordan Valley, tributary rivers, the badia, and at Aqaba.

A small number remain through the winter at wetland sites such as Azraq and Al Khirba as Samra, whilst a few can also be found scattered along rivers such as the Zarqa River.

Tringa glareola
Wood Sandpiper

AR: Taytawi al-gheeyad
GE: Bruchwasserläufer

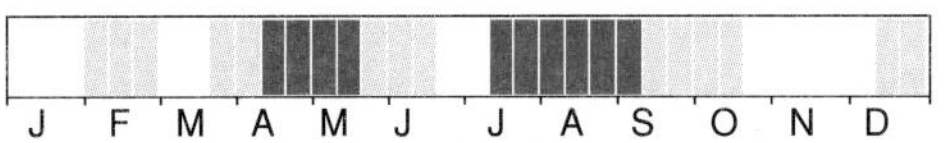

A very common passage bird at wetland sites from late March to mid May (peaking late April), and mid June to mid October (peaking late August to early September). The largest concentrations in spring are usually at Azraq (300 in April 1985), and in autumn at Al Khirba as Samra (100 on 17th and 24 August). There is a considerable turn-over of birds at Azraq in spring, and flocks depart at dusk, circling and calling before they head off north. Passage flocks can also be seen on the move at Aqaba (42 flying north on 11 May). It is rather rare away from these three sites, with only a few records from Kafrayn Reservoir, Shaumari, Wadi al Butm, Ar Ruwayshid, and Ghadir Burqu'. It is also rare in winter, with December singles at Al Khirba as Samra and Azraq, and two at the latter site from 5 February 1979.

Xenus cinereus
Terek Sandpiper

AR: Taytawi nakā
GE: Terekwasserläufer

A vagrant with only one record: one at Azraq on 22 June 1990.

Actitis hypoleucos
Common Sandpiper

AR: Taytawi a'ateey ādi
GE: Flußuferläufer

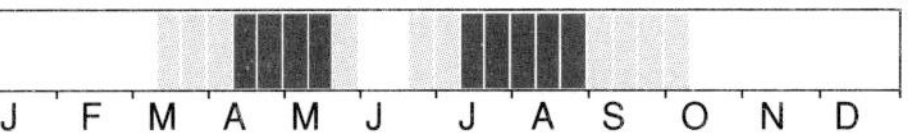

A fairly common spring and autumn migrant, with peaks in late April and late August. Like most waders, it is most often seen at Azraq, but significant numbers also occur in the west, in the Jordan Valley and at Aqaba. It also occasionally turns up on isolated, desert flood pools after periods of rain. Peak counts are 40 at Shuna Reservoir on 27 April, 30 at Al Khirba as Samra on 24 August, 30 at Aqaba on 11 April, and 25 at Kafrayn Reservoir on 21 April.

Its recorded range is from 17 March to 9 October, and records include a few mid-summer birds. Apart from reports of a few at Azraq in December, there are no other winter records.

Arenaria interpres
Turnstone

AR: Qunbar al-mā'a
GE: Steinwälzer

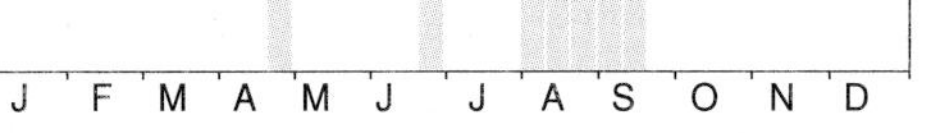

A scarce autumn migrant in late June and then early August to mid September. Up to five have occurred at Al Khirba as Samra and Azraq. One was also seen on the Aqaba hotel beach on 25 April 1985.

Phalaropus lobatus
Red-necked Phalarope

AR: Taytawi mna'ās al-qadam
GE: Odinshühnchen

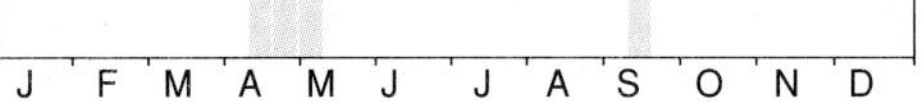

A scarce spring migrant to Azraq during 17 April-7 May, with up to 17 recorded on the flooded qa'. The only other records are from the vicinity of the Dead Sea.

Rare in autumn: one was seen at Azraq on 15-16 September 1963.

Stercorarius pomarinus
Pomarine Skua

AR: Karkar
GE: Spatelraubmöwe

J F M A M J J A S O N D

Three records. Two of these were at Aqaba: one on 25-26 April 1985 and an immature with other skuas there on 20 June 1992. Another, less expected immature was seen on 23 November 1991 on Kafrayn Reservoir, an inland site in the Jordan Valley.

Stercorarius parasiticus
Arctic Skua

AR: Karkar qutbee
GE: Schmarotzerraubmöwe

J F M A M J J A S O N D

A scarce passage migrant offshore at Aqaba, with records of up to four during mid April to mid May, and in early August. Larger numbers can occur in mid summer, with a loose flock of 75 seen there on 19 June 1992, and at least 20 the next day.

Stercorarius longicaudus
Long-tailed Skua

AR: Karkar taweel ath-thanab
GE: Falkenraubmöwe

J F M A M J J A S O N D

A very rare migrant: adults have been seen at the head of the Gulf of Aqaba on 12-13 May 1991, 20 June 1992, and 15 April 1993.

Larus leucophthalmus
White-eyed Gull

AR: Rumj al-mā'a (An-nawras al-abyad al-ayn)
GE: Weißaugenmöwe

?????
J F M A M J J A S O N D

A variable number are present offshore at Aqaba from spring through to late autumn. Numbers are small but vary from year to year, and up to 12 were seen in autumn 1991. These are wandering, non-breeding birds, probably from the nearest colony on Tiran Island at the mouth of the Gulf of Aqaba.

Larus ichthyaetus
Great Black-headed Gull

AR: Nawras es-samak al-kabeer
GE: Fischmöwe

J F M A M J J A S O N D

A rare migrant to the Gulf of Aqaba, with a few singles in mid to late April (although it could easily occur in winter also). Inland at Azraq, there is one record on 18 April 1986. These few records show the species to be considerably rarer than in Israel, where it has become a locally common winter visitor; this contrast is largely due to habitat differences.

Larus minutus
Little Gull

AR: An-nawras es-sagheer
GE: Zwergmöwe

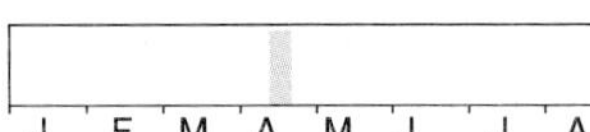

A very rare migrant. The only records are: one at Aqaba on 11-12 April 1985 and records of one in late September and two in early October at Azraq.

Larus ridibundus
Black-headed Gull

AR: Nawras aswad er-rās
GE: Lachmöwe

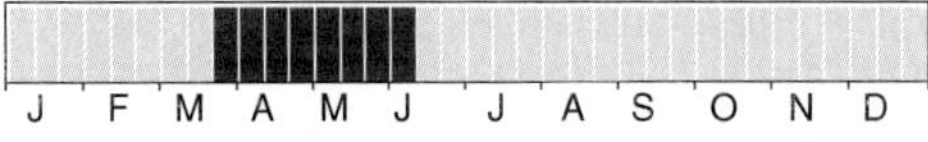

Most numerous in winter and on spring passage, this species might be seen in any month. Peak spring counts are of 200 at Aqaba in April, and 90 at Shuna Reservoir on 27 April. A small number of non-breeding birds remain through the summer, with 20-25 second-summer birds at Shuna Reservoir and Al Khirba as Samra in June and July.

It is a very common winter visitor to the Jordan Valley, with flocks of up to 200 near the Jordan River, and around pools and reservoirs. It also winters in reasonable numbers at Aqaba and Azraq.

There are occasionally records of migrants away from water, such as one near Qasr al Kharana on 31 March 1990, and five east of Al Karak on 10 April 1990.

Larus cirrocephalus
Grey-headed Gull

AR: Nawras ramādi er-rās
GE: Graukopfmöwe

Vagrant: an adult (or subadult) seen flying west at Aqaba on 30 March 1989 is presumed to have been the same second-summer bird which stayed at neighbouring Eilat from 15 March to 4 April in that year.

Larus genei
Slender-billed Gull

AR: Nawras mustadeq al-menqār
GE: Dünnschnabelmöwe

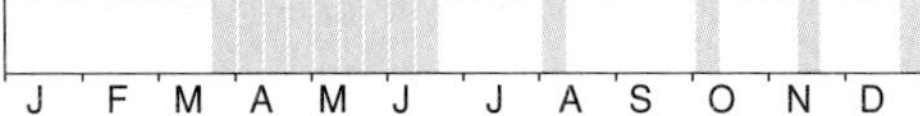

An uncommon spring passage bird at Aqaba and inland wetlands, with a known range from 23 March to 18 May. Up to 30 have been seen at Aqaba. Inland maxima include eight at Azraq, nine at Shuna Reservoir, and one at Al Umari. A few occasionally remain at Qa' al Azraq to mid June, but there has been no proof of breeding. Ones and twos can be seen at Aqaba in nearly every month, including during the winter.

Larus audouinii
Audouin's Gull

AR: Nawras edween
GE: Korallenmöwe

Vagrant: a female was shot at Aqaba on 21 April 1914.

Larus canus
Common Gull

AR: An-nawras (Rumj al-ma'a)
GE: Sturmmöwe

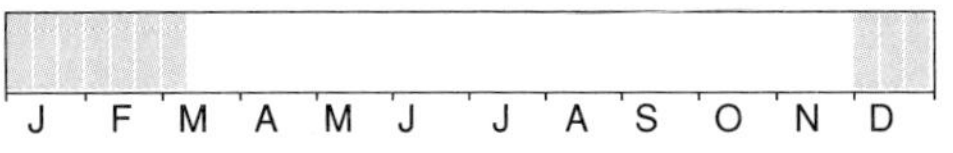

A scarce winter visitor, first recorded in Jordan as recently as 1989. This first sighting was at Azraq on 8 December 1989, but up to eight were seen in the winter of 1991/92. There is also a record at Aqaba on 23 December 1989.

Larus fuscus
Lesser Black-backed Gull

AR: Nawras aswad ath-thaher
GE: Heringsmöwe

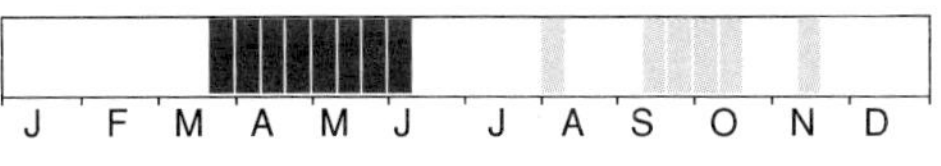

Large flocks are frequently seen on spring passage at Aqaba, with daily counts of up to 100 from early April to early June. Fewer occur during late September to mid October, with a last recorded date of 16 November. Small numbers (up to 16) have occurred inland at Azraq in spring and autumn, and it has been recorded at Shuna Reservoir.

Last century, Canon Tristram remarked that this species was to be found on the uplands of Moab, where it fed on desert snails.

Larus (argentatus) cachinnans
Yellow-legged Gull

AR: An-nawras al-fedi
GE: Weißkopfmöwe

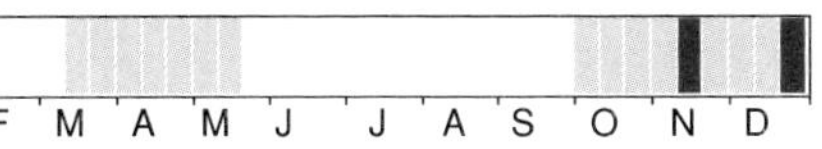

A small number can be found in winter and spring in the Jordan Valley (five at Al Manshiyya) and at Aqaba (up to 40); it is also a winter vagrant at Azraq.

Larus (argentatus) armenicus
Armenian Gull

AR: Nawras armeeni
GE: Armenische Silbermöwe (Armeniermöwe)

Likely to occur at Aqaba (and probably the Jordan Valley) on passage and in winter. The only definite record, however, is of an adult at Aqaba on 12 April 1992.

Larus hyperboreus
Glaucous Gull

GE: Eismöwe

Vagrant: one was shot at Aqaba on 18 April 1914.

Gelochelidon nilotica
Gull-billed Tern

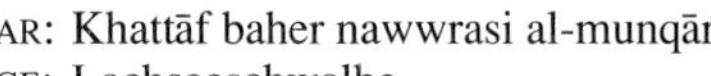
AR: Khattāf baher nawwrasi al-munqār
GE: Lachseeschwalbe

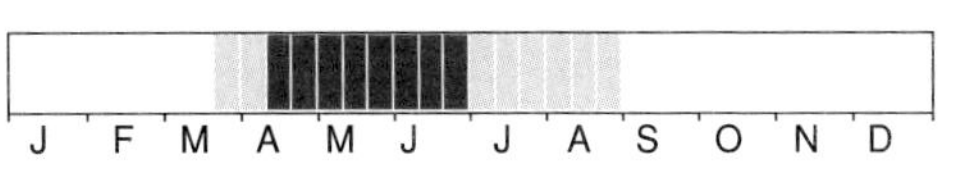

During wet springs, pairs can often be seen patrolling around Qa' al Azraq in the breeding season, although not always over the water. They disturb the breeding Black-winged Stilts and Avocets, whose chicks are amongst the tern's prey. It certainly bred at Azraq in 1991, when adults were seen feeding juveniles in late June and mid July. An egg, possibly of this species, was found at Qa' Khanna in the 1960s.

A fairly common spring and rare autumn migrant. Up to 30 stop off at inland wetlands such as Azraq, Shuna Reservoir, and Al Khirba as Samra, with smaller numbers at Qa' Khanna and Ghadir Burqu'. A maximum of 15 has also been recorded on passage at Aqaba. The only autumn records are in late August, and come from Azraq and Al Khirba as Samra.

Sterna caspia
Caspian Tern

AR: Al-khattāf al-kazweeni
GE: Raubseeschwalbe

Small numbers (up to five) can be seen patrolling up and down the coast at Aqaba throughout the year. They also frequent the sewage works, but there are no suitable beaches for them at rest. The only inland record is of three at Azraq on 23 March 1990.

Sterna bergii
Crested Tern (Swift Tern)

AR: Al-khattāf al-muttawwaj
GE: Eilseeschwalbe

Vagrant: a first-year bird flew up and down the beach at Aqaba on 1 October 1990.

Sterna bengalensis
Lesser Crested Tern

AR: Al-khattāf al-asham
GE: Rüppellseeschwalbe

A vagrant, with two records from Aqaba: one on 15 August 1980, and two on the early date of 30 March 1994.

Sterna sandvicensis
Sandwich Tern

AR: Al-kharshaneh
GE: Brandseeschwalbe

J F M A M J J A S O N D

A scarce spring migrant, both on the coast and inland. Up to three have been recorded at Aqaba and Azraq from April through to June.

Sterna hirundo
Common Tern

AR: Khattāf al-baher al-a'ateeyādi
GE: Flußseeschwalbe

J F M A M J J A S O N D

A fairly common spring migrant at Aqaba from late March to early June. It is usually seen fishing offshore, or resting on one of the quieter beaches or jetties towards the Saudi border. Up to 100 can be seen on any one day.

It is rarer inland, with up to ten seen at Azraq as late as the end of June, and there is a single record of two flying NW across the desert at Qasr al Kharana. The only record from the Jordan Valley is of two at Shuna Reservoir, and the only autumn records in Jordan were at Al Khirba as Samra on 13th and 31 July and 31 August.

An individual showing the characters of the Asiatic race *S. h. longipennis* was photographed at Aqaba on 6 April 1994.

White-eyed Gulls, Aqaba, August 1991

White-winged Black Tern, adult, Qa Hibabiya, May 1991

Whiskered Tern, juvenile, Azraq, September 1989

Whiskered Tern, juvenile, Azraq, September 1989

White-winged Black Terns, Shuna Reservoir, April 1990

White-winged Black Tern, adult, Azraq, May 1991

White-winged Black Terns, Azraq, April 1990

White-winged Black Tern, juvenile, Al Khirba as Samra, August 1991

Spotted Sandgrouse, female, Negev Desert, October 1986 (Paul Doherty)

Barn Owl, Shaumari, September 1990

Scops Owl, Shaumari, September 1990

Little Owl, Lib, December 1990

Long-eared Owl, Shaumari, January 1991

Hume's Tawny Owl, Ein Gedi, Dead Sea, October 1986 (Paul Doherty)

Nightjar, Wadi al Butm, May 1994 (Damian Debski)

Egyptian Nightjar, Azraq, August 1991

Egyptian Nightjar, Azraq, August 1991

Little Green Bee-eater, Fidan, December 1989

Bee-eater, Al Quwayra, April 1990

Smyrna Kingfisher, Sri Lanka, February 1994 (Tim Loseby)

Roller, Shaumari, May 1992

Hoopoe Lark, Qasr al Kharana, May 1990

Desert Lark, annae *subspecies, near Qasr al Kharana, November 1991*

Dunn's Lark, Fidan, June 1990

Desert Lark, Dead Sea, October 1994 (Tim Loseby)

Bar-tailed Desert Lark, Wadi Abu Khushayba, August 1991

Calandra Lark, Ma'in, May 1990

Thick-billed Lark, juvenile, Qasr al Kharana, June 1990

Temminck's Horned Lark, near Qasr Uwaynid, February 1990

Thick-billed Lark, adult, Qa Khanna, May 1990

Short-toed Lark, Abu Dharr, May 1992

Rock Martin, Petra, May 1991

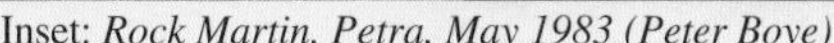

Inset: *Rock Martin, Petra, May 1983 (Peter Boye)*

Red-throated Pipit, Ras an Naqab, October 1994

Red-throated Pipit, winter plumage, Al Amiriyya, October 1990

Long-billed Pipit, near Hammamat Ma'in, May 1990

Tawny Pipit, Wadi ar Rattami, May 1991

Yellow Wagtail, male feldegg *subspecies, Wadi al Yutum, April 1990*

Yellow Wagtail, male "superciliaris" *subspecies, Azraq, May 1992*

Yellow Wagtail, male beema *subspecies, Shaumari, April 1992*

Citrine Wagtail, first-winter, Azraq, September 1990

Yellow-vented Bulbul, Dana, October 1994 (Tim Loseby)

Sterna repressa
White-cheeked Tern

AR: Khattāf thul al-khudood al-baidā'
GE: Weißwangen-Seeschwalbe

J F M A M J J A S O N D

A rare, but probably under-recorded migrant, seen in small numbers offshore at Aqaba in April and August.

Sterna anaethetus
Bridled Tern

AR: Khattāf asham
GE: Zügelseeschwalbe

Up to 18 were seen from the coast in the Gulf of Aqaba during early August 1991. It is likely to be regular there during the summer and early autumn.

Sterna albifrons
Little Tern

AR: Khattāf al-baher as-sagheer
GE: Zwergseeschwalbe

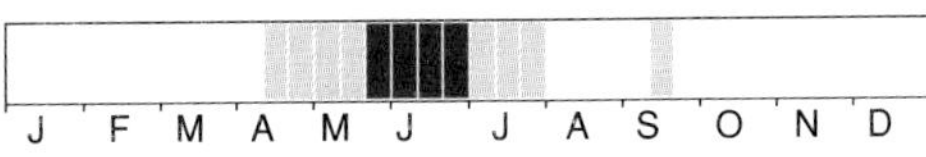

J F M A M J J A S O N D

A few pairs nest at Azraq when the conditions are suitable. Up to 60 summered in 1991, and early in the breeding season a few were seen courtship feeding and visiting islands in the flooded qa'. A single juvenile was seen with an adult in late July.

Otherwise, it is an uncommon spring migrant to Azraq from mid April into May, and was once seen at Qa' Khanna. Singles have been seen on Shuna Reservoir in the Jordan Valley during late April to early June, and small numbers also occur on the Gulf of Aqaba from April to June.

It is very rare in autumn, with one at Azraq on 15 September 1989.

Chlidonias hybridus
Whiskered Tern

AR: Khattāf bahri thu shāreb
GE: Weißbart-Seeschwalbe

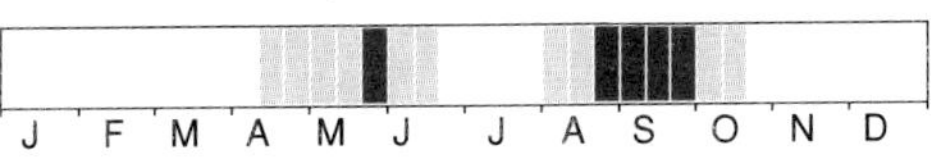

J F M A M J J A S O N D

An uncommon late spring migrant, mainly at inland sites. Small numbers use Azraq, Al Khirba as Samra, and Shuna Reservoir as stop-off points from mid April to mid June, with a peak of 17 at Azraq in late May. It is rare at Aqaba.

In autumn, a few pass through Azraq and Al Khirba as Samra from early August to mid October, but it is again rare at Aqaba.

Chlidonias niger
Black Tern

AR: Al-khattāf al-aswad
GE: Trauerseeschwalbe

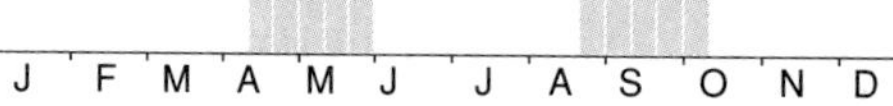

A rare spring migrant to Azraq in April and May, and well out-numbered by the White-winged Black Tern. Flocks of 20-50 have been reported infrequently, but single birds are the norm. A few have also occurred at Azraq, Al Khirba as Samra, and Aqaba in autumn (August to October), and there is one record from Aqaba in April.

Chlidonias leucopterus
White-winged Black Tern

AR: Khattāf bahri aswad abyad al-janāh (Abu raqeh)
GE: Weißflügel-Seeschwalbe

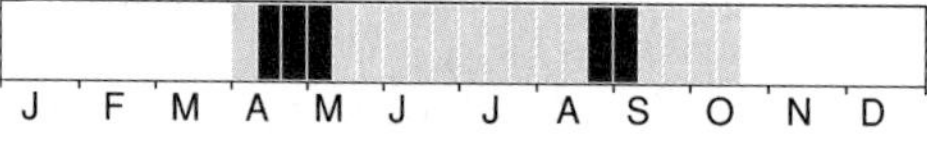

A very common, occasionally abundant passage bird in spring and autumn, mainly to inland flood pools and other areas of open water. From mid April to early May passage birds stop and feed at various sites, the majority occurring over the larger flooded qas in and around the Basalt Desert. Exceptionally large numbers are recorded occasionally, with 1500-2000 estimated over Qa' al Azraq on 26 April 1990 and 600 at Shuna Reservoir on 27 April 1990. It is less common at Aqaba, but 350 migrating birds were counted there in two hours on 15 April 1993. There is an unusual record of one at 1400m, well away from water, over a road at Ain Musa (Petra) on 11 May 1991.

Autumn migration extends from early August through to the end of September, with maximum counts of 150 at Al Khirba as Samra on 31 August 1990, and 46 at Azraq on 1 September 1990. It is relatively localised at this season due to the restricted areas of water available then.

Pterocles coronatus
Crowned Sandgrouse

AR: Qatā mutawwaj
GE: Kronenflughuhn

A local resident of Wadi Araba. Up to 75 birds were seen in the area of Wadi al Fidan and Wadi Abu Dubana during 22 October-16 November 1994.

Pterocles senegallus
Spotted Sandgrouse

AR: Al-qatā al-muraqat
GE: Tropfenflughuhn

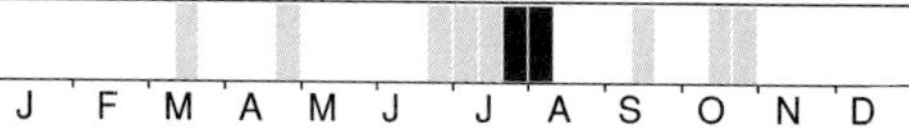

Scattered sightings in the desert in March and April have included pairs in a few cases, and breeding is suspected. Records have come from the Azraq area, between Ar Ruwayshid and Ghadir Burqu', the western Al Jafr Desert (12km north of Ma'an and at Qal'at Fassua), and Wadi Araba (at Fidan).

It may be a resident in Jordan, but it is clearly nomadic, and has not so far been recorded in winter. Birds are most likely to be seen in autumn when small flocks descend on Azraq to drink. Up to 100 were recorded in 1963, but numbers are now much reduced. In late June one drank on the flooded qa', whilst in July and August up to 20 visited the little remaining water near Azraq village. Listen out for the characteristic 'wicko, wicko' call.

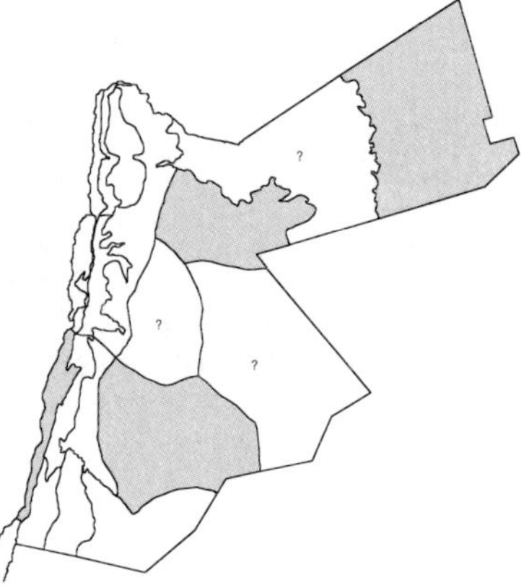

Pterocles exustus
Chestnut-bellied Sandgrouse

AR: Qatā bunni al-baten
GE: Braunbauch-Flughuhn

Last century, Canon Tristram recorded this species as 'very common east of the Jordan River' but, as elsewhere in the region, it has become increasingly rare. Indeed there has only been one documented sighting in Jordan in recent years: a pair was seen 15km west of Azraq in a sand storm on 2 May 1980.

Pterocles orientalis
Black-bellied Sandgrouse

AR: Qatā aswad al-baten
GE: Sandflughuhn

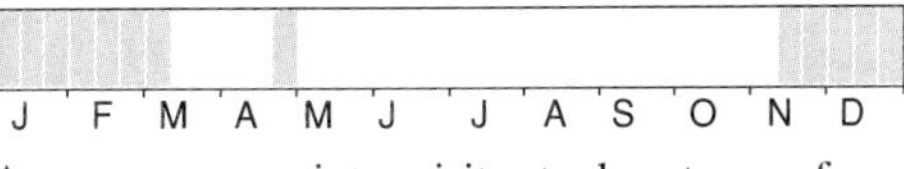

An uncommon winter visitor to desert areas from November to March (rarely April), and most likely to be located by its 'churr … churr' flight call. The Azraq and Shaumari areas used to be favoured sites with flocks of up to 120 occurring to at least 1980. It has not been recorded in these areas recently. Elsewhere, it is probably more widespread in the undulating flint and limestone deserts than the rather scattered winter records suggest.

Pterocles alchata
Pin-tailed Sandgrouse

AR: Kudree
GE: Spießflughuhn

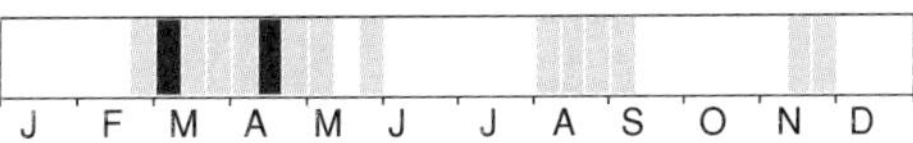

It breeds sporadically in the Azraq and Basalt Deserts, sometimes in such large numbers that its eggs are gathered by the locals in their tens of thousands. Records of this phenomenon are few and second-hand, however, and it is not known exactly where and how frequently it occurs.

It is occasionally fairly common at Shaumari, Azraq, and in the Basalt Desert in late winter and early spring, when groups of up to 200 have been seen flying over. The only records elsewhere are of one seen 10km north of Ma'an, nine at Wadi al Fidan on 13 November 1994, and five over the Amman National Park. Small numbers have also been seen drinking at Azraq in August and September.

Like the Spotted Sandgrouse, this species may be resident in Jordan, but there are very few winter records so far (16 at Risha on 21 November 1989). Its call is a loud, harsh 'catar, catar'.

Columbia livia
Rock Dove

AR: Hamam azraq (Hamam torāni)
GE: Felsentaube

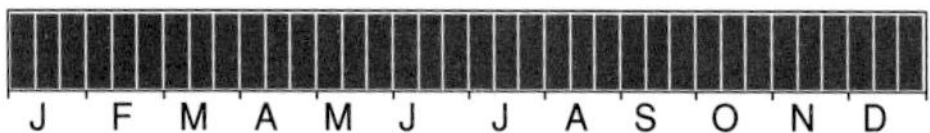

The true, wild Rock Dove is a very common resident breeding species in the mountains of the Rift Margins and in the Rum Desert. Some 80 pairs have been estimated breeding in the Petra area, and another concentration is by the Dead Sea. However, it is generally absent from large expanses of low relief desert in the east, small numbers only occurring where isolated hills or gorges are found.

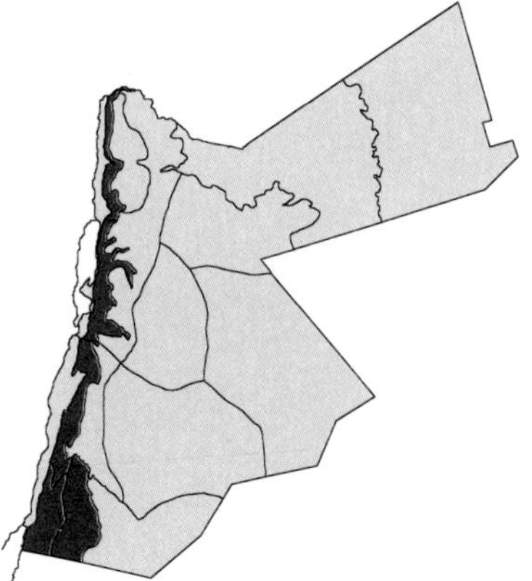

The race *C. l. palaestinae* found in Jordan usually lacks a white rump, but in about a third of birds the rump is white or greyish.

Feral birds are locally abundant in and around habitation. In the early morning, vast numbers commute across the Gulf of Aqaba from their roosts and nests in Eilat to feed on spilled grain in Aqaba port.

Columba oenas
Stock Dove

AR: Hamam barrii
GE: Hohltaube

J F M A M J J A S O N D

A winter visitor to desert regions, mainly rare or unrecorded in most years, but with large influxes in some recent years. It was found in large numbers in parts of the Eastern and Basalt Deserts during the period from 22 November to 21 March in 1990/91 and 1991/92. A bird seen on 16 April is the latest date. The largest numbers have congregated during the late afternoons in the pistachio-lined Wadi al Butm, with an estimated 500 on 21 December 1991. Birds also perch on the high-tension pylons near this site. Other large recent counts include 110 at Qasr al Kharana, 60 at Tell Qorma, 60 near As Safawi, and 27 at Shaumari.

Columba palumbus
Woodpigeon

AR: Warshān
GE: Ringeltaube

It is hard to imagine that last century Canon Tristram could write 'in Gillead I have seen a migration which can only be equalled by the descriptions we read of the flights of the Passenger Pigeons in America'. The only recent records are of singles at Azraq on 27 April 1966, and at Dibbin on 12 January 1990.

Streptopelia decaocto
Collared Dove

AR: Hamam mutawaq
GE: Türkentaube

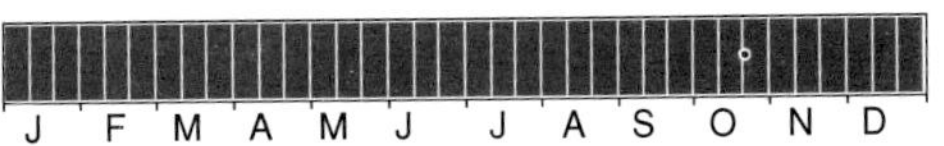

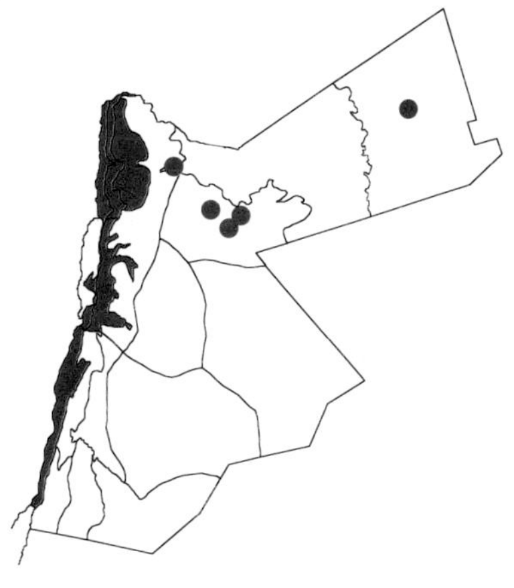

First recorded in Jordan as recently as 1979, this species' range has since expanded so rapidly that it has become a very common resident breeding species in all vegetated areas. The breeding range now includes the Northern Highlands, and irrigated areas such as the Jordan Valley, Southern Ghor, and Shaumari. It is absent from the barren desert regions, including mountainous areas.

It congregates in flocks of 50-150 in autumn and winter, especially in the Jordan Valley, the Northern Highlands, Wadi al Butm, Shaumari, Azraq, and Aqaba.

Streptopelia turtur
Turtle Dove

AR: Hamam ruqti
GE: Turteltaube

Breeds widely and fairly commonly in woods, plantations and orchards in the Northern Highlands and Jordan Valley, and possibly also at Petra.

Elsewhere, it is a very common passage migrant. It is recorded from late March to early July and from early September to early October, mainly in the Rift Margins, but also in the east at Wadi al Butm and Azraq. Large counts include 150 at Suwayma (Dead Sea) on 8 September 1989, 75 at Wadi ash Shita on 29 June 1990, 50 at the Amman National Park on 28 August 1990, and 50 at Azraq on 8 September 1990.

Mass migration was reported in mid March 1923 and late March 1933, and 500 were involved in a fall at Azraq on 28 April 1990.

Streptopelia senegalensis
Palm Dove (Laughing Dove)

AR: Dibseeyeh
GE: Palmtaube

J F M A M J J A S O N D

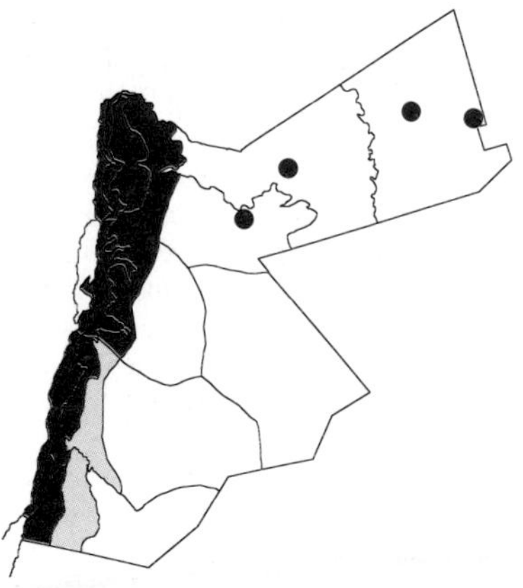

Early observers saw no Palm Doves in Jordan. Although it had probably colonised parts of Jordan slightly earlier, it was first reported in 1977 at Aqaba and Petra. It now breeds commonly in most inhabited, non-desert areas; in the Northern and Southern Highlands, Rift Margins, and from the Jordan Valley south to Aqaba. Away from these western strongholds increasing numbers of pairs are also resident at Azraq, and there have been recent sightings as far east as As Safawi, Ar Ruwayshid, and near the Iraqi border. It is also present rather locally in the Rum Desert, largely restricted to the settlement of Rum itself.

This species has undergone a widespread expansion in the region. Although it was first recorded in Israel in 1938 it had a restricted distribution then, and did not reach the Jordan Valley until the end of the 1960s and Eilat until 1970.

Oena capensis
Namaqua Dove

AR: Hamameh taweelat ith-thanab
GE: Kaptäubchen

J F M A M J J A S O N D

Despite recently colonising adjacent parts of Israel, records remain few in Jordan, and there is no proof of breeding. There are a handful of spring records at Aqaba, including two at the Royal Diving Centre on 30 March 1989. Further north, one was seen at Disi on 27 April 1986, and two were near As Safi on 23 April 1986. At Azraq, probably the most northerly site known for this species, a female was seen flying north on 23 April 1966, and a male was seen on 20 April 1985. One was seen at Shaumari in May 1988.

Psittacula krameri

Ring-necked Parakeet (Rose-ringed Parakeet)

AR: Babagha mutawaqa
GE: Halsbandsittich

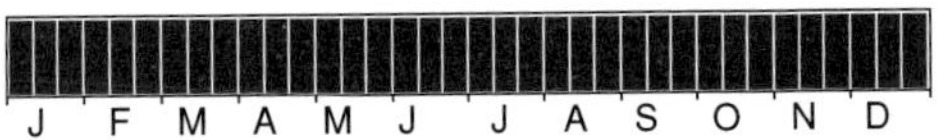

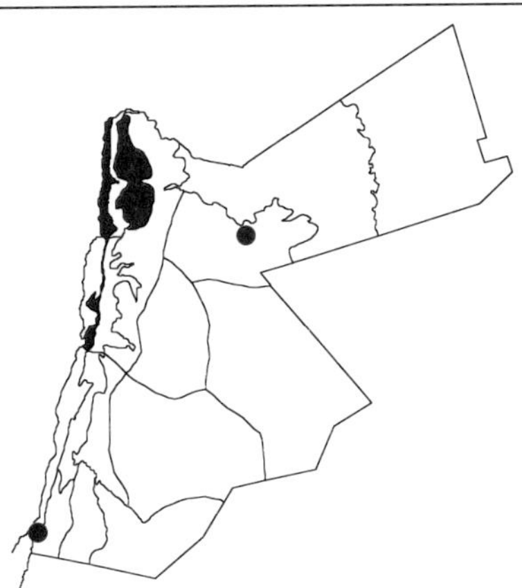

First recorded in Aqaba in 1979, and at Amman and Shaumari in 1987, a feral population of this species is now established in parts of the Northern Highlands, the Jordan Valley and Aqaba, following the escape (or release) of some of the large number of imported birds. A total of 22,250 were imported in 1987-88 alone, mainly from Pakistan. It is found in areas with trees and in agricultural areas and it apparently nests in urban gardens in Amman, though no nest has yet been documented. Communal roosts have been recorded in Amman, with 65 in a single Cypress tree on Jabal Amman on 27 November 1989. A few wanderers or locally introduced birds have been recorded at Azraq and Shaumari.

Clamator glandarius

Great Spotted Cuckoo

AR: Waqwāq muraqat
GE: Häherkuckuck

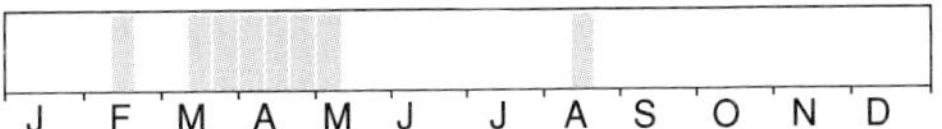

A scarce spring passage bird to the Highlands, Jordan Valley, Wadi Araba, and Azraq. It is typically an early migrant, recorded between February and early May. Although there are no definite instances, breeding is suspected in the northern Jordan Valley. There is only one autumn record, at Shaumari on 12 August 1976.

Cuculus canorus

Cuckoo

AR: Al-waqwāq al-mā'aloof
GE: Kuckuck

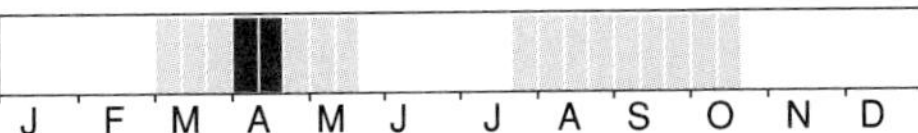

In spring, territorial males can be heard in the open country of the Rift Margins from Wadi Shu'ayb in the north, east of the Dead Sea, and south as far as Wadi Dana, but breeding remains to be proven. Regular sites include Wadi Zerqa Ma'in and Wadi Dana. Potential foster species include Scrub Warbler!

It is also a scarce passage migrant to Petra, Azraq, Shaumari, and other Eastern Desert sites in spring and early autumn. The earliest birds return after 2 March and the latest record is on 17 October.

Tyto alba
Barn Owl

AR: Hāmat
GE: Schleiereule

J F M A M J J A S O N D

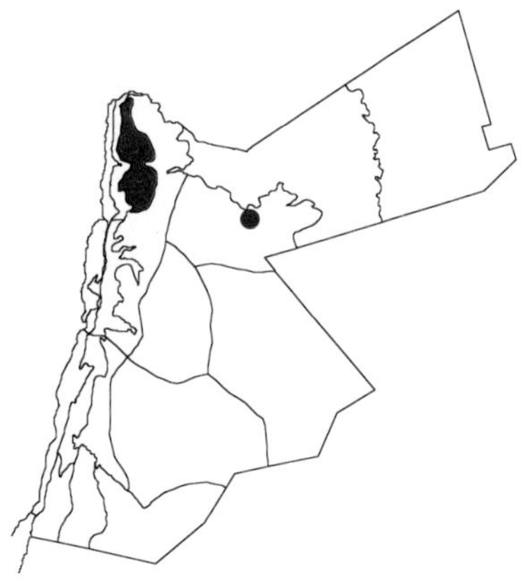

In north-west Jordan, the Barn Owl has recently been proved breeding at Irbid, south of Ar Ramtha, and in the capital, Amman. A pair has also bred regularly at Shaumari following the provision of a nest box in 1986. Previously published records of birds at Azraq and Shaumari in April were interpreted as passage migrants.

The race involved is the pale-breasted, desert form *T. a. erlangeri*.

Otus brucei
Striated Scops Owl (Bruce's Scops Owl)

AR: Boomeh mukhatata
GE: Streifenohreule

J F M A M J J A S O N D

The limited number of records of this elusive species make it difficult to assess its true status, but it may be a rare resident in desert areas with trees. There have been spring records from Azraq, Wadi al Butm and Wadi Rum, and there are also claims that it may breed in the Southern Rift Margins. Statements in the 1960s that this species bred in Jordan were based on the assumption that all the native *Otus* owls were *O. brucei*, which is now known not to be the case.

Otus scops
Scops Owl

AR: Ath-thubej
GE: Zwergohreule

????

J F M A M J J A S O N D

An uncommon migrant breeding species restricted to woodland and scattered trees in the Northern Highlands (for example Irbid, Ajlun and Wadi as Sir), and the Rift Margins south to Petra. After it arrives in late March, it is best located at dusk by its penetrating 'piu' call.

Migrants also pass through the Eastern Desert, and there have been a few records in April and September at Azraq and Shaumari, and one 34km east of Al Mafraq. A high proportion of migrants are unfortunately found as corpses.

Bubo bubo
Eagle Owl

AR: Al-boohe
GE: Uhu

J F M A M J J A S O N D

A rare and localised breeding species in wide-ranging parts of Jordan. In recent years it has been recorded from two sites near Irbid, and also in Wadi Rum and Wadi Dana, but there is little doubt that it is more widespread than this suggests. Last century, it was even to be found in some ruins in Amman, and in the late 1960s it was described as a regular winter visitor to Azraq.

Birds inhabiting the Rum Desert are likely to be of the desert race, or so-called Pharaoh Eagle Owl (*B. (b.) ascalaphus*). These differ from the northern birds (*B. b. interpositus*) in being smaller and paler, and having a distinct barking call.

Ketupa zeylonensis
Brown Fish Owl

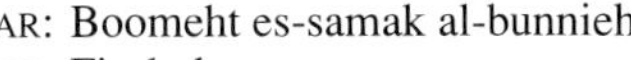

AR: Boomeht es-samak al-bunnieh
GE: Fischuhu

Possibly still a very rare resident along the Yarmuk Valley, and possibly also in the northern Jordan Valley, but both areas are difficult to search for security reasons. There is photographic evidence that one occurred on the Israeli-occupied side of the Yarmuk River at Hammat Gader in 1974-75, and one was reported in Jordan north of Al Znebneh village in 1986.

The current status of this species in its restricted Middle Eastern range is unclear, but it has certainly declined since the 1950s.

Athene noctua
Little Owl

AR: Umm quuieq
GE: Steinkauz

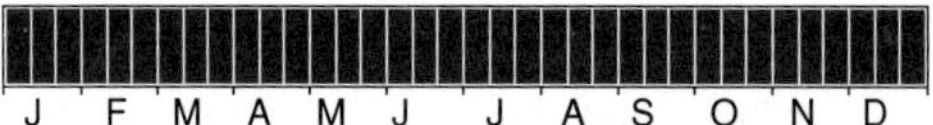

A fairly common bird, confined to the more arid, poorly vegetated regions. It is a typical bird of archaeological ruins, and it also nests in holes in trees, and burrows in flat desert. It is most commonly found in the Dead Sea Rift Margins, around the margins of the Northern Highlands, and in the Northern Steppes. It is found in lower densities further east, in the undulating desert, where birds are restricted to cliffs, gorges and ruins. It is absent from the wooded areas in the north and, rather surprisingly, appears to be very scarce in the mountains of the Southern Rift Margins, Aqaba Mountains, and the Rum Desert.

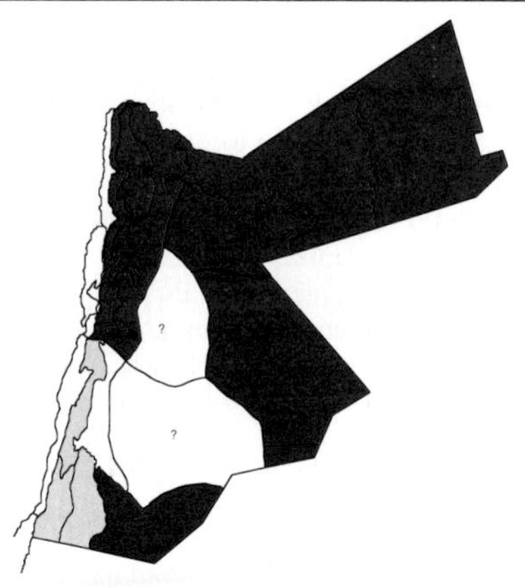

Strix aluco
Tawny Owl

AR: Al-khubal
GE: Waldkauz

J F M A M J J A S O N D

Last century, it was reported to be a not uncommon breeding species in the forests of the Northern Highlands. Whilst camping in that area, Canon Tristram heard it calling night after night, and found one nest in a tree. The next records came one hundred years later, in 1994, when calling birds were heard near Ajlun on 18 and 28 March. Despite the paucity of records, it can be assumed that this nocturnal owl is still a widespread resident of the forests of the Northern Highlands.

Strix butleri
Hume's Tawny Owl

AR: Boomeh butlir
GE: Fahlkauz

This is a truly nocturnal owl of desert mountains, and probably has a fairly widespread distribution in the cliffs and siqs of the Southern Rift Margins and Rum Desert. The natural and man-made cliffs and caves of Petra provide ideal habitat, and up to five birds have been heard calling at dusk. One has even been seen roosting in one of the tombs during the day. Single birds have also been heard on Jabal Umm Ishrin and in Wadi Dana. Other potential breeding areas include the Dead Sea Rift Margins and Aqaba Mountains. In the latter area, feathers were found behind the Marine Science Station, 10km south of Aqaba, in March 1977.

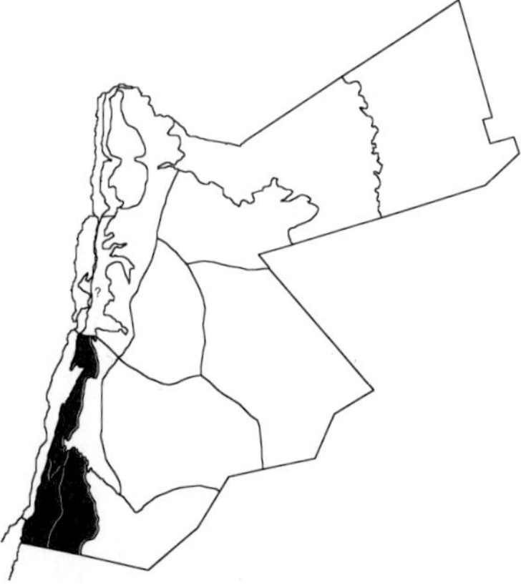

Asio otus
Long-eared Owl

AR: Al-boomeh al-uthuna'a
GE: Waldohreule

J F M A M J J A S O N D

A localised, uncommon winter visitor to the Azraq, Wadi al Butm, Amman, and Jordan Valley areas from late November to mid April. The largest numbers have been at Shaumari, where up to eight roost communally in eucalyptus trees. Additional records from this site in late August and early September suggest either local breeding or early dispersal from nearby.

Asio flammeus
Short-eared Owl

AR: Boomeh sama'a
GE: Sumpfohreule

J F M A M J J A S O N D

A rare bird in Jordan. A few possibly used to winter at Azraq, but the limited number of recent sightings there have been in late April and early May. There is also an undated photograph of a bird taken in the Al Jafr Desert.

Caprimulgus nubicus
Nubian Nightjar

AR: Subad nubi
GE: Nubischer Ziegenmelker

J F M A M J J A S O N D

There are three scattered records, all in 1963: four at Azraq on 19 April, one at Wadi Musa on 28 April, and one at Gibayha on 12 May. Published maps show it to be resident in Wadi Araba north as far as Jericho, but breeding in this region has not been proven within Jordan.

Caprimulgus europaeus
Nightjar

AR: As-subad
GE: Ziegenmelker

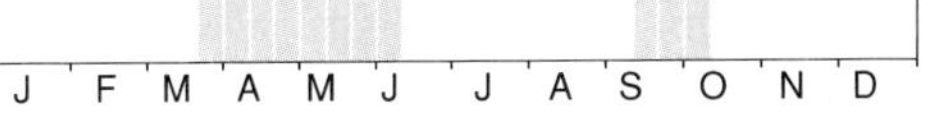

J F M A M J J A S O N D

A rather scarce, but probably under-recorded spring migrant, mainly through the Eastern Desert at sites including Azraq, Shaumari, and Wadi al Butm. Nightjars have been seen fly-catching around the lights at Azraq Resthouse on several occasions; one was even heard reeling at Azraq on 18 April 1969, and there were 11 records (17 birds) at Shaumari during 1975-77. The largest recorded fall concerns six birds found within 500m of each other in Wadi al Butm in mid May 1994. There is one record from the Amman National Park, and feathers have also been found north-east of Zerqa Ma'in. Its recorded ranges are from 25 March to 7 June, and from 28 September to 3 October.

Caprimulgus aegyptius
Egyptian Nightjar

AR: Subad musri
GE: Pharaonenziegenmelker

J F M A M J J A S O N D

May be commoner in the desert than records suggest, but it has nested at least once at Azraq. The nest was found in sparse *Tamarix* on salt-encrusted silt in early June 1969.

It is a summer migrant, and likely to be present from March to September, however, there are only three records in addition to the breeding record given above. One was seen at Azraq on 29 April 1980 and two were photographed at the Azraq fishpools in July and August 1991. The other record is of one in Wadi Rum on 4 May 1963.

Apus apus
Swift

AR: As-sumāmah
GE: Mauersegler

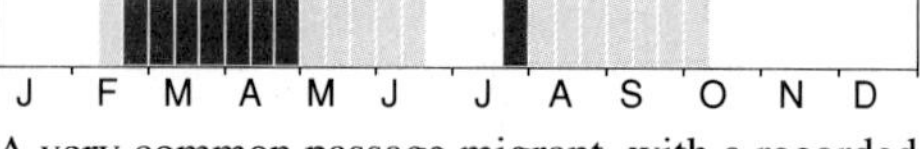

J F M A M J J A S O N D

A very common passage migrant, with a recorded range between 15 February and 1 October, but most numerous in spring between late February and the end of April. It occurs along the Rift Margins and in the Eastern Desert. If it breeds, it is most likely to do so in the north, in the hills east of Jordan Valley.

Apus pallidus
Pallid Swift

AR: As-sumāma ar-rabdā'a
GE: Fahlsegler

J F M A M J J A S O N D

Breeds in the Southern Highlands, where considerable numbers can be seen around Wadi Musa and Petra. Elsewhere in the highlands, and to a lesser extent at Azraq, it is a fairly common spring migrant (peaking mid April to early May), but it is scarce in autumn.

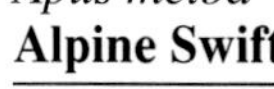

Apus melba
Alpine Swift

AR: Sumāmat as-sorood
GE: Alpensegler

J F M A M J J A S O N D

A common summer migrant, recorded from 22 February to 20 October. It occurs in the Northern Highlands (including frequent birds over Amman) and in the Rift Margins south to Wadi Dana. A record of 100 in Wadi al Hidan on 17 November 1989 suggests that birds may stay later than originally thought.

Although the mapped breeding range includes two areas in the Southern Rift Margin (and another near Az Zarqa), large numbers of birds have also been seen landing on suitable breeding cliffs at Wadi al Hidan.

It is rare in the Eastern Desert, where only a few have ever been seen at Azraq in January-February and in April. There are also surprisingly few records from Aqaba.

Apus affinis
Little Swift

AR: As-sumāmah es-sagheereh
GE: Haussegler

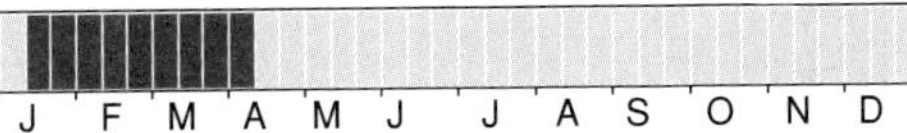

A fairly common, presumed resident of the Rift Valley and Rift Margins, with peak numbers in winter and early spring (but no records for August and September). It breeds on several cliffs in the Northern Rift Margins (Umm Qays, Yarmuk River area) and in the Dead Sea Rift Margin (from Wadi Shu'ayb south to Wadi al Karak), but is absent from the Southern Rift Margin and Rum Desert. In winter, birds often congregate over water in the southern Jordan Valley, with the largest recorded numbers being 50 over Shuna Reservoir on 19 January 1990 and 17 March 1990.

It is a rare migrant to Azraq and Shaumari from February to April.

Halcyon smyrnensis
Smyrna Kingfisher (White-breasted Kingfisher)

AR: Qāwoond (Deek al-beher)
GE: Braunliest

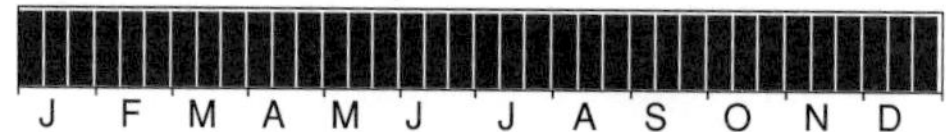

A fairly common resident in the agricultural areas of the Jordan Valley, and in many of its tributaries from the Yarmuk River south to Wadi al Mujib, notably the Zarqa River and Wadi Shu'ayb. It also occurs in the agricultural areas of the Southern Ghor. This kingfisher is as equally at home in lush vegetated areas as it is near water, and it can often be seen perched on telegraph wires waiting to drop on its prey.

A few have been seen in early to mid April on the Aqaba shore, and these may originate from Eilat where they now breed. The only Azraq record dates from August 1922.

Ceryle rudis
Pied Kingfisher

AR: Sa'id as-samak al-abqa
GE: Graufischer

Resident, and presumably breeding in small numbers at the reservoirs in the lower Jordan Valley, at the King Talal Dam, and along the Jordan River. It has been recorded at relatively few sites, reflecting the paucity of suitable open water.

A few wander across the desert to Azraq in autumn and winter (October to March). It is now rare there, but in the 1960s it was reported to be a common sight in the flooded *Tamarix* at the edge of the marsh in October and November.

Alcedo atthis
Kingfisher

AR: Ar-rafrāf
GE: Eisvogel

J F M A M J J A S O N D

An uncommon passage migrant and winter visitor (late August to mid April) to the Jordan Valley, and its tributary valleys south to Wadi al Mujib. It also frequents the Dead Sea area, Aqaba and Azraq at the same seasons. A migrant on flood water in Wadi al Butm on 30 September 1994 illustrates its ability to migrate across desert areas.

It is suspected that breeding may have occurred at Azraq in the past, and it may nest along the Jordan River.

Merops orientalis
Little Green Bee-eater

AR: Al-warwār al-akhdar as-sagheer
GE: Smaragdspint

J F M A M J J A S O N D

Not recorded in Jordan until 1979, but now known to be resident in small numbers from south of Aqaba, north along Wadi Araba as far as As Safi. Birds are typically found in open acacia woodland or on road-side wires, but they nest in burrows in sandy wadi banks. Birds occasionally wander further north, for example, five were seen at the mouth of Wadi al Mujib on 21 December 1990.

The race found in Wadi Araba is the blue-throated, Arabian race *M. o. cyanophrys*, as opposed to the Egyptian race *cleopatra*.

Merops superciliosus
Blue-cheeked Bee-eater

AR: Al-warwār al-eraqi
GE: Blauwangenspint

J F M A M J J A S O N D

An isolated breeding colony formerly thrived in the Azraq marshes, with up to 40 pairs estimated in the 1960s. They nested in burrows, largely on islands where the soil was soft beneath a hard crust. There is no evidence of this colony existing after 1969.

Small groups of up to four birds have occasionally been recorded on passage at Aqaba in spring, and there are also records from the Jordan Valley, As Safi and Ar Ruwayshid. It also passes through Azraq from August to early October, but far less frequently now than in the past.

Merops apiaster
Bee-eater

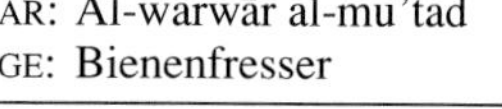

AR: Al-warwār al-mu'tad
GE: Bienenfresser

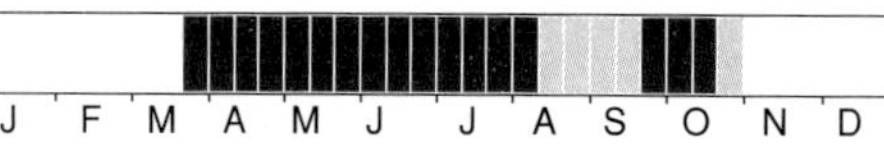

Surprisingly few breeding colonies are known in Jordan. Although nesting birds have been located in the Northern Highlands, the Rift Margins and Sharra Highlands, they well may be more numerous than records suggest. Large feeding flocks (up to 200) around the Amman National Park in summer imply that a colony may be present in that vicinity.

It is, nevertheless, a very common migrant and summer visitor from late March to late October. Migrants have been reported widely from Aqaba northwards along the whole length of the Rift Margins, with a maximum of 500 roosting at Aqaba on 3 May 1990, and 100 on 30 September 1990. In the interior deserts, birds have been seen at Ras an Naqab, Wadi Sahb al Abyad and Azraq. It also occurs at Shaumari, where it is more numerous in autumn than in spring.

Migrants often pass high overhead, but they are very vocal, and can be located by their far-carrying 'quilp' and 'kroop' calls.

Coracias garrulus
Roller

AR: Ash-shaqrāq al-mu'tād
GE: Blauracke

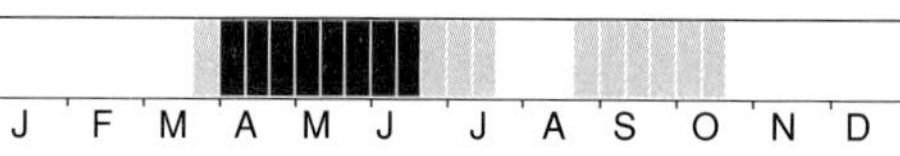

A scarce migrant breeding species to the wadis flowing into the Jordan Valley. Mid summer records and evidence of breeding comes from the South Shuna-Kafrayn, Wadi as Sir and Zerqa Ma'in areas.

Otherwise, it is a fairly common spring (peak early May), and less common autumn (peak late September and early October) migrant to many areas. Small groups can sometimes be observed on passage; for example 25 were seen flying WNW at Azraq on 28 April and 3 May 1965, with 20 at the Amman National Park on 24 April 1990.

Upupa epops
Hoopoe

AR: Al-hudhud
GE: Wiedehopf

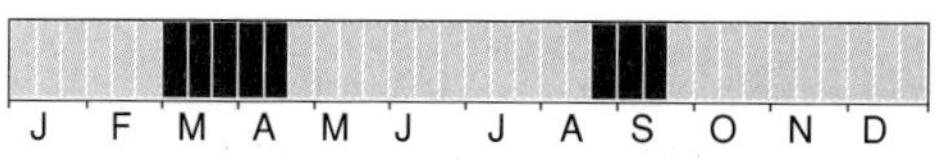

The Hoopoe can be seen in Jordan in all months, but it is most numerous as a spring migrant.

In the highlands, it is a fairly common summer visitor from late February to November. A few breed in the Northern Highlands, and in the Southern Highlands 3-6 pairs bred in 10km² at Petra in 1983. Their 'poo-poo-poo' call can also often be heard in spring above Wadi Dana.

It is a fairly common migrant to many areas, including the Eastern Desert and Aqaba, where numbers peak during early March to mid April. Fewer are seen in autumn from late August to the end of October.

The warmer climate of the Jordan Valley allows the Hoopoe to be a resident there, with small numbers breeding, for example at Shuna Reservoir.

Jynx torquilla
Wryneck

AR: Al-liwa'a
GE: Wendehals

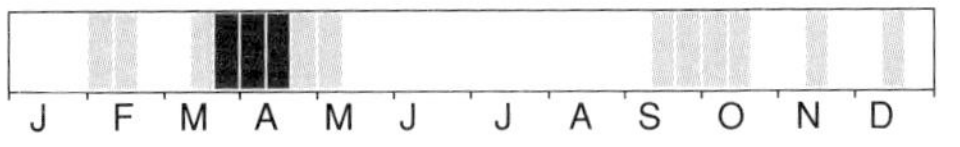

A rather scarce spring migrant (mainly late March to mid April), but rarer in autumn (September and October). It has been recorded at widely scattered sites in the west from Aqaba to Amman, plus Azraq and Wadi al Butm in the east. It is not restricted to wooded areas on migration, when it can turn up in deserts with only scrub cover. It tends to be easier to locate there.

There is one true winter record in the Jordan Valley, at South Shuna on 15 December 1989, with others in this region in November and February.

Dendrocopos syriacus
Syrian Woodpecker

AR: Naqār al-khasheb as-souri
GE: Blutspecht

J F M A M J J A S O N D

A local resident, to be found breeding in orchards, pines, oaks, and wooded wadis in the Northern Highlands, for example at Umm Qays, Ajlun, Dibbin, Wadi as Sir, and Wadi ash Shita. In the south its range has contracted due to the loss of its woodland habitat, but in the north, the spread of olive orchards can only have helped the species. A few were seen in 1909 in the steep gorges of the Moab plateau, and one was shot in Wadi al Wala just below sea-level.

Eremalauda dunni
Dunn's Lark

GE: Einödlerche

J F M A M J J A S O N D

The Dunn's Lark has occurred and bred, although perhaps only erratically, at localities in Wadi Araba, and in the Eastern and Basalt Deserts.

A nest was found in Wadi ash Shaumari in 1965, and at that time other birds were seen in Wadi Rajil (between Al Umari and Tell Qorma), and on a silt pan 27km west of Ar Ruwayshid. At these sites it was found on rough sandy ground with scattered low shrubs in wadi spreads within limestone desert. There are few recent reports from the above areas.

At Wadi Abu Dubana (Fidan), on the flanks of Wadi Araba, up to ten, including singing birds, were seen in 1990 and 1994. It is assumed that this population was associated with the 1988/89 winter influx into Wadi Araba (previously noted only in Israel).

Ammomanes cincturus
Bar-tailed Desert Lark

AR: Qubarat al-badyā mukhatat ith-thanab
GE: Sandlerche

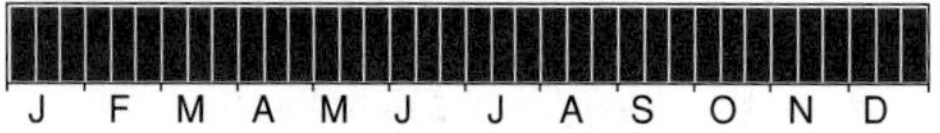

A widely distributed but uncommon bird, found in the Eastern Desert, Ar Ruwayshid Desert, on silty wadi fills in the Basalt Desert, also in Wadi Araba, and in the more open parts of the Rum Desert. At Azraq it is associated with open stony hammada, and it prefers parts with sandy patches and at least some low shrubs. It is thought to be a resident in the above areas, although most records are between March and October. A winter record of ten on sands near Mahattat Rum on 22 December 1989 is suggestive of local movements, as birds are not usually found in this area.

This lark is best located during its characteristic song flight: a 'chu-wee' whistle, repeated monotonously during an undulating flight.

Ammomanes deserti
Desert Lark

AR: Qubarat al-badyā
GE: Steinlerche

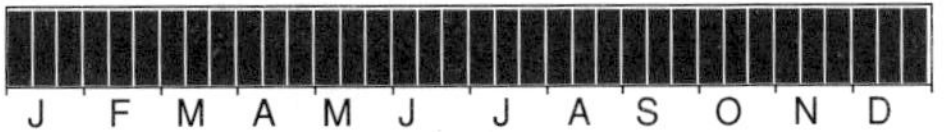

A widespread, common resident of rocky desert habitats, found in the Rift Margin wadis from Wadi Shu'ayb south to Aqaba, in the Rum Desert, the Basalt Desert, and more patchily on escarpments and wadis of the central desert watersheds. Three races, differentiated on the basis of their coloration, are described in Jordan: *deserti* (dark grey-brown) recorded at Aqaba, *isabellinus* (paler and greyer) occurring through most of Jordan, and *annae* (dark slate-grey) found on the flint and black basalt deserts of central and northern Jordan. Pale individuals have been reported coexisting with dark birds, a phenomenon also noted elsewhere in Arabia.

Alaemon alaudipes
Hoopoe Lark

AR: Al-makā'a
GE: Wüstenläuferlerche

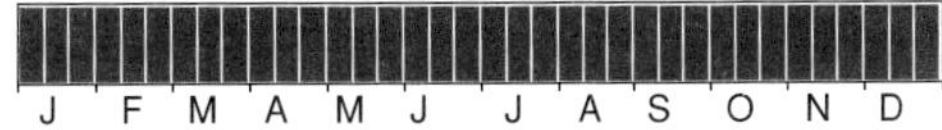

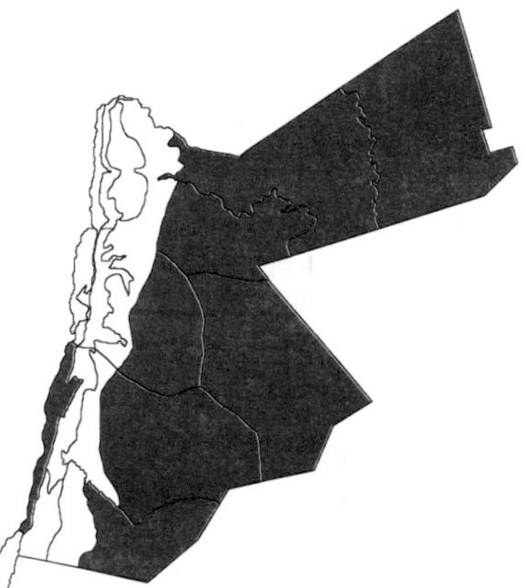

A fairly common resident bird across the eastern and south-eastern deserts (including the Basalt and Ar Ruwayshid Deserts), and also in Wadi Araba. It is almost entirely confined to flat sandy wadis with extensive, and sometimes fairly dense low shrublets. It is usually paired or solitary, but small groups of up to six (totalling 15) were seen in the Wadi al Jilat area on 17 February 1990. A few also occur on the eastern margin of the Northern Steppes, but only where the steppe habitat has suffered desertification. At present, the only records from the Rum Desert are in October and December.

The evocative, but melancholy song will remain a strong memory of the desert. It consists of drawn-out, high-pitched, out-of-key whistles, and is given from a bush or in a brief, up-then-down song flight.

Although mainly an insect eater, it was once observed digging a small lizard from its burrow. It killed the lizard with some difficulty by stabbing it, but then discarded it. Most field guides show birds to be a pale sandy colour, but greyish hues are not uncommon, especially on the flint and basalt areas.

Rhamphocoris clotbey
Thick-billed Lark

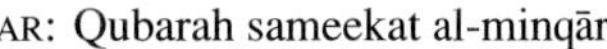
AR: Qubarah sameekat al-minqār
GE: Knackerlerche

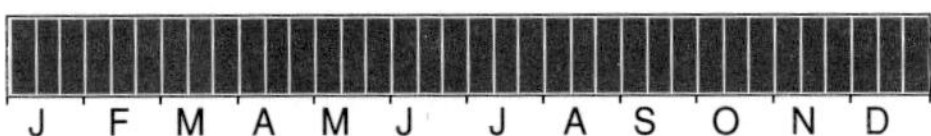

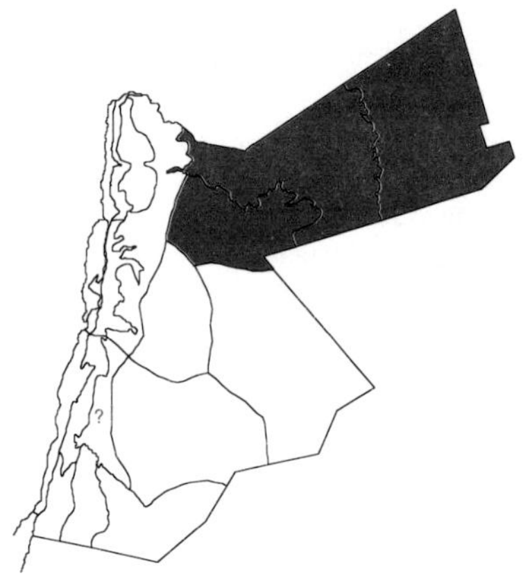

One of the specialities of Jordan, this species is a scarce resident of the Eastern, Basalt, and Ar Ruwayshid Deserts. It is usually found on low relief flint hammada desert (Qa' al Hibabiya, Qasr al Kharana and Wadi al Butm), but it also occurs in wadis within the basalt boulder fields (Wadi Rajil, east of As Safawi, and Wadi as Sibhi), and on limestone (south-east of Ar Ruwayshid). Furthermore there have been isolated records from steppe habitat on the margins of the Sharra Highlands, and a separate population may exist there.

The outsized bill, well streaked breast, and Redshank-like flight pattern make for easy identification, but it breeds at such low densities that locating it is a major obstacle.

Melanocorypha calandra
Calandra Lark

AR: 'Olol
GE: Kalanderlerche

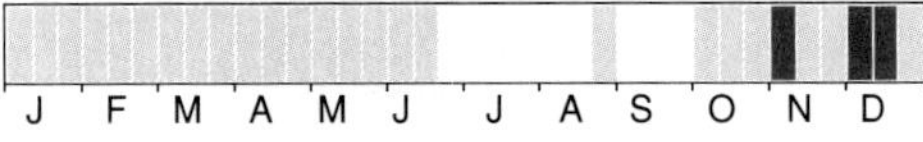

A very common winter visitor, and rather scarce breeder in agricultural and steppe country surrounding the Northern Highlands. From October and through the winter, it frequents ploughed fields in groups of up to 50, but a flock of 700 was seen at Umm ar Rasas on 1 December 1989, and 1800 were seen near Al Qadisiyya on 5 October 1994. It only rarely occurs in true desert areas, and it is a winter vagrant to Azraq.

Smaller numbers stay to breed in crops in the Northern Highlands and Steppes. In spring it can be heard singing, for example, around the Amman National Park, and from the Madaba to Hammamat Ma'in road. The song is rather similar to that of Skylark, but is full of mimicry, and is given either from a perch or from high in the sky. When displaying in flight it shows off its black underwing with stiff wingbeats.

Melanocorypha bimaculata
Bimaculated Lark

AR: Al-'olola (Al-mutawaq as-sagheer)
GE: Bergkalanderlerche

A scarce early spring migrant in the highland fringe and Eastern Desert, mainly in March, but a few also occur until late April. It is usually seen in small flocks of up to nine birds, but 30 were seen at Azraq on 30 March 1988.

The only autumn records are from Azraq in October 1922 and on 12 October 1990.

Calandrella brachydactyla
Short-toed Lark

AR: Al-o'lai'aleh
GE: Kurzzehenlerche

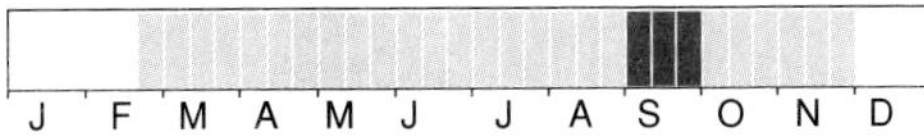

A locally very common migrant to, and uncommon breeding species in the margins of the Northern Highlands and deserts. Present from early March to end November.

A few breed in arable areas in the Northern Highlands, and Steppes, such as the Amman National Park and near Dhiban. A small population also bred in cultivated land and in desert at Azraq, at least in the 1960s.

Otherwise, it is a migrant through desert areas from early March to early April, and from early September to early October. At Azraq and Ghadir Burqu' it is primarily an autumn migrant, with up to 400 congregating to drink at the small wetland sites, especially in late September. It is absent from Jordan in winter.

Calandrella rufescens
Lesser Short-toed Lark

AR: Al-o'lai'aleh es-sagheereh
GE: Stummellerche

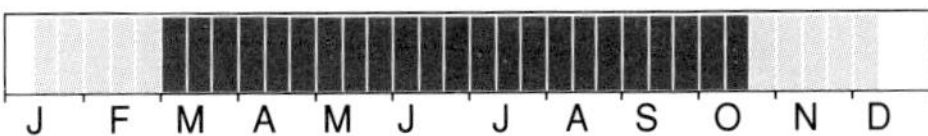

A very common breeding species in the Eastern Desert, particularly around Azraq. It can also be found on Rift Margin agricultural land, and a few occur in the Basalt and Ar Ruwayshid Deserts.

Elsewhere, such as the Rum Desert, it invades inconsiderable numbers when conditions become suitable after rains (as in spring 1991). It is found commonly in a variety of habitats at Azraq (cultivation, dry marsh, qa' edges and desert).

Large flocks congregate at wetland sites at Azraq from June to October. It is absent from most areas in winter, but it remained at Azraq in some numbers in the past, suggesting a local seasonal movement from the desert.

Galerida cristata
Crested Lark

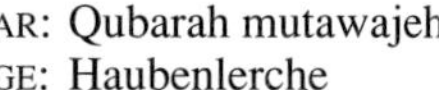

AR: Qubarah mutawajeh
GE: Haubenlerche

J F M A M J J A S O N D

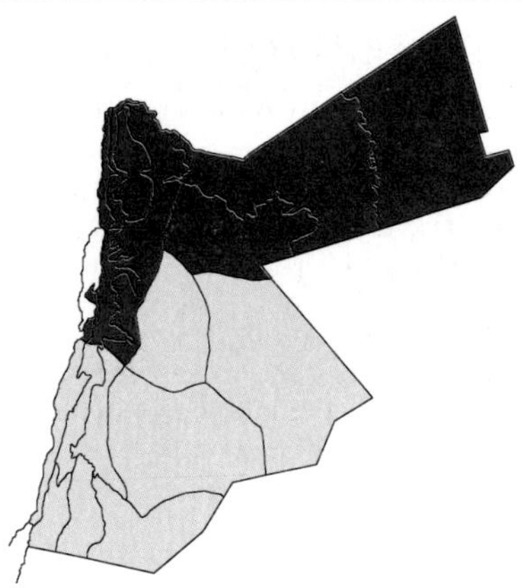

In the northern half of the country, the Crested Lark is a very common resident in a wide variety of agricultural and rural habitats. These include sites in the Jordan Valley, Dead Sea Rift Margins, Northern Highlands, Eastern, Basalt, and Ar Ruwayshid Deserts. It is far less common in the southern half of the country, and is largely absent from the south-eastern deserts, Petra mountains, and Wadi Araba. However, it is present in cultivated areas in the south, such as the Disi irrigation project (Rum Desert).

Lullula arborea
Woodlark

AR: Qubarat al-gheyād
GE: Heidelerche

J F M A M J J A S O N D

A fairly common winter visitor and rare passage bird to the Rift Margins, Highlands and Steppes of north-western Jordan. It typically occurs in small flocks of 3-27, in open, rocky, ploughed land in the uplands, usually above 500m, but it can also occur in open pine forest. It can be seen from mid October to mid March in the Amman-Na'ur, Dibbin-Najde, Lib-Mukawir, and Wadi al Wala areas. One seen at sea-level in the lower Zarqa River in early November was presumably a migrant, as was one in Wadi al Butm on 24 May 1990.

In addition, birds have been recorded singing in suitable breeding habitat in the uplands north of Wadi Dana in late March and early April 1992 and 1994, and near Ajlun on 5 April 1993. Both sites are at altitudes of about 1200m.

Alauda arvensis
Skylark

AR: Qubarat al-haqel
GE: Feldlerche

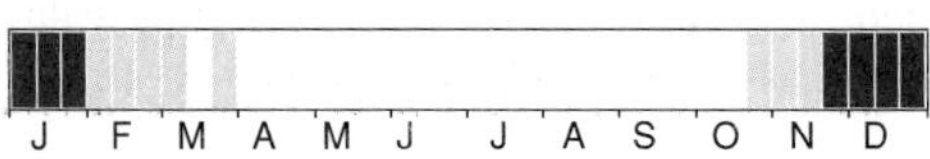

A very common winter visitor to agricultural land in the Jordan Valley, the Northern Steppes, Eastern Desert, and Azraq Oasis. It may also be regular in the Ar Ruwayshid Desert (220 at Risha on 21 November 1989). Its favoured habitat is ploughed arable land, and it is found in flocks of 30-150 (maximum 320) during late November to late January, and less commonly from late October to early March.

Eremophila bilopha
Temminck's Horned Lark

AR: Qubarat tmenak al-qarnā'a
GE: Saharaohrenlerche

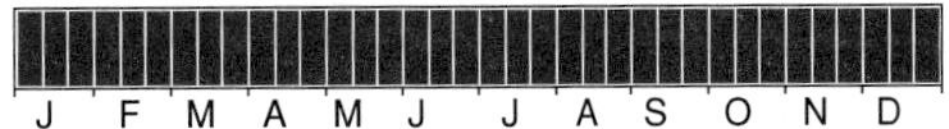

This is the commonest and most widespread breeding lark of the non-mountainous Jordanian hammada deserts. As such, it is a resident in the deserts of the north, centre, south-east, and far north-east as well as on the Basalt Desert, although at some sites, for example Shaumari, observations show it may be partly nomadic. Around Azraq, it prefers flint hammada or bouldery tracts with low and thinly scattered shrublets. A few also occur on the eastern limit of the Northern Steppes. It is decidedly scarce further south in the Ma'an area, and is absent from the more sandy Rum Desert, and from Wadi Araba. Six seen at the base of the Ras an Naqab escarpment on 8 April 1990 are the furthest south recorded.

A few visit Azraq wetland sites to drink, but it is clearly not a typical member of this community.

Riparia riparia
Sand Martin

AR: Khattāf ash-shawāti
GE: Uferschwalbe

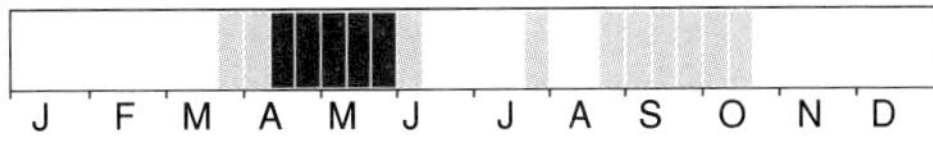

An abundant migrant in spring and autumn to be found widely throughout the country then. Passage flocks can be seen at Aqaba, typically having to battle north against strong headwinds. Hundreds also head east to the south of Amman. Azraq oasis is an established stop-over site, and pre-roost congregations of several thousand can be seen wheeling over the reed-beds and marshes on spring evenings. On migration, birds also cross large expanses of desert, following the lines of wadis.

Northward passage extends from late March to late May, and in autumn it returns in smaller numbers from early September to mid October. It has been recorded in the Jordan Valley as early as February.

Ptyonoprogne fuligula
Rock Martin (Pale Crag Martin)

AR: Khattāf ash-shawāheen al-bahet
GE: Steinschwalbe

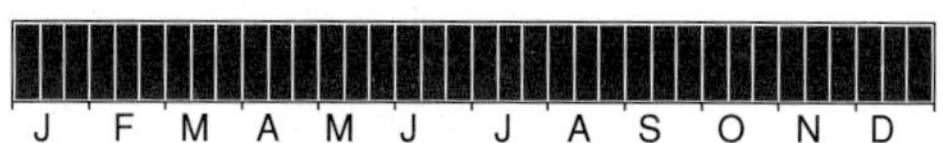

A very common resident of the arid mountains, gorges and crags of the Rift Margins from the Dead Sea south to Aqaba, and also in the Rum Desert. Large numbers can be seen in spring at Petra, where 100-150 pairs were estimated breeding in $10km^2$ in 1983. Here, they nest in man-made as well as in natural holes and crevices.

Whether birds wander outside this breeding range at other seasons is unclear. Although there are records of vagrants turning up at Azraq (3 flying north-west on 16-17 April 1963), separating this species from Crag Martin is notoriously difficult.

Ptyonoprogne rupestris
Crag Martin

AR: Khattāf ash-shawāheen
GE: Felsenschwalbe

J F M A M J J A S O N D

Probably an uncommon winter visitor and passage migrant, mainly to western areas, but the situation is unclear due to confusion with the resident Rock Martins.

In winter, small numbers have been seen in the southern Jordan Valley and Southern Ghor, hawking over reservoirs, marshes and banana plantations. All of these habitats are outside the Rock Martin's normal range. In the 1960s, it was also recorded along the Rift Margins from Wadi Shu'ayb south to Wadi Musa, near As Safi, and at Wadi Rum, between 21 April to 1 May. Most were moving between west and north. One, associating with a Rock Martin, entered a cave at Ar Rashadiyya. It has also been recorded as a vagrant in the Eastern Desert, with two records at Azraq during 20-22 April, and one at Wadi al Butm on 31 March 1990.

This species is some 15% larger than the resident Rock Martin, being browner, with a dark mottled throat; it also has contrasting dark underwing and upperwing coverts. However, some individuals are indistinguishable apart from their size!

Hirundo rustica
Swallow

AR: Snounou
GE: Rauchschwalbe

J F M A M J J A S O N D

The nominate race occurs as an abundant migrant in spring and autumn. Spring passage peaks in mid April to early May, with a lesser autumn passage from late September to late October. The latest date for a migrant is 14 November, and the earliest contender occurred on 20 January.

It occurs widely at Aqaba and in the Highlands and Deserts. Visible migration can be witnessed along ridges, wadis, and even the line of the Desert Highway northward in spring and south in autumn. It often congregates over water in flocks of hundreds, if not thousands, especially if migration is

held up by poor weather, for example 2000 over flooded Qa' al Hibabiya on 1 May 1991. Roosts of several thousand birds also occur in the Azraq reed-beds.

In addition, the rufous-bellied race *H. r. transitiva* is a common resident along the length of the Jordan Valley, with birds breeding in most of the villages, and flocking over the reservoirs in winter (for example up to 150 concentrated over Shuna Reservoir on 26 January 1990). Outside the Jordan Valley, there is a winter record of 34 (of unknown race) at Al Khirba as Samra on 6 December 1990.

Hirundo daurica
Red-rumped Swallow

AR: Snounou ahmar al-ajez
GE: Rötelschwalbe

A fairly common summer visitor and passage migrant, breeding locally in the Northern Highlands. It is present in good numbers from mid March to early October, but the earliest recorded date is 26 February. On passage, it can be seen along the Jordan Valley and highlands and at Aqaba, especially in early April. It breeds near habitation and under bridges, mainly in the wadis of the Northern Rift Margins and Highlands, but also as far south as Al Karak.

Delichon urbica
House Martin

AR: Khattāf ad-dowāhi
GE: Mehlschwalbe

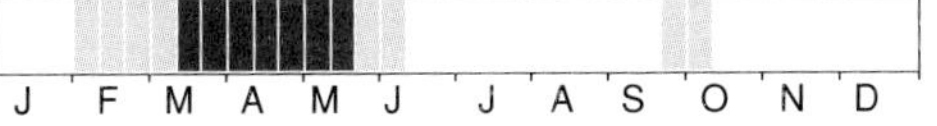

A fairly common spring migrant, passing through over a protracted period from early February to early June. It is most common in the Rift Valley and Rift Margins, with peaks of 80 at Ras an Naqab on 9 May and 40 at Wadi al Mujib on the early date of 9 February. It is scarce to the east. Although up to 100 were recorded at Azraq in the 1960s, ten at Shaumari on 18 April 1992 is the recent maximum.

It is decidedly rare in autumn, with singles at Azraq on 22 September 1989, and by the Zarqa River on 6 October 1989.

Anthus novaeseelandiae
Richard's Pipit

AR: Jashnet retshard
GE: Spornpieper

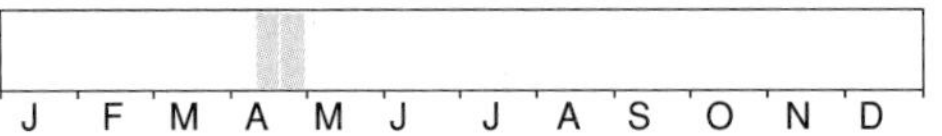

A rare migrant at Azraq, with a small number of individuals recorded over several years during the period 15-25 April.

Anthus campestris
Tawny Pipit

AR: Al-jashneh as-safra (Abu tomra sahrāwi)
GE: Brachpieper

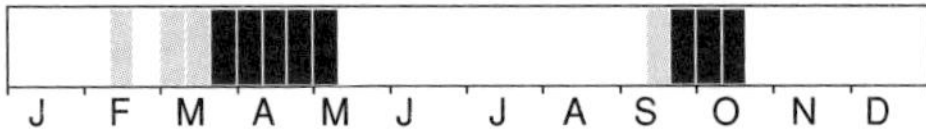

A rather scarce passage migrant during early March to early May, and mid September to mid October. The earliest record is at Azraq on 19 February. It is most likely to be seen in small numbers in the Eastern Desert, Rift Margins, and at Aqaba.

Territorial behaviour was observed at Busayra on 2 May 1955, and at Azraq and Wadi al Butm in the 1960s. In the light of recent observations, however, breeding appears unlikely.

Anthus similis
Long-billed Pipit

AR: Al-jashneh thāt al-minqār at-taweel
GE: Langschnabelpieper

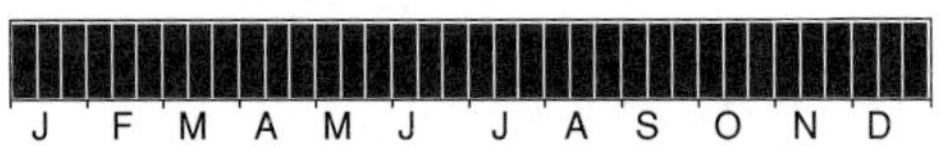

A localised resident, most likely to be seen in the Rift Margins and Northern Highlands from the Yarmuk River south to Wadi al Mujib and east as far as the wadis around the city of Amman. It is less common in the Southern Rift Margins (At Tafila to Petra), and was seen at Wadi Rum in the 1960s. It prefers dry, steep, grassy and stony slopes with boulders and low scrubs, usually within wadis. In spring, it is best located by its simple 'tir-ee ... tiu' song, which is usually delivered monotonously from a rock perch or in flight. There is a report of one at Azraq on 2 May 1980.

Anthus trivialis
Tree Pipit

AR: Abu tamra al-ashjār
GE: Baumpieper

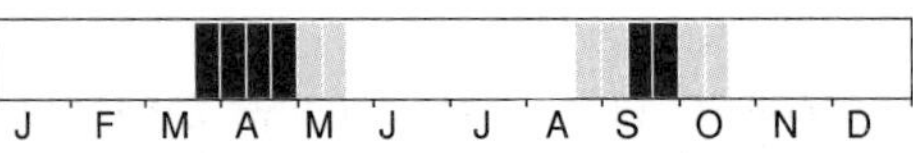

An uncommon passage migrant in spring (peaking in mid April), and rarer in autumn (mid to late September). It is most frequently recorded from the Aqaba and Azraq areas, but it can also be expected to pass through many Rift Valley and Rift Margin localities.

Anthus pratensis
Meadow Pipit

AR: Jashnet al-gheyt
GE: Wiesenpieper

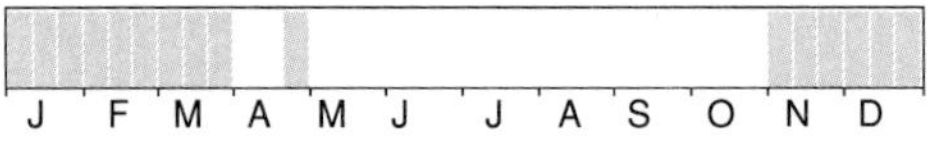

A winter visitor in small numbers to the Northern Highlands, Jordan Valley, Dead Sea, and Al Khirba as Samra. The largest recorded flock of 22 was seen at the Amman National Park on 17 December 1991. The species typically occurs from early November to late March, but two were seen near Nijil on 25 April 1963. It is rare at Azraq and Shaumari, where its niche is apparently occupied by the Red-throated Pipit.

Anthus cervinus
Red-throated Pipit

AR: Abu tamra al-muhmar az-zor
GE: Rotkehlpieper

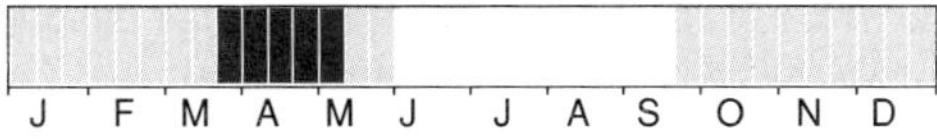

A common spring passage bird, also seen less commonly in autumn and winter. It is most common at Azraq in mid April, where counts of up to 100 have been made. Elsewhere, it can be seen, typically at or near water, across the country from Aqaba to the Dead Sea, and also at temporary desert flood pools.

Significant numbers used to winter at Azraq, with an estimated population of 50-100 birds. Recent observations reveal a decline in numbers in Jordan (probably due to habitat loss), with only a scattering of late autumn and winter records from Azraq, Al Khirba as Samra, Aqaba, and the Dead Sea.

Anthus spinoletta
Water Pipit

AR: Jashnet al-ma'a (Abu tomrat al-ma'a)
GE: Bergpieper

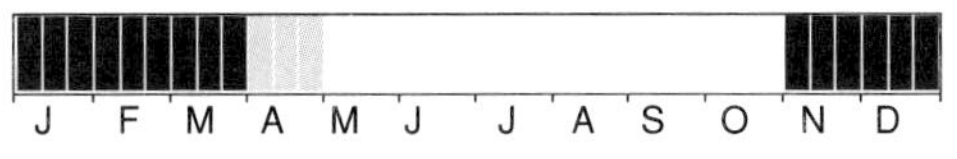

A common winter visitor to wetland sites from early November to the end of March, a few lingering into April. The principal site is Azraq, but it can also be seen at Al Khirba as Samra and along the Zarqa River. In the 1960s, thousands were seen on the soft mud and patchy water of the Azraq qa' in January, but numbers have now decreased. Even when the qa' has flooded in recent years, numbers have rarely exceeded 80 birds.

In the lower Jordan Valley small numbers occur at the reservoirs, the Suwayma marsh, and also in the ploughed fields. It is a rarity at Aqaba, and a late migrant was seen near Ash Shawbak on 24 April 1963.

Motacilla flava
Yellow Wagtail

AR: Thu'ara safra
GE: Schafstelze

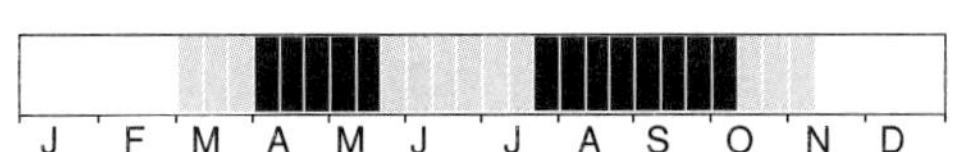

A small isolated population breeds at Azraq, although it may be restricted to wet years. The race involved is *M. f. feldegg*, but birds resembling *flava* also occur in the breeding population.

A very common passage migrant to wetland sites, especially Azraq, in both spring and autumn, peaking in mid April and late September. Flocks of up to 150 can congregate at favoured sites, usually damp grassy areas with a supply of insect food. Up to 500 birds have been counted at Azraq in mid April. Actively migrating birds are frequently seen at Aqaba, but not normally as abundant as the 750 seen on 15 April 1993. It can also be seen more rarely away from water, when tired migrants crossing the desert seek any shade, even under vehicles. It is absent in winter from 1 November to 2 March.

Six or seven races commonly pass through Jordan: *M. f. beema* (Sykes'), *feldegg* (Black-headed), *flava* (Blue-headed), *lutea* (Kirghiz Steppes Yellow), *"superciliaris"* (superciliated Black-headed), *thunbergi* (Grey-headed), and also birds resembling *cinereocapilla* (Ashy-headed). The Black-headed Wagtail is by far the most numerous race, followed in abundance by the Sykes' and Grey-headed races.

Motacilla citreola
Citrine Wagtail

AR: Thu'ara laimooneeyeh
GE: Zitronenstelze

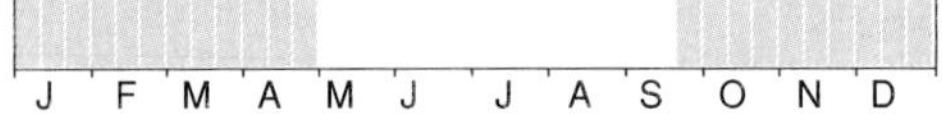

An uncommon passage migrant at wetland sites, with adults from mid March to as late as early June, and then mainly first-year birds from early August to mid October. Most records are of one or two birds at Azraq, with others from Ghadir Burqu', Al Khirba as Samra, and Suwayma.

A record of a pair at Al Khirba as Samra on 7 June 1990 was curious, and a breeding attempt in Jordan cannot be ruled out in the future.

Motacilla cinerea
Grey Wagtail

AR: Thu'ara ramādiyeh
GE: Gebirgsstelze

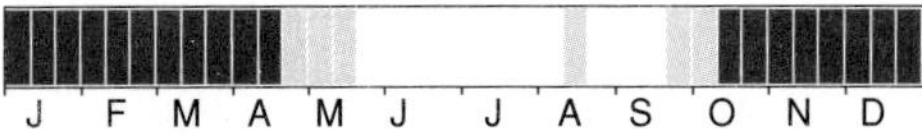

An uncommon winter visitor and passage migrant to flowing wadis in western Jordan, from Pella south to Wadi al Mujib. It also occurs in small numbers at Aqaba, Wadi Rum, Wadi Dana, Petra, and Azraq. It has been recorded from late September to late March, a few lingering to late April.

Motacilla alba alba
White Wagtail

AR: Thu'ara baidā
GE: Bachstelze

J F M A M J J A S O N D

A very common winter visitor and passage migrant, widely recorded in the Northern Highlands, northern desert, Basalt Desert, Jordan Valley, and Wadi Araba, including the Dead Sea, Azraq, Petra, and Aqaba areas. Thousands were seen at Azraq in winter in the 1960s, but the recent peak of only 100 there reflects the reduction in suitable habitat. It roosts communally in a variety of habitats, ranging from reeds along the Zarqa River to trees in the Marriott Hotel car park in urban Amman.

It has been recorded from late September to mid April, with a few staying to mid May. However, one on the Zarqa River on 11 August 1991 was distinctly early, and suggestive of local breeding.

Pycnonotus leucogenys
White-cheeked Bulbul

AR: Al-bulbul thu al-khudood al-baidā'
GE: Weißohrbülbül

Vagrant: one at Aqaba on 9 April 1990. This is a common cage bird locally, so the status of this bird in Jordan must remain somewhat uncertain.

Pycnonotus xanthopygos
Yellow-vented Bulbul

AR: Al-bulbul
GE: Gelbsteißbülbül

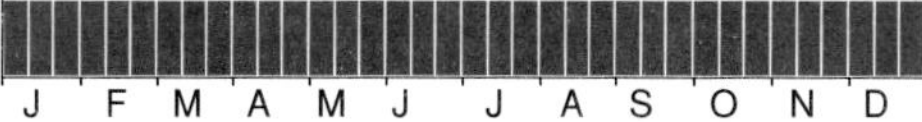

A very common resident in the Jordan Valley, and also widespread in the Highlands from Umm Qays south to Aqaba. Its typical habitat is oleander scrub in wadi bottoms, but it is also present in semi-urban habitats. It is rarely seen in the east at Al Khirba as Samra, and it is absent from desert areas, including Azraq. Its colonisation of Jordan may be recent, as it was not listed by Colonel Meinertzhagen in 1954.

Troglodytes troglodytes
Wren

AR: As-sa'u (Saksukat al-hitān)
GE: Zaunkönig

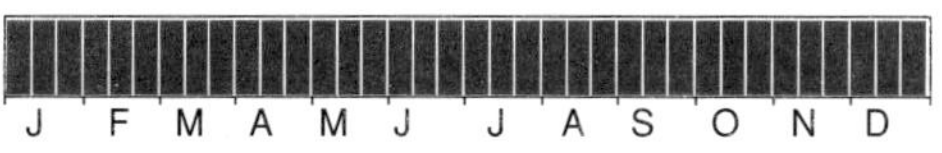

A small resident population occurs in the Northern Highlands, centred on the pine and oak forests of Dibbin and Ajlun. It is not a particularly common bird, but it occurs alongside other Mediterranean species such as Blackbird, Jay and Blue Tit. In addition, up to two birds in Wadi as Sir in November and December, and a bird heard singing in Wadi Dana on 12 April 1993 were to the south of this range.

Prunella modularis
Dunnock

AR: Asfur ash-shauk as-sagheer
GE: Heckenbraunelle

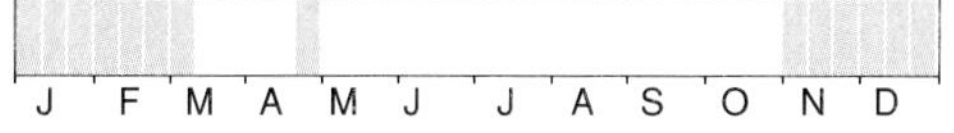

A local, scarce winter visitor, mainly to oleander-lined wadis in the Northern Highlands and Dead Sea Rift Margins. A few individuals have been recorded at Rumaymin, Wadi as Sir, and Wadi al Wala ranging from 20 November to 2 March. It has also occurred as a vagrant at Shaumari (8 November) and Azraq (27 April).

Cercotrichas galactotes
Rufous Bush Robin (Rufous Bush Chat)

AR: Abu-henā'a al-ahrāsh
GE: Heckensänger

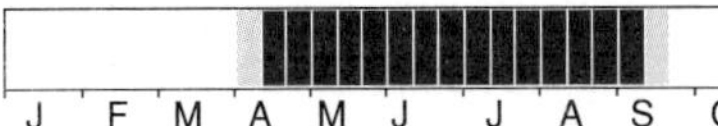

A common migrant and summer visitor from early April to mid September. It breeds in a variety of habitats dominated by bushes and scrub, particularly *Tamarix* in more desert areas, and hawthorn scrub in the highlands. It is found widely in the Northern Highlands and Jordan Valley, and at As Safi and Azraq. South of Wadi al Wala, it has been recorded breeding only at Petra, and at Aqaba it occurs as a scarce April migrant.

Its song is rich and musical, and somewhat reminiscent of the song of the Robin.

Erithacus rubecula
Robin

AR: Abu al-henā'a
GE: Rothehlchen

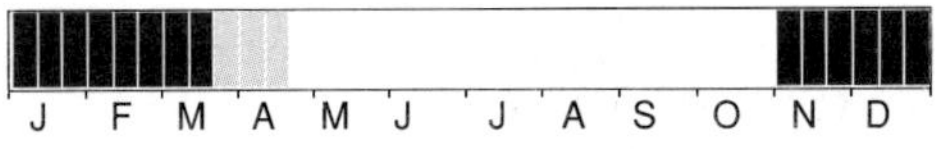

A common winter visitor to the Northern Highlands, especially the vegetated wadis, gardens and pine forests. Concentrations are usually low, but up to 20 have been recorded in some wadis in November. A few also occur in drier habitats at Azraq, Shaumari, the Jordan Valley, Dead Sea, Wadi Araba, Petra, and Aqaba. A daily maximum of 60 at Dana in late November 1994 suggests a large influx. Records range from early November to mid April.

Luscinia luscinia
Thrush Nightingale

AR: Al-hazār
GE: Sprosser

J F M A M J J A S O N D

An uncommon migrant, particularly in desert areas from the Dead Sea to Azraq and south to Aqaba, and in the wadi vegetation of the Rum Desert. In the Northern Highlands, it may occur more frequently than the records suggest, as it tends to be difficult to locate. It typically skulks below bushes such as White Broom *Retama raetum* in desert wadis, where it can appear in local concentrations, for example a fall of 13 in Wadi Rum on 2 May 1963, and 11 at Aqaba on 29 April 1985. It occurs mainly from early April to early May, and less commonly in September and October.

Luscinia megarhynchos
Nightingale

AR: Al-'andaleeb
GE: Nachtigall

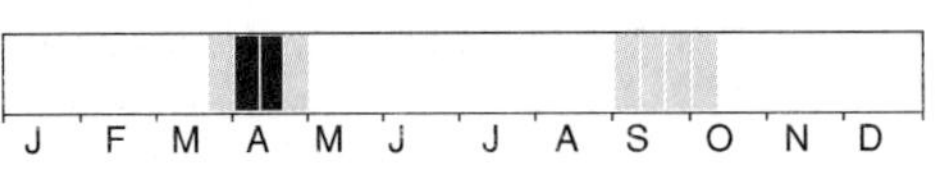

May breed along the Jordan River.

An uncommon migrant to Azraq, Shaumari and adjacent desert, highlands, Wadi Araba, and Aqaba during late March to early May, and rarely in September and October. Peak spring passage occurs on average about 10 days earlier than Thrush Nightingale.

Luscinia svecica
Bluethroat

AR: Al-musaher
GE: Blaukehlchen

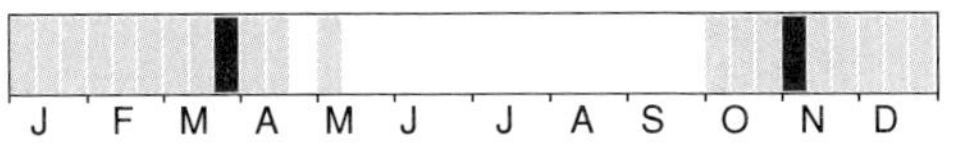

An uncommon passage migrant and winter visitor, with small numbers at many wetland sites in the rift, in Rift Margin wadis, at Al Khirba as Samra sewage works, and Azraq (where a winter population of 50-100 birds was estimated in the 1960s). It has been recorded mainly from mid October to mid April, with peaks in early November and late March. Extreme early and late dates respectively are 3 October and 5 May. White-spotted race *L. s. cyanecula* and red-spotted *svecica* both occur.

Irania gutturalis
White-throated Robin

AR: Abu al-henā'a abiad az-zor
GE: Weißkehlsänger

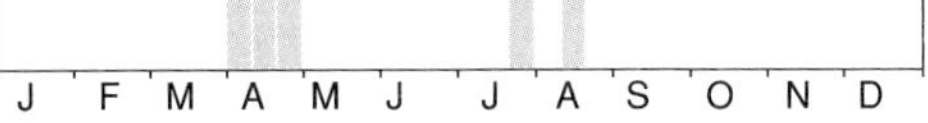

A scarce spring passage bird recorded during the period 5-29 April. Ones and twos have been recorded in open scrub and bushy areas in the Northern Highlands, Eastern Desert, Ar Ruwayshid Desert, and at Wadi al Mujib.

Records of six males and a female at a drilling rig in the Risha area on 26 July 1990, two at the Risha Gasfield on 27-28 July, and one on 12 August suggest early return passage in the far north-east of the country, but it is not known how exceptional these records are.

Phoenicurus ochruros
Black Redstart

AR: Humirā'a dulbasā'a
GE: Hausrotschwanz

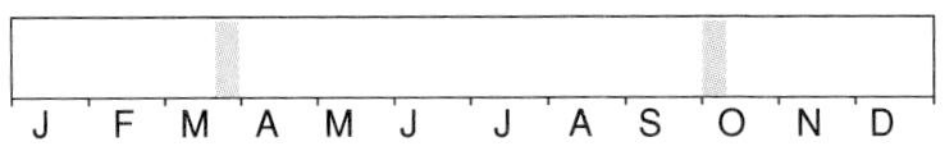

A common winter visitor from early November to early March, with a few passage birds from early October to early May. It is to be found in open, rocky hillsides in the Northern Highlands, including the Amman suburbs, Azraq area, Basalt Desert, Jordan Valley, Dead Sea, Petra, and in the Rum Desert.

A pair frequented a stone dyke near Ar Rabba in the central highlands on 21 April 1963 – this is the only suggestion of breeding in Jordan (the race was not recorded).

Rufous-bellied races of Black Redstart

J F M A M J J A S O N D

Rufous-bellied birds of the race *P. o. semirufus* or *phoenicuroides* occur rarely, but predominantly in late March at Azraq, the Rift Margins, and in the Rum Desert. A concentration of birds above Wadi Dana in early October 1994 may suggest that birds have been overlooked somewhat.

Phoenicurus phoenicurus
Redstart

AR: Al-humirā'a
GE: Gartenrotschwanz

J F M A M J J A S O N D

A common migrant from late February to late May, and mid August to mid November. The earliest record is from Azraq on 1 February. It occurs widely in the highlands and desert in a range of habitats from open oak woodland to low, wadi scrub. Occasionally, weather conditions force large mass arrivals, such as 600 at Azraq and Shaumari on 28 April 1990, and 100 at Qasr Amra on 16 April 1993.

SAMAMISICUS RACE OF REDSTART

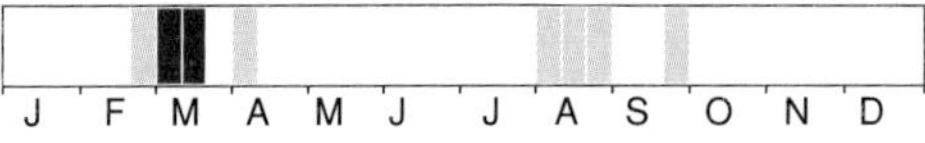

Birds of the south-west Asian race *P. p. samamisicus* (males with conspicuous white wing-panels) are uncommon, but regularly seen in small numbers. It is most easily seen in the Northern Highlands and Jordan Valley during March, but also occurs less frequently from late February to early April, and early August to late September. It occurs more rarely in the Southern Rift Margins, in the desert, and at Shaumari.

Cercomela melanura
Blackstart

AR: Qulayi aswad ith-thanab
GE: Schwarzschanz

J F M A M J J A S O N D

A characteristic, common resident of the arid, rather bare wadis of the Rift Margins, from the Yarmuk River in the north to Aqaba in the south. It is most numerous on the flanks of the Jordan Valley and Dead Sea, and its range extends east-

wards up tributaries such as the Zarqa River, Wadi as Sir, Wadi al Wala, and Wadi al Mujib. It also occurs in the Aqaba Mountains and in the acacias of Wadi Araba. It is generally absent above altitudes of 500m, but at Petra a few pairs breed up to 930m. It is absent from the Rum Desert.

Saxicola rubetra
Whinchat

AR: Ablaq al-haqil
GE: Braunkehlchen

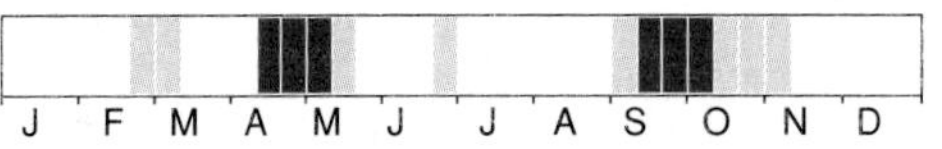

An uncommon migrant, mainly to desert regions from at least mid April to mid May, and more commonly from early September to early November (peak in late September). A few early birds have been recorded six weeks prior to the main arrival, with records on 23 February and 9 March. Whinchats are most likely to be found in the Eastern Desert, where they occasionally occur in mass groundings of migrants, for example 200 at Azraq and Shaumari on 28 April 1990.

Rufous Bush Robin, Azraq, August 1991

Thrush Nightingale, Azraq, April 1992

Bluethroat, male, Azraq, October 1990

Blackstart, Dead Sea, October 1994 (Tim Loseby)

Redstart, male samamisicus *subspecies, Wadi al Jilat, March 1990*

Isabelline Wheatear, Wadi Batn al Ghul, March 1990

Black-eared Wheatear, male, Dana, May 1994 (Damian Debski)

Desert Wheatear, male, Azraq, December 1990

Finsch's Wheatear, male, Turkmenistan, June 1992 (Tim Loseby)

Red-rumped Wheatear, male, Qasr al Kharana, May 1990

White-crowned Black Wheatear, first- or second-year bird, Rum, October 1994 (Time Loseby)

Mourning Wheatear, Ras an Naqab, October 1994 (Tim Loseby)

Mourning Wheatear, black morph, east of As Safawi, September 1994 (Richard Porter)

Rock Thrush, winter-plumaged male, Wadi Musa, October 1994 (Tim Loseby)

Spectacled Warbler, Ar Rashadiyya, October 1994 (Tim Loseby)

Scrub Warbler, Petra, May 1983 (Peter Boye)

Arabian Warbler, Hazeva, Wadi Araba, October 1986 (Paul Doherty)

Red-breasted Flycatcher, Shaumari, November 1991

Orange-tufted Sunbird, juvenile, Dana, May 1994 (Damian Debski)

Ficedula *flycatcher, first-winter, Shaumari, September 1989*

Orange-tufted Sunbird, male, Dana, May 1994 (Damian Debski)

Blue Tit, Dibbin Forest, February 1992

Golden Oriole, male, Shaumari, September 1990

Red-backed Shrike, first-winter, Aqaba, September 1990

Masked Shrike, adult, Wadi ash Shita, May 1991

Masked Shrike, first-winter, Shaumari, September 1989

Woodchat Shrike, adult, March 1993 (Steve Harley)

Jay, Dibbin Forest, June 1990

Fan-tailed Raven, Masada, Dead Sea, April 1986 (Paul Doherty)

Dead Sea Sparrow, male, Eilat, December 1987 (Paul Doherty)

Spanish Sparrow, winter plumage, South Shuna, November 1991

Rock Sparrow, Dana, October 1994 (Tim Loseby)

Tristram's Grackles, Dana, October 1994 (Tim Loseby)

Indian House Crows, Aqaba, October 1994 (Tim Loseby)

Trumpeter Finch, female or immature, Shaumari, September 1990

Tristram's Serin, Eilat, November 1985 (Paul Doherty)

Chaffinch and Yellowhammer, Sakib, December 1990

Sinai Rosefinch, male, Dana, October 1994 (Tim Loseby)

Sinai Rosefinch, female, Dana, October 1994 (Tim Loseby)

Desert Finch, male, Turkmenistan, June 1992 (Tim Loseby)

House Bunting, male, Petra, May 1983 (Peter Boye)

Ortolan Bunting, female/immature, Dana, October 1994 (Tim Loseby)

Cretzschmar's Bunting, male, Israel, April 1992 (Paul Doherty)

Black-headed Bunting, male, Turkey, June 1992

Corn Bunting, Amman National Park, April 1990

Saxicola torquata
Stonechat

AR: Qulayi mutawaq
GE: Schwarzkehlchen

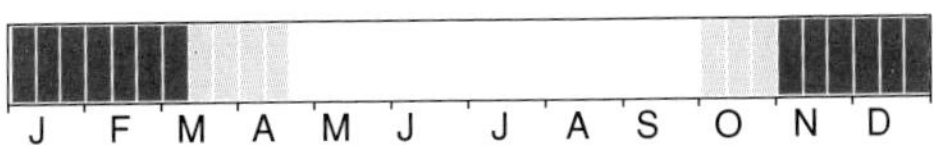

The European race *S. t. rubicola* is a common winter visitor to many parts of Jordan from early October to early March, although a few remain to mid April. Birds frequent open, bushy areas in the Northern Highlands, Jordan Valley and Azraq areas, and are less common in the Southern Highlands and at Aqaba.

EASTERN RACES OF STONECHAT

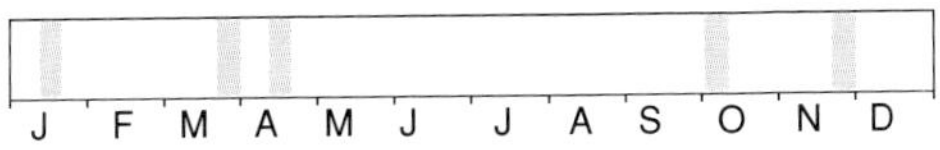

Birds of the eastern races *S. t. maura* or *stejnegeri* have occurred rarely in the Northern Highlands, Rift Margins and at Azraq in January, March-April, October, and November.

Oenanthe isabellina
Isabelline Wheatear

AR: Al-ablaq al-ash hab
GE: Isabellsteinschmätzer

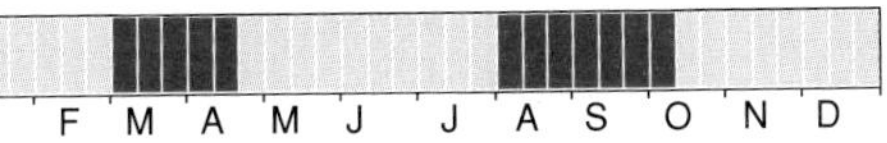

A common breeding bird of the steppic habitat, found on the Sharra Highlands from Al Karak and Ash Shawbak south to Ras an Naqab. It is probably a summer visitor to these highlands, which lie between 1200m and 1600m above sea-level. Here it is possible to see the distinctive song flight, in which birds fly up with fluttering wing beats and tail fanned, and then glide down with tail and wings spread.

At many sites in the Rift Margins, Northern Highlands, and Eastern Desert (including Azraq) this is a fairly common migrant from early February to mid April, and early August to early October. A few also remain through the winter on the agricultural land of the Northern Steppes around Umm ar Rasas, Madaba and Queen Alia International Airport, and also in the Eastern Desert.

Oenanthe oenanthe
Wheatear (Northern Wheatear)

AR: Abu blaiq
GE: Steinschmätzer

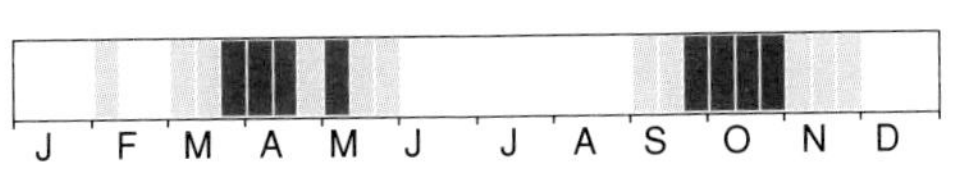

An uncommon migrant in spring and autumn, mainly to the Northern Highlands and Steppes, Eastern Desert, and Aqaba, although it also occurs widely along the Rift Margins and in other Desert areas. Peak spring passage occurs in early to mid April (early March to mid May), and smaller numbers pass through between early September and late November. The earliest recorded date is 7 February at Azraq.

Oenanthe (pleschanka) cypriaca
Cyprus Pied Wheatear

AR: Ablaq qubrusii
GE: Zypern-Steinschmätzer

J F M A M J J A S O N D

In recent years, it has become apparent that this is a scarce early spring migrant through Jordan from mid March to early April. Up to three have been recorded from Azraq, Shaumari, between Umm aj Jimal and Azraq (Basalt Desert), and possibly also at Wadi Dana.

Past records of 'Pied Wheatears' in Jordan may instead have been Cyprus Pied Wheatears. These additional sightings range from 9 March to 26 April, with other reports of birds at Azraq and Wadi Araba in November and December.

Oenanthe hispanica
Black-eared Wheatear

AR: Ablaq aswad al-uthun
GE: Mittelmeer-Steinschmätzer

J F M A M J J A S O N D

Breeds fairly commonly on stony slopes with scattered bushes in the Northern Highlands, and south to Ma'an. It is found on high ground, often in agricultural areas and orchards, and it may nest in road cuttings. An apparently established pair was present at Azraq in 1965, but breeding was not proved there.

This wheatear also occurs fairly commonly and widely on passage in the Eastern Desert, Northern Highlands, Rift Margins, Rum Desert, and at Aqaba. It is present from early March to mid October, with a few lingering into early November. The earliest recorded arrival is in the second half of February. Spring passage peaks in early to mid April, with a further, autumn peak in early to mid September.

Males of both black-throated and white-throated forms occur, but all birds are of the eastern race *O. h. melanoleuca*.

Oenanthe deserti
Desert Wheatear

AR: Ablaq al-badya
GE: Wüstensteinschmätzer

J F M A M J J A S O N D

A widespread resident of desert habitats, largely avoiding hills and mountains. It is found in all the desert regions including Wadi Araba and the Rum Desert. It is a particularly characteristic member of the Eastern Desert and Azraq avifauna, breeding in silt dune areas, patches of *Juncus* at the edge of dried-out marshland, and in wadis with both high and low cover and in flat or rough ground. In the past, it also bred on *Nitraria* islands in the deeply flooded Azraq marshes.

A few records at altitudes of up to 1400m in the Sharra Highlands may indicate a further population in this area.

There may be some degree of dispersal in winter, as there are fewer records in the north at this time.

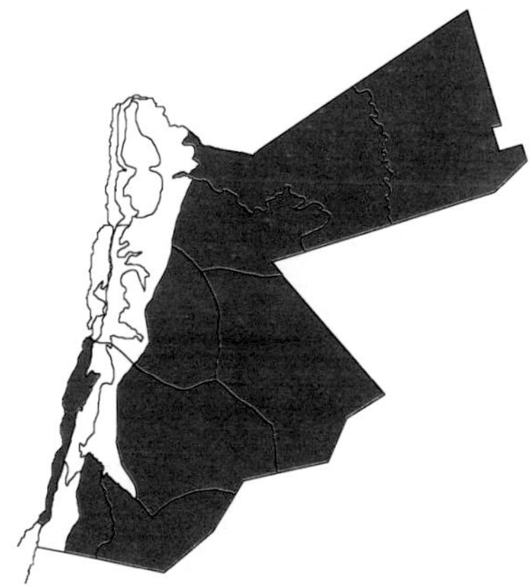

There is evidence of a slight spring passage at Aqaba, and of an autumn passage on the Northern Steppes and Dead Sea Rift Margins.

Oenanthe finschii
Finsch's Wheatear

AR: Al-ablaq al-arabi
GE: Felsensteinschmätzer

J F M A M J J A S O N D

A fairly common winter visitor to sparsely vegetated areas of the Northern Highlands including the Amman suburbs, to the Northern and Central Rift Margins, the Northern Steppes, Eastern Desert, and Basalt Desert. There is one record from an irrigated area at Disi (Rum Desert). A winter range has also been mapped along the road crossing north-east Jordan to Iraq.

It has been recorded from 18 October to early March, but stragglers can remain until 27 April. Finsch's Wheatears generally occupy the niche occupied by Black-eared Wheatears in summer, so care should be taken with identification in the transition periods.

Oenanthe moesta
Red-rumped Wheatear

AR: Al-ablaq ahmar al-ajez
GE: Fahlbürzel-Steinschmätzer

J F M A M J J A S O N D

A localised resident in at least two areas of desert. In the Central and Eastern Deserts from Suwaqa to Shaumari, pairs nest in rodent burrows in low, sandy wadis, for example near Qasr al Kharana. There are also isolated populations in steppic habitat in the Sharra Highlands north of Ma'an, and east of Ash Shawbak. Other areas may be occupied: it has been recorded on the margin of the Northern Steppes, south of Wadi Rum, and in the Rift Margin north-west of Ras an Naqab.

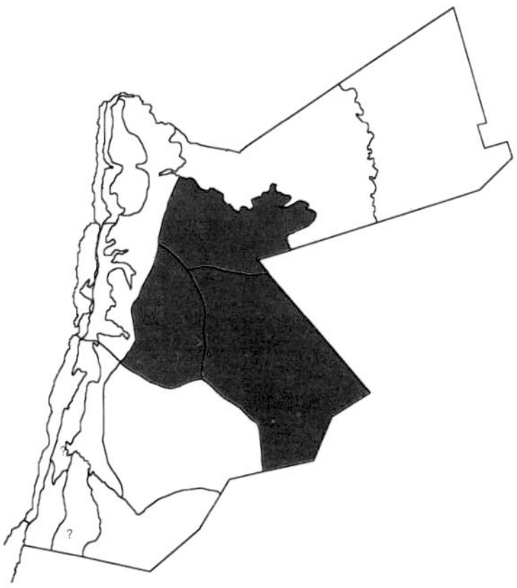

Oenanthe xanthoprymna
Red-tailed Wheatear

AR: Ablaq ahmar ith-thanab
GE: Rostbürzel-Steinschmätzer

A vagrant to the Eastern Desert, with singles 24km south-east of Azraq on 23 April 1955, and at Shaumari on 9 November 1975. A male *O. x. xanthoprymna* was also seen north of Fidan (Wadi Araba) on 14 November 1994.

Oenanthe lugens
Mourning Wheatear

AR: Al-ablaq al-hazeen
GE: Schwarzrücken-Steinschmätzer

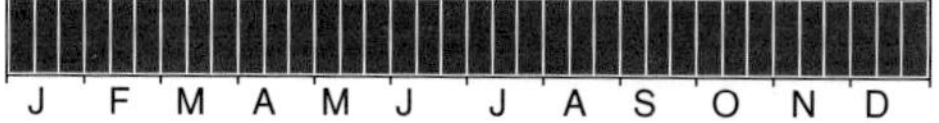

A characteristic bird of the Rift Margin fauna, found from Mount Nebo south to Aqaba, and east to the Rum Desert. It nests in crevices and under rocks in arid, sparsely-vegetated areas containing steep-sided, rocky wadis. The birds typically build a platform of small stones by the nest entrance, as do Temminck's Horned Larks. It is also found on the low limestone escarpments and wadis which make up the watershed between the Central, Al Jafr, and Wadi as Sarhan Deserts. There is an isolated cluster of observations in limestone-flint country east of Azraq. Records of typical morph birds in the Basalt Desert are rare, but they are said to form mixed pairs with dark morph birds (see below). It is not found on the shores of the Dead Sea, where it is replaced by the White-crowned Black Wheatear there.

Black morph of Mourning Wheatear

Birds of the distinctive *black morph* are restricted to the eastern Basalt Desert, but they are neither common nor ubiquitous there. Most sightings come from the Azraq to Ar Ruwayshid road, where they frequent road cuttings, boulder piles, and abandoned telegraph poles in addition to natural bluffs and wadi sides. They are generally absent from the featureless, rolling, boulder fields, and none have been seen at Ghadir Burqu', Umm aj Jimal, or on a 100km transect from Azraq to Ar Ruwayshid south of the main road. There are two records of presumed non-breeding black morph birds to the south of the basalt: at Shaumari in February-March 1976, and east of the Azraq to Al Umari road on 6 March 1992.

Oenanthe monacha
Hooded Wheatear

AR: Ablaq thu qalnsoweh
GE: Kappensteinschmätzer

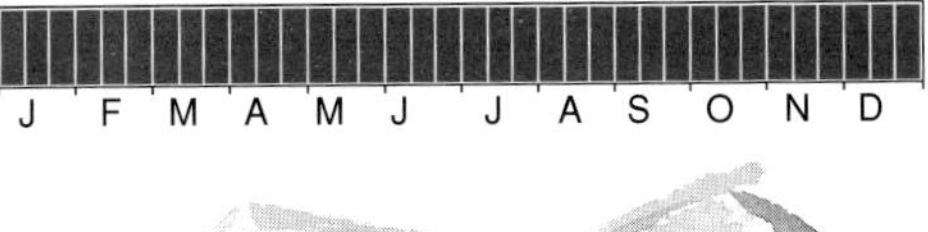

A thinly distributed resident of arid, rocky terrain in the Rift Margins and Rum Desert. The eastern shores of the Dead Sea appear to be a favoured haunt. Although it has been seen in Wadi Dana in the Southern Rift Margins, it has been recorded only once at Petra. It is a notoriously difficult species to find, possibly due to their large and widely spaced territories in mainly inaccessible habitat.

Oenanthe leucopyga
White-crowned Black Wheatear

AR: Al-ablaq al-aswad thu al-qeneh al-baida'a
GE: Saharasteinschmätzer

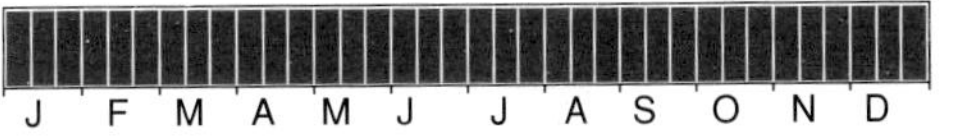

A common resident of the arid and rocky Rift Margins, from the northern shores of the Dead Sea to the Aqaba Mountains, and in the Rum Desert, and Al Mudawwara Desert east to Batn al Ghul. It is a true desert wheatear, and typically replaces the Mourning Wheatear in habitats with most rocks, cliffs and gorges, although there is some overlap in distribution. A population may exist in the eastern Basalt Desert, but this needs confirmation. A female was seen at Shaumari on 20 March 1994.

In the Rum Desert, its diet has been seen to include scorpions and the poisonous locust *Peokiloceros bufonius*.

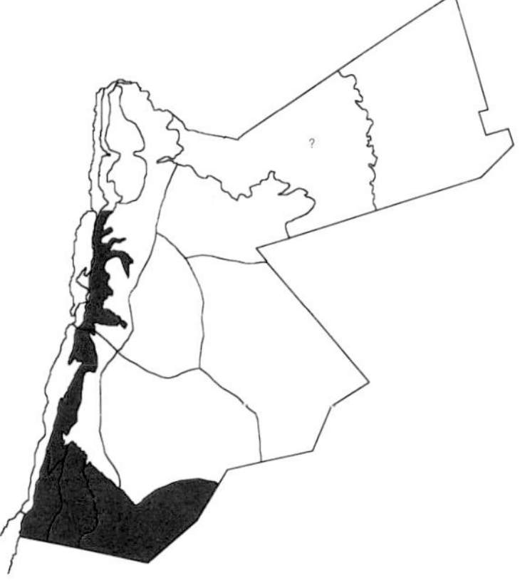

Monticola saxatilis
Rock Thrush

AR: Sumenet as-sokhoor
GE: Steinrötel

J F M A M J J A S O N D

A scarce spring migrant from late March to early May, recorded mainly in the arid regions of the south and east. Small numbers occur in the Rum Desert, Sharra Highlands, Southern Rift Margins, Aqaba Mountains, Eastern Desert, and Central Desert. Five at Wadi Rum on 4-5 April 1994 is a large count. It has been only once recorded in autumn: one south of Wadi Musa on 7 October 1994.

Monticola solitarius
Blue Rock Thrush

AR: Sumenet as-sokhoor az-zerqa'a
GE: Blaumerle

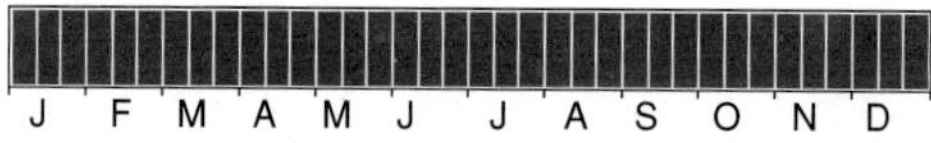

Nests locally in the Rift Margin highlands and wadis, from the Zarqa River south to Petra. It is resident in its breeding range, but dispersal or passage is also evident in other areas.

It is a scarce early spring migrant at Azraq, Shaumari, Wadi al Butm, and Ras an Naqab in late February to early April. Autumn passage appears to be more prevalent in the far east, with nine at Risha on 12 October 1989 and two at Ghadir Burqu' on 30 September 1994.

Turdus torquatus
Ring Ouzel

AR: Ad-dujj al-mutawaq
GE: Ringdrossel

Vagrant: a male collected in Wadi Musa, near Petra on 18 November 1986 is displayed in the Jordan Natural History Museum, Irbid.

Turdus merula
Blackbird

AR: Sahroor
GE: Amsel

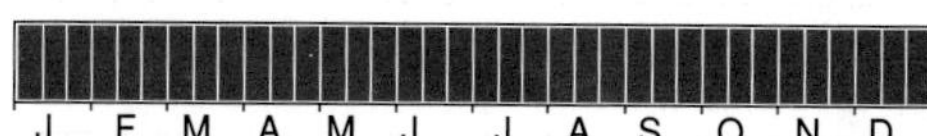

A fairly common resident of the oaks, olives and pines in the Northern Highlands from Umm Qays south to Na'ur, including the gardens of Amman. Records from Wadi Dana in April, May and October also suggest the possibility of breeding much further south.

The resident population is augmented by a substantial autumn/winter influx; flocks of up to 20 have been counted at Dibbin and Wadi as Sir. Small numbers also reach the Jordan Valley, Dead Sea, Wadi al Mujib and Petra in winter, and a few have been recorded as far east as Azraq and Shaumari during November to March.

Turdus pilaris
Fieldfare

AR: Al-dujj as-sagheer
GE: Wacholderdrossel

J F M A M J J A S O N D

An uncommon winter visitor to the Northern Highlands, and the Wadi al Butm-Azraq area. Up to 22 have been seen at the Amman National Park, but Wadi al Butm is a more regular winter site, with flocks of up to 60 frequenting the *Pistacia atlantica* trees. There is also a record of 100 birds at Dana on 23 November 1994. It has been recorded from 22 November to 3 March.

Turdus philomelos
Song Thrush

AR: As-summaneh al-motrebeh
GE: Singdrossel

J F M A M J J A S O N D

A common winter visitor to the Northern Highlands, particularly in the pine woods, orchards, and vegetated wadis. Peaks counts are as follows: 150 at Dibbin Forest, 27 at Najde, 25 at the Amman National Park, 20 at Wadi as Sir, and 12 at Marj al Hammam. Elsewhere, it can be seen in small numbers in the Jordan Valley, and at Wadi Dana, Petra, Wadi Rum, Aqaba, Wadi al Butm, Azraq, and Shaumari. A daily maximum of 113 birds at Dana in late November 1994, coincided with an influx of other thrushes. It has been recorded from early November to as late as 21 April.

Turdus iliacus
Redwing

AR: As-summaneh al-ghareedeh
GE: Rotdrossel

Vagrant: one at Azraq on 23 January 1979, and one at Dana on 23 November 1994.

Turdus viscivorus
Mistle Thrush

AR: Summanet ad-dabaq
GE: Misteldrossel

J F M A M J J A S O N D

A scarce winter visitor to the Northern Highlands and Azraq areas from early November to mid March. It usually occurs in small numbers, but 15 were seen at Najde, near Dibbin on 16 February 1990. The three recorded in acacia desert 10km south of Aqaba on 2 December 1989 were well out of the normal winter range of this species.

Cettia cettia
Cetti's Warbler

AR: Hazijeh senni esh-sharqieh
GE: Seidensänger

J F M A M J J A S O N D

In the last five to ten years, a small resident population has become established along the Jordan River, and in several of the lush wadis leading down into the Rift Valley. It is now possible to see, or at least hear, this species from Wadi al Yabis as far south as Wadi Dana and Petra. However, it has not colonised Azraq, where it remains a surprisingly rare winter and spring visitor between November and April.

Cisticola juncidis
Fan-tailed Warbler

AR: Zuraiqa qusābi
GE: Cistensänger

J F M A M J J A S O N D

In the 1960s, Azraq oasis contained a resident breeding population of perhaps 30-60 pairs. These were found at the spring outfalls and in low marsh vegetation. Even by 1985, however, only one singing male could be found, and the breeding population has now totally disappeared. Its range is patchy elsewhere; birds have been seen in the Jordan Valley, Southern Ghor, and by the Zarqa River, where a small number may breed in cultivated land.

Prinia gracilis
Graceful Warbler

AR: Al-fuseeh (Abu zua'aer)
GE: Streifenprinie

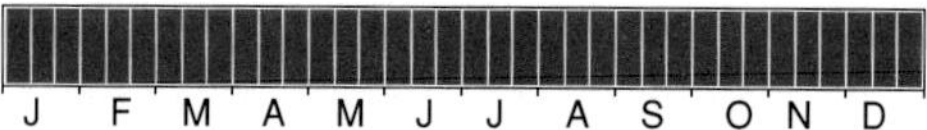

A widespread and common resident of cultivated and natural scrub habitats in the Jordan Valley, along the shores of the Dead Sea, in the Southern Ghor, and in the Northern Highlands and Rift Margins from Umm Qays as far south as Wadi al Hasa. In the east, it is restricted to irrigated areas, such as Al Khirba as Samra and the Azraq oasis, and it colonised Shaumari sometime after 1977.

It is rare in the south and south-east of the country where, in desert regions, it is largely replaced by the Scrub Warbler. There are a few records from Aqaba and Wadi Araba in April and December.

Scotocerca inquieta
Scrub Warbler

AR: Hazijet al-heesh al-mukhatateh
GE: Wüstenprinie

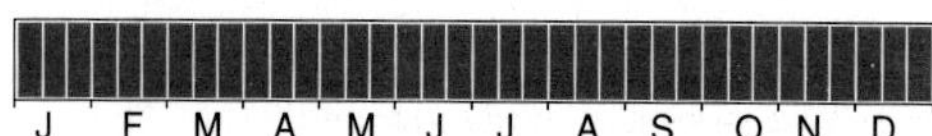

A common resident of the arid Rift Margins from Wadi Zerqa Ma'in south to Petra, the Rum Desert, and wadis in at least the Eastern, Al Jafr, and Wadi as Sarhan Deserts. It breeds where patches of shrubs occur on stony desert, and in those wadis and wadi spreads where low and widely scattered shrublets give way to thicker and taller vegetation. About 50 breeding pairs were estimated in a $10km^2$ area of Petra in 1983.

The ranges of Scrub and Graceful Warbler only rarely overlap, but this occurs around Azraq and Shaumari, and along the upper boundary of the Rift Margins between Wadi as Sir and Wadi al Mujib. It is largely absent from the shores of the Dead Sea and in Wadi Araba, though there are a few records in December.

Locustella naevia
Grasshopper Warbler

AR: Khansha'a al-jarād
GE: Feldschwirl

Vagrant: single birds singing at Azraq on 28 April 1980 and 29 April 1983.

Locustella fluviatilis
River Warbler

AR: Khansha'a al-mā'a
GE: Schlagschwirl

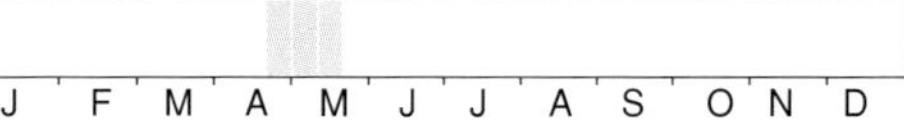

A rare, late spring migrant, with records of singles from Azraq, Ghadir Burqu', At Tafila (1914), Wadi Rum and Aqaba between 24 April and 13 May.

Locustella luscinioides
Savi's Warbler

AR: Al-kansha'a as-sagheer
GE: Rohrschwirl

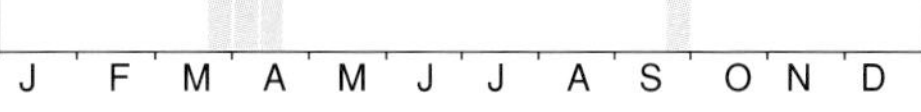

A few were heard reeling in the Azraq marshes in the 1960s and subsequently, up to 1985. One was seen collecting nest material, so it is fair to assume a small population bred there. There have been no recent records of singing birds, and the habitat is now lost.

Migrants have been seen at Shaumari on 23 March 1976, Azraq Resthouse on 19-20 April 1984, and Ghadir Burqu' on 21 September 1991.

Acrocephalus melanopogon
Moustached Warbler

AR: Hazejah umm ash-shāreb
GE: Mariskensänger

Birds of the eastern race *A. m. mimica* were a common resident at Azraq in the 1960s, with maybe 100-200 breeding pairs. They could be found at the edge of the tallest reeds, in low reed and sedge beds and in dense growths of *Tamarix*. The species was still present in January-February 1979, with 25-50 birds recorded. However, the drying of the marshes has since seen the demise of this species at Azraq. There were a few spring records up to 1988, but there have been only rare winter sightings since then.

Birds may also winter along the Jordan River, and one was seen at As Safi on 15 November 1991. Migrant birds were seen at Azraq on 20 April 1963 (the nominate race, as distinct from the local breeding race), and near Al Jafr on 6 May 1963.

Acrocephalus paludicola
Aquatic Warbler

AR: Hazejat al-mā'a
GE: Seggenrohrsänger

Vagrant: one at Azraq on 3 May 1965.

Acrocephalus schoenobaenus
Sedge Warbler

AR: Hazejat es-sa'ad (Umm Noah)
GE: Schilfrohrsänger

J F M A M J J A S O N D

An uncommon migrant, mainly to the Azraq and Aqaba areas. It was formerly more common at Azraq, and is reported to have even bred there in the 1960s. Small numbers now occur from late March to early June, and during September. The earliest recorded arrival date is 26 February.

Acrocephalus palustris
Marsh Warbler

AR: Hazejat al-bata'eh
GE: Sumpfrohrsänger

A vagrant, with a record of five birds seen in bean fields at Azraq on 11-12 May 1966.

Acrocephalus scirpaceus
Reed Warbler

AR: Hazejat al-qasab
GE: Teichrohrsänger

J F M A M J J A S O N D

In the 1960s, the population in the Azraq reedbeds was estimated to be at least 90 pairs, probably 300, and perhaps over 400 pairs. It was surprisingly recorded defending territory, even in late November to January. It is still present at Azraq, but in much reduced numbers. Many pairs were also seen in 1963 along the Jordan River at the King Abdullah and King Hussein Bridges, and singing males have been heard recently in reeds at Kafrayn and Wadi Zerqa Ma'in.

It also occurs as a scarce migrant, between 5 April and 24 May. It can be seen mainly at wetland sites, and particularly at Azraq. However, out-of-context migrants have been seen in desert scrub in the Eastern Desert, Wadi Araba and Wadi Rum.

In recent years it has been present at Azraq from mid April to early October, but not in winter as it had been in the 1960s.

Acrocephalus stentoreus
Clamorous Reed Warbler

AR: Hazejat al-qasab as-sayyāha
GE: Stentorrohrsänger

J F M A M J J A S O N D

In the 1960s, there were a small number of singing males (up to seven) in the tall reed-beds at Azraq, suggesting that an isolated population was resident there. Recent records at Azraq have been very few, and, if not singing, care should be taken to rule out migrant Great Reed Warblers. Elsewhere, it is most likely resident along the Yarmuk River, Jordan River, and at As Safi.

Acrocephalus arundinaceous
Great Reed Warbler

AR: Hazejat al-qasab al-kabira
GE: Drosselrohrsänger

J F M A M J J A S O N D

This species formerly bred commonly in the tallest reed-beds at Azraq (22 singing males in 1966), but there is no recent evidence, even of singing birds. Otherwise, it is a scarce spring migrant to Aqaba, Azraq, Suwayma, and Wadi ar Rattami during 23 March to 14 May. There is only one autumn record: at Azraq on 15 September 1990.

Hippolais pallida
Olivaceous Warbler

AR: Hazejat zaytoonieh
GE: Blaßspötter

J F M A M J J A S O N D

A fairly common migrant breeding species in the Rift Margin highlands from the Zarqa River south to Petra, including the Amman suburbs. It may also breed in the Jordan Valley.

As a migrant through many parts of Jordan, it occurs fairly commonly in the Jordan Valley, Wadi Araba, Northern Highlands, Eastern Desert, Rum Desert, and at Aqaba. Migrants are evident from late March to late May, with the earliest spring record dated 17 March. Autumn passage may start as early as late July, but it is most apparent from early August to mid September.

Hippolais caligata
Booted Warbler

AR: Al-hāzeja al-mutaniqqila
GE: Buschspötter

J F M A M J J A S O N D

A rare passage bird at Azraq from 15 April to 12 May and during 8-12 September. Previously, many birds now thought to be Olivaceous Warblers were confused with Booted Warblers, and this species was thus thought to be a more common migrant than is now apparent. Recent records are largely unsubstantiated, but one sighting of up to four at the Risha Gasfield during 27 July to 12 August 1990 is noteworthy.

Hippolais languida
Upcher's Warbler

AR: Hazejat ash-shajar
GE: Dornspötter

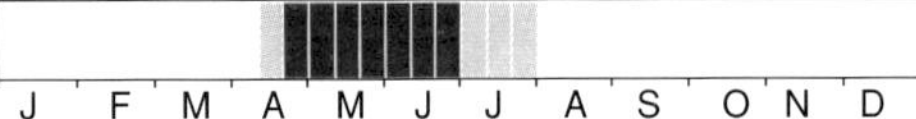

J F M A M J J A S O N D

A small breeding population has recently been discovered in hawthorn and scrub vegetation near the Amman National Park, where it is present from late April to at least late July. It may prove to be widespread in similar habitats in the Northern Highlands, and could even be a breeding species in the Southern Rift Margins around Dana.

Small numbers also occur on spring passage at widely scattered localities, including the Dead Sea Rift Margins, Eastern Desert, Amman suburbs, and Wadi Rum. The species has been recorded from 18 April to 25 May, with one at the Risha Gasfield on 27 July 1990.

Hippolais olivetorum
Olive-tree Warbler

AR: Hazejat ashjar al-zaytoon
GE: Olivenspötter

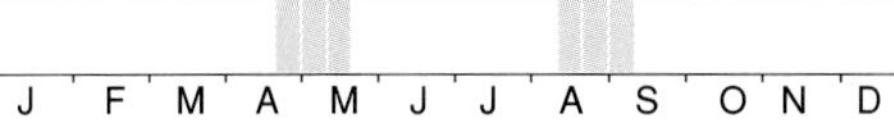

A rare spring migrant from late April to mid May, mainly to sparsely vegetated areas at Aqaba, Wadi Rum, Petra, and the Jordan River. It is more of a rarity in autumn with singles at the Risha Gasfield on 12 August 1990, and at Azraq on 4-6 September 1963.

Hippolais icterina
Icterine Warbler

AR: Hazejah laimooneeyat as-sader
GE: Gelbspötter

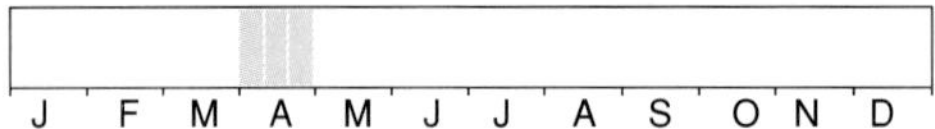

A very rare spring migrant with five records at Azraq in the period 8-28 April.

Sylvia conspicillata
Spectacled Warbler

AR: Dakhla um nadārā
GE: Brillengrasmücke

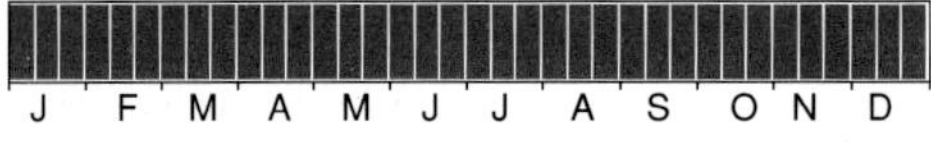

In the highlands of western Jordan, where it is appears to be resident, the Spectacled Warbler occurs in low, thorny scrub habitats. It breeds at low densities in suitable parts of the Northern Highlands, Dead Sea Rift Margins, and Sharra Mountains.

In winter small numbers wander to desert sites in Wadi Araba, the Southern Ghor, Eastern Desert and Azraq, where they occur from October to March.

Sylvia cantillans
Subalpine Warbler

AR: Dakhlat es-sarood
GE: Weißbart-Grasmücke

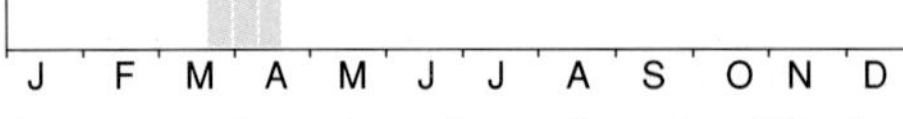

A scarce early spring migrant from late March to mid April, recorded at Aqaba, Wadi Rum, Petra, Wadi Dana, Dibbin, Azraq, and Shaumari. None have been seen in autumn.

Sylvia mystacea
Ménétries's Warbler

AR: Dakhla ra'asa'a
GE: Tamariskengrasmücke

Vagrant: a pair at Shaumari on 24 April 1965, and one at Fidan on 24 March 1989.

Sylvia melanocephala
Sardinian Warbler

AR: Dakhla lā'ssa
GE: Samtkopf-Grasmücke

J F M A M J J A S O N D

A common resident species, breeding in low scrub and garigue habitats in the Highlands and Rift Margins from Ar Ramtha south to Wadi Dana, and most easily located by hearing a burst of its loud, rattling song.

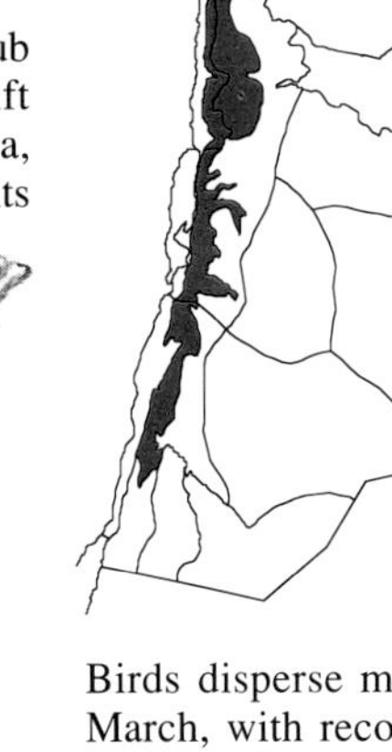

Birds disperse more widely during October to March, with records from Aqaba, Wadi Araba, the Dead Sea, the Jordan Valley, and wadis in the Eastern Desert and Azraq area. A few individuals linger in these non-breeding areas to about mid April, and paired behaviour has been noted at Azraq.

Sylvia melanothorax
Cyprus Warbler

AR: Dakhla qubrusiyya
GE: Schuppengrasmücke

There are three records of males in acacia-lined wadis near Fidan during 17-20 November 1994. Based on observations on the Israeli side of Wadi Araba, it is likely to be an uncommon bird on passage (October and February-March) and in winter.

Sylvia rueppelli
Rüppell's Warbler

AR: Nadiqa qusābi
GE: Maskengrasmücke

J F M A M J J A S O N D

A scarce early spring migrant, recorded from late February through to mid April mainly in the western part of the country. It typically occurs in desert areas with low scrub and broom bushes, and it is often associated with Lesser Whitethroats. There are single records from Aqaba, Qal'at Fassua, Fidan, Al Karak and Jarash. In the east, it is a rarity at Azraq and Shaumari, but four males were seen at Wadi ar Rattami on 11 April 1985. None have yet been seen in autumn.

Sylvia nana
Desert Warbler

AR: Showaleh
GE: Wüstengrasmücke

??? ???
J F M A M J J A S O N D

A rarity, to be found in low shrubs in desert wadis in spring and winter, although probably more widespread in winter than the few records suggest. Singles have been seen at Ghor as Safi in December 1883, Azraq on 18 April 1965 and 24-25 April 1966, Wadi Batn al Ghul, north of Al Mudawwara on 5 February 1990 (two on 7th), and at three localities around Wadi Abu Dubana (Fidan) during 13-18 November 1994. The Wadi Batn al Ghul birds showed a close feeding association with Desert Wheatears – a habit also noted between other wheatears and *Sylvia* warblers in Israel, Egypt, and the United Arab Emirates.

Sylvia leucomelaena
Arabian Warbler

AR: Hazejah arabieh
GE: Akaziengrasmücke (Blanford-Grasmücke)

J F M A M J J A S O N D

A localised resident of Wadi Araba, found exclusively in acacia woodland. It was first identified in Jordan in 1963, and there were no further records until 1988. It can be seen as far north as As Safi, but is most easily located in the Fidan and Feinan areas. A record to the south-east of Aqaba on 12 April 1992 may represent a local wanderer.

This isolated population, at the northern limit of the species' range, has been assigned to a separate subspecies *S. l. negevensis.*

Sylvia hortensis
Orphean Warbler

AR: Dakhlat al-basāteen
GE: Orpheusgrasmücke

J F M A M J J A S O N D

May breed locally in the Southern Rift Margins, as several territorial males have been recorded in and above Wadi Dana in April. The song of the eastern race *S. h. crassirostris* consists of loud phrases of jerky, fluty notes and chucklings, and is reminiscent of the song of a Nightingale.

Otherwise, this is a scarce spring migrant to the Jordan Valley, Rift Margins, Northern Highlands, and Rum Desert during early March to late April. There are few records from the east, even at Azraq, and no records at all in autumn.

Sylvia nisoria
Barred Warbler

AR: Dakhlat mukhattata
GE: Sperbergrasmücke

J F M A M J J A S O N D

A scarce migrant to the Eastern Desert (including Azraq), the Highlands, Rift Valley, and Rum Desert during mid April to late May, and late August to late September. Passage in the west appears to be restricted to the spring, whilst at Azraq, Shaumari, and Wadi al Butm it also occurs in autumn, with one record on 12 June 1977.

Sylvia curruca
Lesser Whitethroat

AR: Zuraiqa feranieh sughrā
GE: Klappergrasmücke

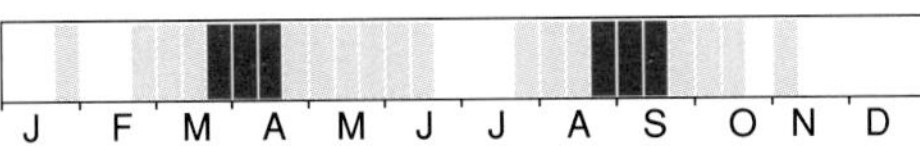

A scarce breeding bird of pine woods in the Northern Highlands, at sites such as Dibbin Forest, and the ridge above Wadi as Sir. On the basis of their distinct song and distribution, these breeding birds are likely to belong to the race *S. c. caucasica*. Breeding was first proven in 1990.

A very common migrant throughout Jordan, occurring widely in the Rift Valley, Rift Margins, Highlands, and Deserts. Spring passage begins in early March, with peak numbers in early April. Passage is particularly obvious in desert regions, with its 'tic' calls apparently coming from every broom bush, acacia tree and clump of vegetation. The autumn peak is in early September, with a few occurring into mid October. With records from Azraq on 29 January, and 21st and 26 February 1979, it appears that a few birds may occasionally winter in that area.

Sylvia communis
Whitethroat

AR: Az-zuraiqa al-feranieh
GE: Dorngrasmücke

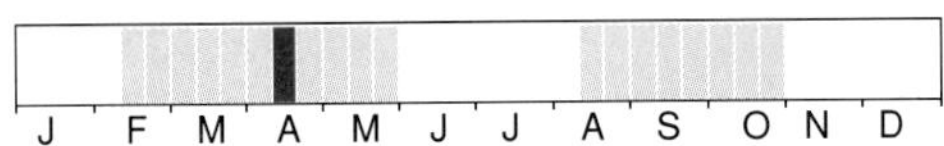

An uncommon migrant, mainly in the Eastern Desert, Northern Highlands, Rift Margins and Aqaba, from mid February to late May, and again from mid August to late October.

Singing birds recorded in the northern Jordan Valley suggest that it may breed in that region.

Sylvia borin
Garden Warbler

AR: Al-qurqufnieh
GE: Gartengrasmücke

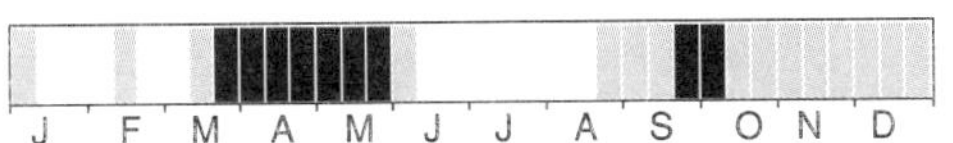

Nowadays an uncommon migrant, with small numbers passing through in early to late May, and again in early September to early October. Numbers are apparently much reduced in comparison with the 1960s, when it was classed as abundant, with up to 100 at Azraq on a single day. The earliest recorded date is 16 April.

It is now recorded mainly at Aqaba, and in the vegetated desert areas at Wadi al Butm and Azraq, but it has also occurred at the Amman National Park, and at Wadi al Hasa in the Highlands.

Sylvia atricapilla
Blackcap

AR: Abu qalansowah
GE: Mönchsgrasmücke

J F M A M J J A S O N D

Spring sees large numbers in many regions from late March to late May, and a few are also seen in autumn in a protracted period from late August to late November. It is the second most numerous migrant warbler after Lesser Whitethroat, and occurs commonly in the Rift Valley, Rift Margins, Highlands, Eastern Desert, and Rum Desert. A few remain in winter in the Northern Highlands.

Phylloscopus bonelli
Bonelli's Warbler

AR: Naqsharat bonely
GE: Wanderlaubsänger

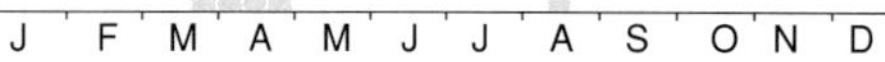

The three fledged young seen in Aleppo Pines at Dibbin Forest on 11 August 1991 constitute the first and only evidence of breeding in Jordan. The 'tchip' call they made is that characteristic of the eastern race *P. b. orientalis.* Otherwise, this same race of the Bonelli's Warbler is a scarce spring migrant, recorded at Aqaba, along the Rift Margins, and at Azraq-Shaumari in late March to late April. Fifteen at Wadi al Mujib on 1 April 1994 is a large concentration. None have yet been seen on autumn passage.

Phylloscopus sibilatrix
Wood Warbler

AR: Naqsharat al-ghab
GE: Waldlaubsänger

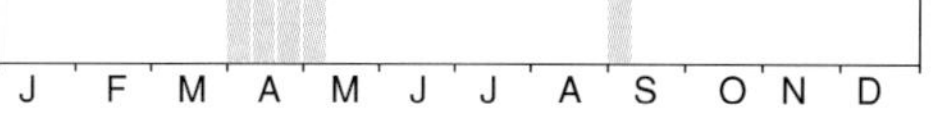

A scarce spring migrant to widely scattered sites at Aqaba, in the Rift Margin highlands, Rum Desert, Wadi al Butm, and Azraq-Shaumari. It has been recorded from early April to early May, but is most likely to be seen during the period 10-18 April. It is rare in autumn, with one at Wadi as Sir on 7 September 1991, and one at Azraq in November 1964.

Phylloscopus neglectus
Plain Willow Warbler (Plain Leaf Warbler)

GE: Eichenlaubsänger

Vagrant: one at Azraq on 18 April 1963.

Phylloscopus collybita
Chiffchaff

AR: Naqsharah thābyeh
GE: Zilpzalp

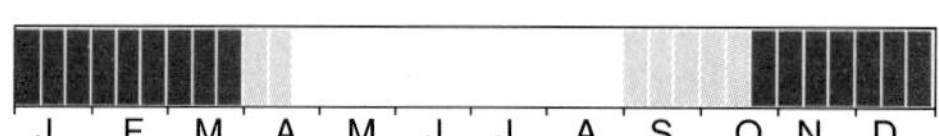

A fairly common migrant and winter visitor to many parts of Jordan. The race involved is thought to be chiefly *P. c. abietinus*, based on its pale, only slightly yellowish plumage, and plaintive 'swee-oo' call. Recent observations show that it is present from November to April in the Northern Highlands, Dead Sea, Petra, Wadi Araba, and Aqaba areas. Further east, it is found only at Azraq and Shaumari, and it avoids the sparsely vegetated desert wadis in winter. Spring migration is particularly evident in late March, with a few lingering to early May. Autumn birds return as early as the beginning of September, but most arrive after the main Willow Warbler passage.

Phylloscopus trochilus
Willow Warbler

AR: Naqsharat as-sufsuf
GE: Fitis

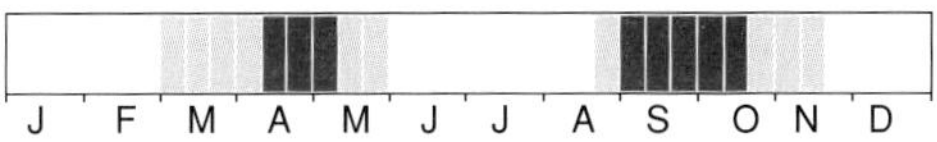

A common migrant, being most numerous in late April and mid September. Spring migration is evident from early March to late May, and on autumn passage it occurs from late August to mid November. It is most frequent in the Eastern Desert (including Azraq), and the Northern Highlands, but it also occurs along the Rift Margins and in remote desert wadi bushes. It can occur in large falls, for example 250+ in the Azraq-Shaumari area on 28 April 1990.

Both the *P. t. trochilus* and *acredula* races are involved, and *yakutensis* has also been trapped.

Regulus regulus
Goldcrest

AR: Sa'ut mutawwajah bel-thahab
GE: Wintergoldhähnchen

The two recent records in pine woods of the Northern Highlands are the first records for Jordan: one in the Amman National Park on 1 December 1989, and the other in Dibbin Forest on 16 February 1990.

Muscicapa striata
Spotted Flycatcher

AR: Khãtef ath-thubab al-monaqatt
GE: Grauschnäpper

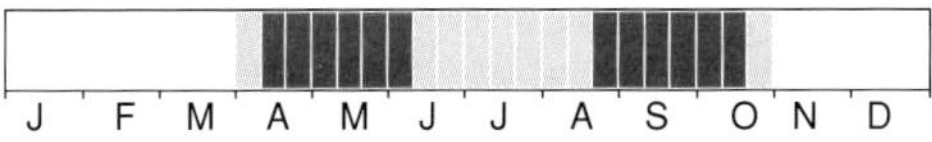

A few nest in the Northern Highlands, for example in pines at the Amman National Park, and also in Wadi ash Shita. Breeding was first proved in 1990.

Birds occur commonly on passage, mainly between mid April and early June, and again between late August and mid October. It is a widespread visitor to many areas, but is particularly frequent at Aqaba, Azraq, Wadi al Butm, and Shaumari. However, it can turn up almost anywhere, including remote wadis in the desert. It can occur in large falls, for example 150+ at Azraq-Shaumari on 28 April 1990. The extreme dates for this summer migrant are 5 April and 20 October.

Ficedula parva
Red-breasted Flycatcher

AR: Khãtef ath-thubãb ahmar ar-rãs
GE: Zwergschnäpper

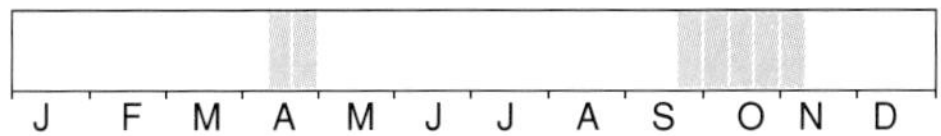

A rare passage migrant. In spring, it has occurred as a vagrant at Aqaba, Shaumari and Amman, but only between 16-28 April; one was also trapped at Azraq in spring.

In addition, it appears to be a regular, albeit scarce late autumn migrant to Shaumari, with ones and twos recorded between 28 September and 1 November. Other singles were seen along the Zarqa River on 27 October 1989, and at Feinan on 21 October 1994.

Ficedula semitorquata
Semi-collared Flycatcher

AR: Khātef ath-thubab an-nisf mutawaq
GE: Halbringschnäpper

?
J F M A M J J A S O N D

A scarce spring passage bird between late March and early May. It is most frequent at Shaumari and Wadi al Butm, but it has also been reported from Azraq, Na'ur, Petra and Wadi Rum. The species is difficult to separate from the other *Ficedula* flycatchers in autumn, but a possible was seen at Shaumari on 15 September 1989.

Ficedula albicollis
Collared Flycatcher

AR: Khātef ath-thubab al-mutawaq
GE: Halsbandschnäpper

?
J F M A M J J A S O N D

A scarce spring passage bird between late March and mid May. Up to four have been seen on any one day at Azraq, Shaumari, Wadi al Butm, Wadi al Wala, and Petra. In autumn, a possible was seen at Shaumari on 12 October 1990.

Ficedula hypoleuca
Pied Flycatcher

AR: Khātef ath-thubab al-abqa'a
GE: Trauerschnäpper

J F M A M J J A S O N D

A scarce spring passage bird between late March and early May. It is most frequently seen in the Eastern Desert at Azraq, Shaumari, and Wadi al Butm, but it has also been seen at Aqaba and As Suwayfiyya (Amman).

Turdoides squamiceps
Brown Babbler (Arabian Babbler)

AR: Tharthareh arabieh
GE: Graudrossling

J F M A M J J A S O N D

A characteristic bird of the Rift Valley fauna, breeding along the shores of the Dead Sea, and in Wadi Araba from As Safi and Wadi al Fidan south to Aqaba. It is typically found in deserts near *Tamarix*, palms, or acacias. At higher altitudes, which it avoids in Israel, it breeds at Petra (7-11 pairs in 1983), and probably in Wadi Umm Ishrin (Rum Desert). Further north, birds are also found in the lower-most Zarqa River.

It is a gregarious bird, often seen moving through an area in noisy groups of up to 20, giving the high whistling 'piu' contact call. It has a complex breeding system involving co-operative behaviour within the group.

Parus caeruleus
Blue Tit

AR: Qurquf azraq
GE: Blaumeise

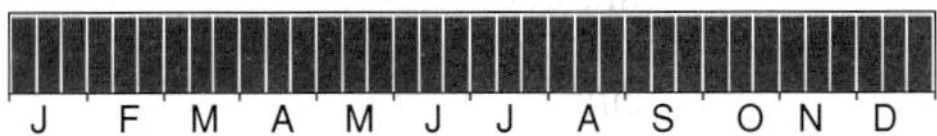

A small resident population occurs in the Northern Highlands of Jordan, some 500km from the nearest mapped breeding range in the Taurus Mountains of Turkey. Birds were first recorded in Wadi as Sir in April 1893, but there were no further sightings for 91 years until they were rediscovered in 1984. They are most easily seen in the remnants of pine forest at Dibbin, but they have also been recorded in other habitats, including oak woods at Qal'at ar Rabat (Ajlun), Ibbin, Najde, Wadi al Yabis, and in the Zubiya reserve. One near Sport City, Amman in October 1994 is the southern-most record to date. Breeding was first proven in 1990.

Parus major
Great Tit

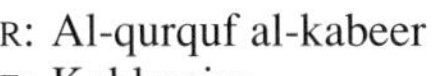

AR: Al-qurquf al-kabeer
GE: Kohlmeise

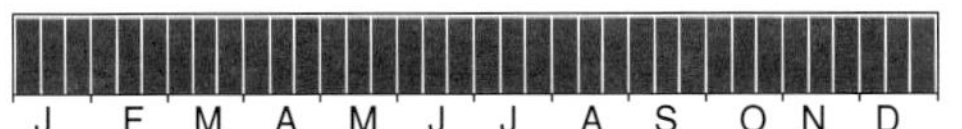

A resident, breeding fairly commonly in the woods, orchards, and gardens of the Northern Highlands and northern Rift Margins (from Irbid south to the Amman National Park). There is an apparently isolated population in the Southern Rift Margins around Wadi Dana and Petra. Some 4-6 breeding pairs were estimated at Petra in 1983. Here, they prefer scattered Juniper trees and oleander-lined wadis. Birds have also been seen at Pella (Jordan Valley) on 19 January 1990 and 17 March 1994.

Tichodroma muraria
Wallcreeper

AR: Ad-dāb
GE: Mauerläufer

The only record of this species in Jordan is of two in Wadi al Mujib in spring 1897. In northern Israel, it is a scarce, but regular winter visitor to cliff walls, and it could well be waiting to be found in the wadis of at least the Northern Highlands.

Remiz pendulinus
Penduline Tit

AR: Ar-rmaiz
GE: Beutelmeise

J F M A M J J A S O N D

Small numbers of this species winter along the Jordan River, in the Southern Ghor, and at Azraq. However, it could prove to be quite common in the lush vegetation on the banks of the Jordan River if exploration were easier there. At least nine were seen at Al Manshiyya on 8 November 1990, and five at Damiya on 8 November 1991. Up to four were also seen at a small marsh near As Safi in December 1991. A light spring passage is also apparent at Azraq during April.

Nectarinia osea
Orange-tufted Sunbird (Palestine Sunbird)

AR: Toma'ir felesteeny
GE: Jerichonektarvogel

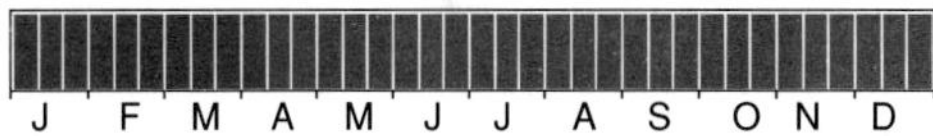

Formerly restricted to the Jordan Valley and the vicinity of the Dead Sea, this species has now expanded its range along the whole length of the Rift Margin highlands. There are old records from Petra, but then a gap of 61 years before it was recorded again in 1975. It is a common, resident breeding species from the Zarqa River south to Petra, with 40-50 breeding pairs estimated at the latter site in 1983. It occurs in Amman as a garden bird, feeding on nectar from the many flowering plants. In the wadis, it is concentrated where oleander grows. There may be some local movement within its range, as birds follow the flowering of plants through the year.

Small numbers have been seen at Aqaba and Wadi Araba from October to April, but there are insufficient data to determine if birds are resident in these areas. It has not been observed in the Azraq area so far, and there are only two records at Wadi Rum (six on 24-25 April 1983, and two on 18 April 1990).

Oriolus oriolus
Golden Oriole

AR: As-safarieh
GE: Pirol

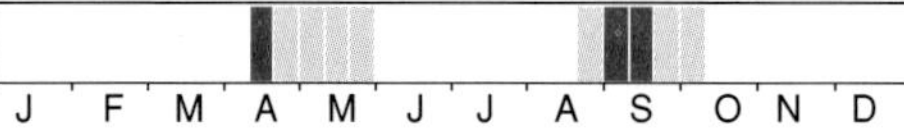

Shaumari in early to mid September is the best place to see this species, when up to 15 have been seen in the eucalyptus trees. A few are seen from mid April to late May, but more pass through during late August to early October. In addition to Shaumari and the Eastern Desert, it occurs in the Northern Highlands, Rift Margin highlands, and at Aqaba (12 in hotel gardens on 27 April). It can also occur in remote desert wadis.

Lanius isabellinus
Isabelline Shrike

AR: Burqeh shahba'a muhmarat ith-thanab
GE: Isabellwürger

J F M A M J J A S O N D

A rare migrant, occasionally visiting Azraq and Shaumari in late April and early May, with one also observed at Wadi Rum on 28 April 1963. In autumn, a single bird was seen at Azraq on 2 November 1991, and another occurred south of Aqaba on 13 October 1993.

Lanius collurio
Red-backed Shrike

AR: Jazzār ahmar ath-thahar
GE: Neuntöter

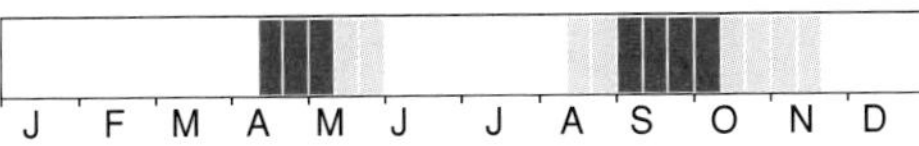

One of the two commonest shrikes occurring on passage both in spring (mid April to late May) and autumn (late August to mid November). Peak passage usually occurs around the first two weeks of May, and occasional massive falls have been witnessed, for example 500 in the Azraq-Shaumari area on 28 April 1990. It is a rather late migrant, with none recorded before 17 April. Autumn passage is equally obvious, and peaks in mid September. It can be observed most widely in the Northern Highlands and Eastern Desert, but it can also be found along the length of the Rift Margins as far south as Aqaba.

Lanius minor
Lesser Grey Shrike

AR: Duqnāsh tardee
GE: Schwarzstirnwüger

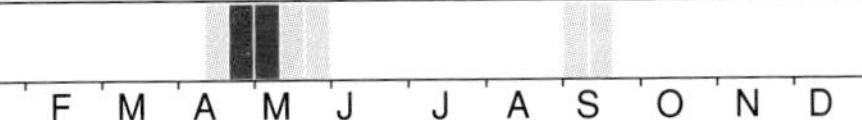

A regular late spring migrant in the Eastern Desert, but usually occurring in rather small numbers. It is recorded most often in late April to early May (once on 13 April), with rare mass arrivals, for example 68 between Ar Ruwayshid and Azraq on 30 April 1965. It is less frequent in the west, and is not often seen along the Rift Margins. It is rare in autumn, with a few seen at Azraq in early to mid September.

Lanius excubitor
Great Grey Shrike

AR: Jazzar al-badieh
GE: Raubwürger

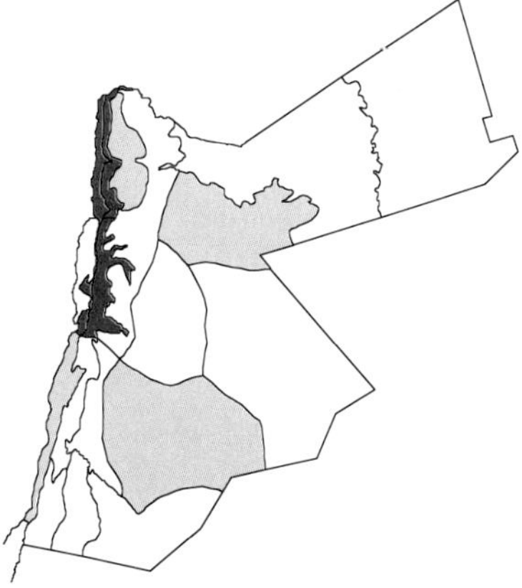

A fairly common resident breeding species of semi-arid areas where there are trees or bushes, for example in the southern Jordan Valley, the Rift Margins from Mahis south to Wadi al Hasa, in Wadi Araba, and in the Eastern Desert (Wadi al Butm, Azraq, Shaumari, and Al Jafr). It is found more widely outside the breeding season, especially in winter, but it still appears to be absent from the Rum Desert and much of the Northern Highlands.

Lanius senator
Woodchat Shrike

AR: Duqnāsh shāmee
GE: Rotkopfwürger

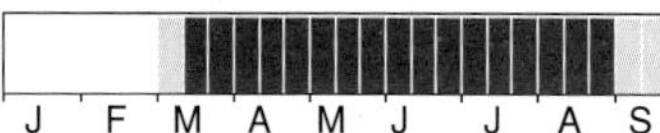

A common summer visitor from early March to mid September. It occurs as a migrant in many areas, and breeds in woods, olive groves and orchards in the Rift Margin highlands from Umm Qays south to Ash Shawbak.

It is a widespread migrant to the Rift Margin highlands and Eastern Desert, but is less common in the Rift Valley and Rum Desert. Peak passage is in early April, but it can still be seen in non-breeding areas as late as early June. Autumn passage is slight (especially in the east), and reflects the dispersal of breeding birds from late August onwards.

Lanius nubicus
Masked Shrike

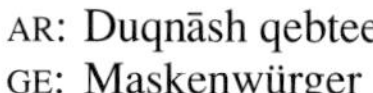

AR: Duqnāsh qebtee
GE: Maskenwürger

J F M A M J J A S O N D

A fairly common summer visitor and migrant from late March to late October. A small number breed in the open woodland and orchards of the Northern Highlands from Jarash south to the Amman National Park, and a few may also breed at Petra, in the Rift Valley, and in the Rum Desert.

It occurs on spring passage quite widely from Aqaba, Wadi Araba, and the Rift Margin highlands to the Eastern Desert. Peak passage occurs in April, but the last spring bird at a non-breeding site was seen on 1 June. There are few signs of a marked autumn passage, apart from post-breeding dispersal in the highlands, and a few in the Azraq area from late August to early October.

Garrulus glandarius
Jay

AR: Al-qeeq
GE: Eichelhäher

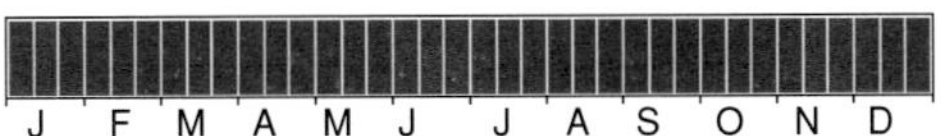

A locally fairly common resident of pine and oak forests in the Northern Highlands from the Yarmuk River south to Wadi ash Shita, including the Dibbin Forest.

The race involved is *G. g. atricapillus,* which has a dark crown and moustachial on an otherwise pale head.

Corvus monedula
Jackdaw

AR: Ghurāb ez-zar'a
GE: Dohle

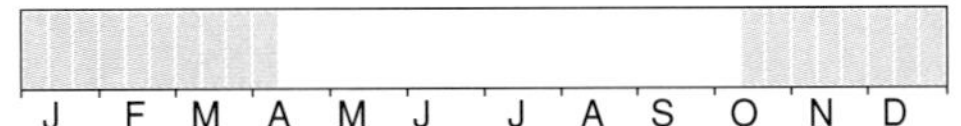

Six adults were seen at Pella on 4 April 1993, and two of these were feeding young in a small, natural cave. The birds had prominent white napes. Jackdaws were again present at this site in March 1994.

Although apparently more common in the past in the Northern Highlands and on the Moab plateau, it is now a scarce winter visitor to the Jordan Valley, Northern Highlands, and Azraq from October to March. A flock of 50 was seen at Ajlun on 27 March 1988, but numbers are otherwise small.

Corvus splendens
Indian House Crow

AR: Ghurāb al-manazil al-hendy
GE: Glanzkrähe

J F M A M J J A S O N D

A small resident population has become established in the extensive palms at Aqaba since 1979. A population of at least 10 to 20 pairs is now estimated in the town, with concentrations in the areas of mature palms along the coast. The colonisation of Aqaba, along with Suez (Egypt), is thought to have resulted from birds arriving via ships.

Birds rarely wander far, even south along the coast, so two records from the Rum Desert are noteworthy: one at Wadi Rum on 17 April 1987, and three at Disi on 19 April 1987.

Corvus frugilegus
Rook

AR: Ghurāb al-qayith
GE: Saatkrähe

In December 1891, Hart 'met with a small flock and shot one' in the Jordan Valley. Although it is a regular winterer in Israel, the only recent sighting in Jordan is one reported between As Salt and the Dead Sea on 15 April 1986.

Corvus corone cornix
Hooded Crow

AR: Zagh
GE: Aaskrähe

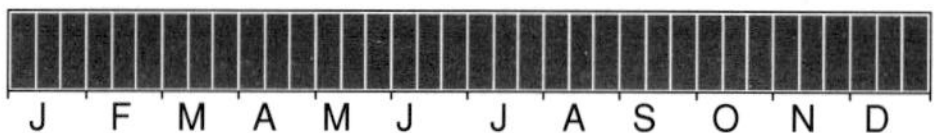

A common resident breeding species in the Northern Highlands (from Irbid south to Amman), and also the northern Jordan Valley (from Al Manshiyya south to Dayr Alla). It favours wooded habitats, either natural or planted, and occurs in urban areas as well as in the more remote forests. The largest recorded flocks are those in Dibbin Forest, where up to 75 have been seen in mid June.

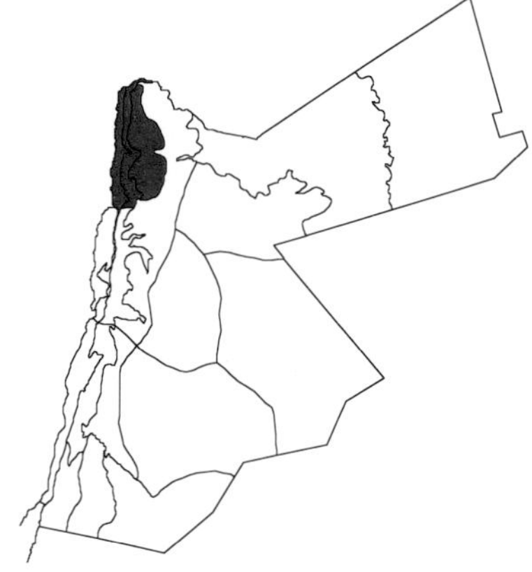

Corvus ruficollis
Brown-necked Raven

AR: Ghurāb o'haimir al-a'noq
GE: Wüstenrabe

A common and widespread resident of arid regions, being absent only from the northern Jordan Valley, Northern Rift Margins and Highlands, and adjacent Steppes. It is found in the Rift Margins and Highlands from South Shuna south to Aqaba. Further east on the desert plateaux, it is particularly common along the line of the Desert Highway, where it nests on high-tension pylons. It also occurs widely in the Rum Desert, where scavenging winter flocks of up to 60 can often be seen at Al Qatrana, Disi, and Wadi Rum. Flocks also gather by the roadside north of Aqaba, attracted by the large number of lorries, and presumably also by rubbish.

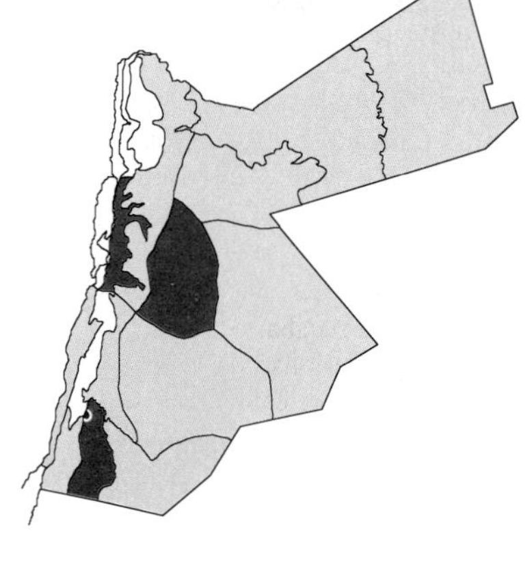

Interestingly, there are very few records from the Southern Rift Margins (for example Wadi Dana and Petra), where it is largely replaced by Fan-tailed Ravens. It is also rather scarce in the Eastern Desert around Azraq, although this may represent a recent decline.

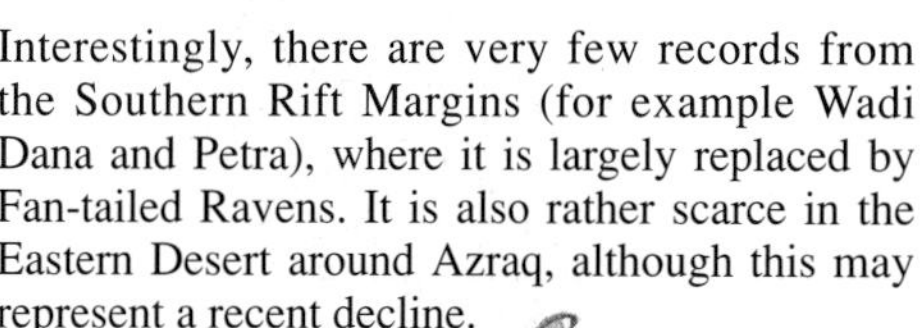

Corvus corvus
Raven

AR: Al-ghurāb
GE: Kolkrabe

It appears that the Common Raven was widespread in northern and western Jordan until quite recently. It was formerly a common resident in Amman, and even in the 1960s was recorded in the Jarash-Amman area, to the east in the Basalt Desert, and in the south at Al Karak, Ash Shawbak and Wadi Dana. There are apparently no ravens now remaining in the Northern Highlands, and in other areas only Brown-necked Ravens have been identified with certainty. In future, sightings of potential Common Ravens should be fully checked out.

Corvus rhipidurus
Fan-tailed Raven

AR: Ghurāb marwahi ith-thanab
GE: Borstenrabe

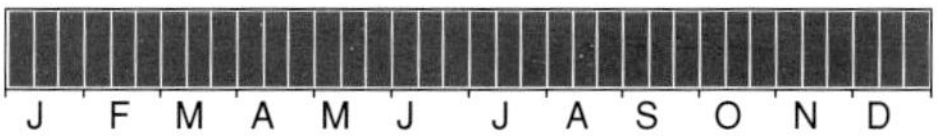

J F M A M J J A S O N D

A common resident of the Rift Margin mountains and wadis from the northern end of the Dead Sea south to Aqaba, although it also occurs rather locally in the Rum Desert, and occasionally wanders into Wadi Araba. The four prime areas are: the north-eastern shores of the Dead Sea, Wadi al Karak, Petra, and behind Aqaba, where flocks up to 120 strong of this gregarious bird can be seen. About 30 breeding pairs were estimated in $10km^2$ at Petra in 1983.

Onychognathus tristramii
Tristram's Grackle

AR: Sowadieh
GE: Tristramstar

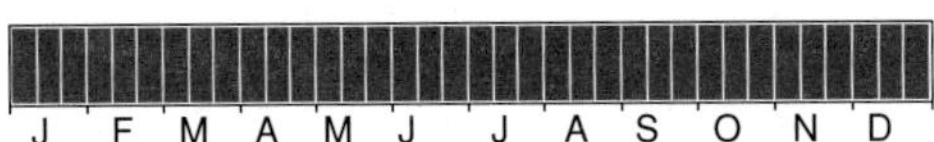

J F M A M J J A S O N D

A characteristic resident of the Rift Margin wadis, from the northern end of the Dead Sea south to Aqaba, and also in the Rum Desert. It is locally common, especially at its strong-holds by the Dead Sea, Wadi Dana and Petra. It congregates in flocks of up to 370 in autumn and winter. At Petra in 1983, about 30 breeding pairs were estimated in $10km^2$, and all were west of the central valley. Birds from the Wadi Rum cliffs can be seen at Rum village, and others visit the suburbs of Aqaba, where they presumably scavenge for food.

It is a gregarious bird, whose loud, melodious whistle calls, 'wee-oouu-eee', often echo off the rock walls as a group flies past, flashing the orange patches in its wings.

Sturnus vulgaris
Starling

AR: Zarzoor
GE: Star

J F M A M J J A S O N D

An uncommon to abundant winter visitor to the Jordan Valley and northern deserts, with numbers varying from year to year. In recent years, it has been an uncommon winter visitor (early November to early March), with flocks of up to 80-100 in the Jordan Valley, and Eastern and Basalt Deserts, particularly near habitation. A roost of 100,000 birds was reported in 1942 at the Yarmuk estuary reservoir. In contrast, none were seen by the author in the winter of 1991/92. The southernmost records are from Dhiban and Petra. It has been recorded from 21 October to 21 April.

Sturnus roseus
Rose-coloured Starling

AR: As-sumarmar
GE: Rosenstar

J F M A M J J A S O N D

A very rare late spring migrant to the Eastern Desert with singles at Azraq on 11-12 May 1966, and at Shaumari on 13th, 28th and 29 May 1976.

Passer domesticus
House Sparrow

AR: Asfur doree
GE: Haussperling

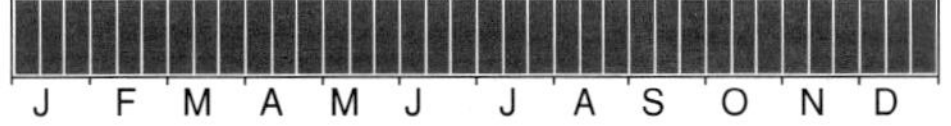

A widespread and very common resident, clearly associated with man, and found in all but the most barren, uninhabited desert. It is even found in remote areas containing just a single house. It is quick to colonise new areas. There was an apparent increase at Azraq in the 1960s and 1970s as the town grew; it colonised Bayir police post in the 1970s and Shaumari since 1976-77. It is also a new arrival at Petra, associated with the increased numbers of tourists. There were 25 at a temporary camp in the Ar Ruwayshid Desert and it took only three months for them to discover a road builder's camp near Bayir, 86km south of the previous camp.

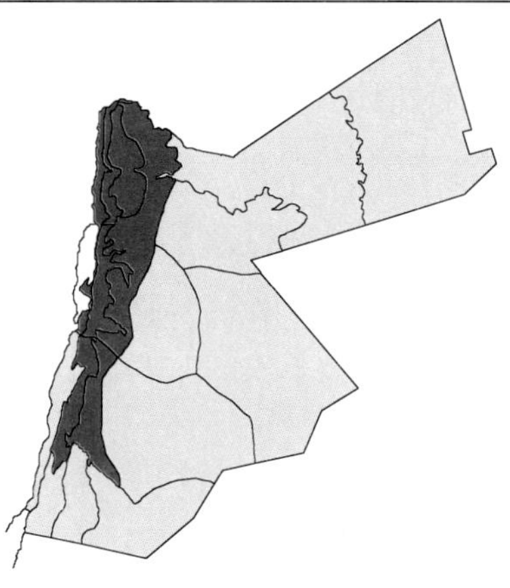

Passer hispaniolensis
Spanish Sparrow

AR: Asfur esbanee
GE: Weidensperling

A localised breeding bird, restricted to the lush valleys flowing down to the Jordan Valley and Dead Sea, where it nests colonially in stands of poplars. It is found in most wadis from Wadi Shu'ayb as far south as Wadi al Hasa, but it may well occur further north too.

It is found more widely and commonly in winter, especially in desert areas. It frequently forms flocks of 50-100, and sometimes assembles in large roosts containing up to 1000 birds. In the Rift Valley, flocks can be seen at Aqaba, Fidan, As Safi, on the shores of the Dead Sea, and in the southern Jordan Valley. In the Eastern Desert, it can be found in winter at vegetated areas such as Wadi al Butm, Azraq and Shaumari. Flocks also winter in Wadi al Mujib. A few have also been recorded at Wadi Rum and at the Disi irrigation project in winter.

Passer moabiticus
Dead Sea Sparrow

AR: Asfur al-baher al-maiet
GE: Moabsperling

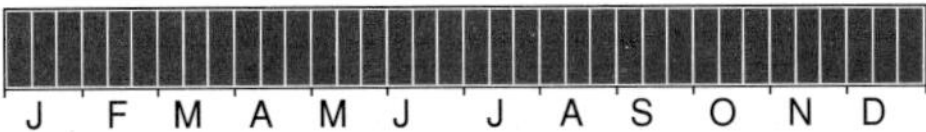

Breeds in loose colonies in the *Tamarix* thickets which line the banks of the Jordan River, and locally along the shores of the Dead Sea. A good place to observe a breeding colony is at Suwayma on the north shore of the Dead Sea, west of the Resthouse. The nests are large, untidy, pin-cushions of twigs. One of the original sites, discovered last century, was at the mouth of Wadi al Hasa in the Ghor as Safi, but it is not known if this site is still occupied.

It forms flocks in winter, often associated with Spanish Sparrows, and these wander widely in the fields of the southern Jordan Valley, and to a lesser extent in Wadi Araba. Up to 250 were counted at South Shuna on 26 January 1990, and 10 were seen at Fidan on 24 December 1989. Away from the Rift Valley, the only record is of about 30 in Wadi Zarbi, near Al Rusayfa on 6 February 1965.

Petronia brachydactyla
Pale Rock Sparrow

AR: Asfur sakhree saharawee
GE: Fahlsperling

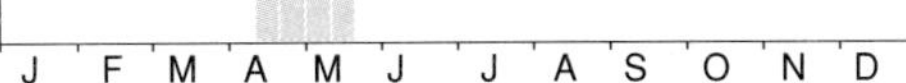

The only breeding record comes from Dana, where two singing males and an adult feeding two juveniles were observed on 18 May 1994. In the 1960s, it was also considered to be a possible breeding species in the Azraq area, but there is no firm evidence to support this.

As a spring migrant, it is clearly quite numerous in some years, and absent in others. It was recorded as a common migrant at Azraq in the 1960s, with 237 bird-days between late April and early May. Flocks of 30-80 were seen in 1985, migrating in a NE to S direction at several sites around Azraq, and singing birds were located near Ar Ruwayshid, Wadi ash Shaumari, and Azraq in the same year.

Other recent reports are few. They have been concentrated at Al Karak, Al Lajjun, Petra, and Wadi Rum during 10-25 April.

Petronia petronia
Rock Sparrow

AR: Al-asfur as-sakhree
GE: Steinsperling

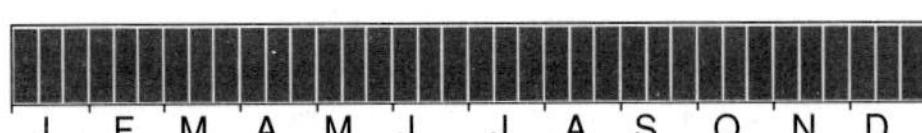

A fairly common resident of the arid Rift Margin highlands from the Zarqa River south to Petra. At Petra, it breeds in colonies of up to 30 pairs in the most narrow, deep and precipitous wadis; a total of 80+ pairs was estimated breeding in 1983. In addition to its favoured habitat of mountain wadis, it also apparently nests in mature trees on open cultivated slopes in the Northern Highlands.

Fringilla coelebs
Chaffinch

AR: As-sun'aj
GE: Buchfink

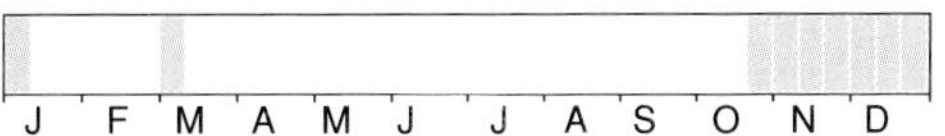

A locally very common winter visitor to the Northern Highlands, Southern Rift Margins, and the Jordan Valley, where it has been recorded between 22 October and 24 March. Substantial roosts can be found in the pine forests at Dibbin and the Amman National Park, with many birds flying in from the surrounding feeding areas. It is a fairly common winter visitor to the wadis at Petra, with 100 present in early March 1992. Only small numbers occur both further south, for example at Wadi Rum, and further east at Shaumari and Azraq.

Fringilla montifringilla
Brambling

AR: Sharshur jabali
GE: Bergfink

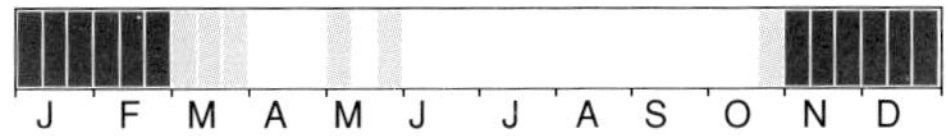

An uncommon winter visitor to the Northern Highlands, recorded at Dibbin, Wadi as Sir, and the western Amman suburbs between 1 November and 6 March. In the east, it is also a very rare late autumn migrant at Shaumari and Azraq (25 October to 10 November).

Serinus serinus
Serin

AR: Al-na'ar al-'orobee
GE: Girlitz

J F M A M J J A S O N D

Not a regular breeding species, but a pair with four recently fledged young was seen at Petra on 5th and 8 May 1983.

A common winter visitor in the Northern Highlands from Umm Qays south to Wadi al Mujib, and also in the Jordan Valley mainly from early November to late February. It often occurs in moderately large flocks, and also roosts communally: 140 at the Amman National Park on 9 November 1991, 100 by the Zarqa River on 24 November 1990, 80 at Kafrayn on 26 January 1990, and 65 at Pella on 19 January 1990. A few birds linger into early spring and can be heard singing.

Smaller numbers occur at Petra, and it is a vagrant to the Eastern Desert, with singles at Shaumari on 28 May 1976 and 10 February 1990.

Serinus syriacus
Tristram's Serin (Syrian Serin)

AR: Al-na'ar
GE: Zederngirlitz

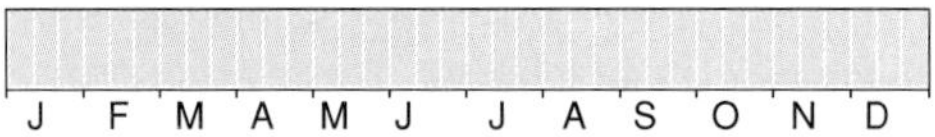

J F M A M J J A S O N D

An isolated, and presumed resident population frequents open, oak and juniper woodland near the top of the rift escarpment at Wadi Dana. 25 to 30 birds, including pairs and juveniles, were seen as long ago as April 1963. In recent years, birds have been seen in mid May, mid June and early October, with at least 20 there on 28 November 1991.

Small numbers occur in winter, often associated with Goldfinch flocks, and there are records from Shaumari, Petra and Kufr Sum (north of Irbid). A few also pass through the Northern Highlands (Umm Qays, Dibbin, Wadi as Sir, Amman National Park and Mount Nebo) in late March to mid April. A few start to sing in spring, but these are presumably en route to breed further north in the foothills of Jabal Sheikh (Mount Hermon).

Carduelis chloris
Greenfinch

AR: Al-khudairee
GE: Grünling

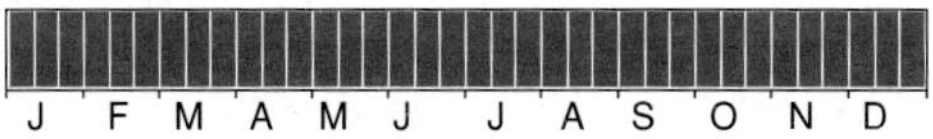

J F M A M J J A S O N D

A very common resident, mainly in wooded areas of the Northern Highlands and Dead Sea Rift Margins, from Umm Qays south to Wadi al Mujib, and possibly even at At Tafila.

In winter, a few wander to other areas, such as Petra, the Jordan Valley, and the Basalt and Eastern Deserts.

Carduelis carduelis
Goldfinch

AR: Hasoon
GE: Stieglitz

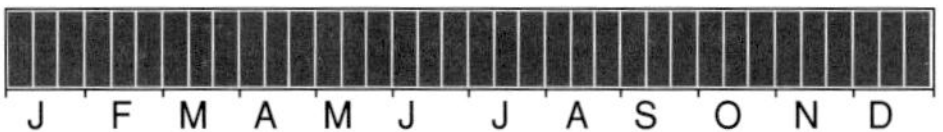

A very common resident, recorded in the Highlands from Umm Qays south to Petra, with 20 pairs breeding at the latter site in 1983. The only records further south are of a single bird at Ras an Naqab, and several at Disi.

Some descend to the Jordan Valley in winter, and a few have also reached Azraq: a singing male in 1965, a pair in 1966 and one on 6 February 1979.

Carduelis spinus
Siskin

AR: Summilee
GE: Erlenzeisig

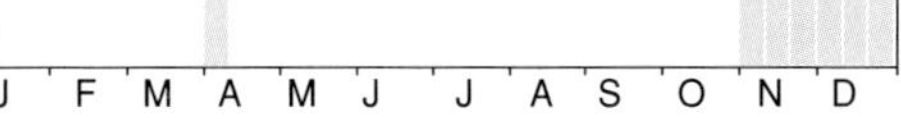

A localised, and rather uncommon winter visitor to the Dibbin Forest, and possibly to other pine forests in the Northern Highlands. Up to 25 have

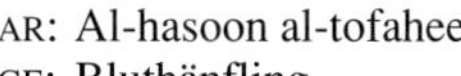

been recorded at Dibbin in November and December. One was also seen above Wadi as Sir on 1 January 1991, with migrants further afield at Shaumari (22 November 1990), Petra (3 April 1994), and Aqaba (20 November 1990).

Carduelis cannabina
Linnet

AR: Al-hasoon al-tofahee
GE: Bluthänfling

A common resident breeding species in the Northern Highlands, and in the Dead Sea Rift Margins south to at least Wadi al Mujib, but less commonly as far south as Wadi Dana and Petra. It was reported as breeding at these Southern Rift Margin localities in the 1960s, but it now appears to be only a scarce spring migrant there.

There is dispersal, or possibly an influx of birds during early November to mid March, with small flocks to be found in the desert fringe of the Northern Steppes, and in the Jordan Valley. It is also a winter vagrant to the Eastern Desert, with up to 25 at Azraq, Shaumari and Wadi al Butm. One was also seen well to the south at Disi on 6 February 1990.

Rhodospiza obsoleta
Desert Finch

AR: Al-asfure al-wardi as-sahrawee
GE: Weißflügelgimpel

J F M A M J J A S O N D

A resident of the Azraq oasis, southern Jordan Valley, and the Northern Steppes, where it is assumed to breed. Although formerly scarce in Jordan (the first record was in 1976), this species is now a regular, fairly common resident, breeding in small numbers in the Azraq and Shaumari areas. Other favoured areas include the plains of Irbid, Ar Ramtha and Al Mafraq, as well as Suwayma (Dead Sea). The recent increases in the amount of agriculture and planting of trees in desert areas are thought to have contributed to the spread of this species, especially in the Azraq area.

Outside the breeding season, small flocks can be found in the general areas where they breed, for example 47 at Azraq on 14 November 1989, 25 at Al Khirba as Samra on 30 August 1991, and 30 at Suwayma on 10 March 1992. The only record in the south is of three at Disi on 4 April 1994.

Bucanetes githagineus
Trumpeter Finch

AR: Az-zameer
GE: Wüstengimpel

J F M A M J J A S O N D

A fairly common resident species, recorded in nearly all the desert areas, where it is far more widespread than previously published maps suggest. It prefers rocky areas with cliffs and gorges and limited vegetation. It is most often seen in the Eastern Desert, Wadi as Sarhan, Basalt Desert, and Rum Desert, but it is also one of the few species to be found in the Al Mudawwara Desert.

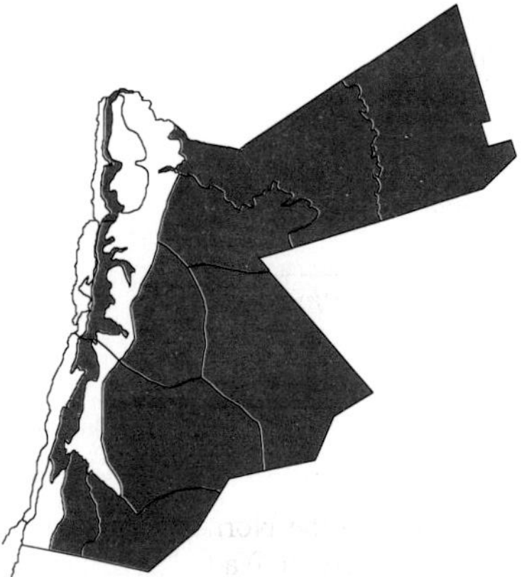

It is less common along the Rift Margins, but has been recorded from the Zarqa River south to Petra. 10-15 pairs were reported breeding at the latter site in 1983, but it is nomadic, and may not breed in some years.

Its song must rank as one of Jordan's most bizarre. It is an unmistakable drawn-out, nasal buzzing or, more descriptively, is like a plastic toy trumpet.

Carpodacus erythrinus
Scarlet Rosefinch

AR: Asfur wardi mu'tād
GE: Karmingimpel

Vagrant: a juvenile female was caught at Azraq on 8 September 1963.

Carpodacus synoicus
Sinai Rosefinch

AR: Asfur wardi sena'ie
GE: Sinaigimpel (Einödgimpel)

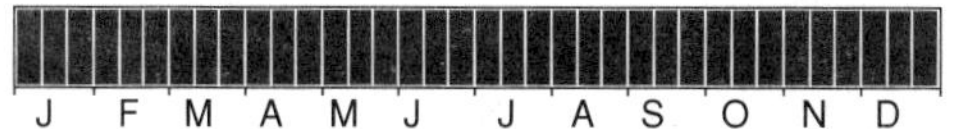

A characteristic resident of the Southern Rift Margins and Rum Desert, in areas where there are outcrops of red sandstone rocks. It has been recorded from near As Safi south to Petra, and in the south from Ras an Naqab to the jabals around Wadi Rum. It was first identified in Jordan at Petra in 1912; before then it was thought to be restricted to Sinai.

There can be no better place to see this bird than amongst the gorges and monuments of Petra, where the Wood Warbler-like trilling song and 'chig' call help to locate it if it is not feeding next to the tracks. It also makes frequent use of drinking sites, such as cisterns, puddles and springs. Some 60-80 breeding pairs were estimated in 10km^2 at Petra in 1983.

In the autumn of 1994, a small man-made drinking pool at Dana attracted many (possibly hundreds) to drink. An unusually large flock of 130 birds was also counted above Dana village on 12 October 1994.

To the north of these regular sites five were seen by the Dead Sea, at the mouth of Wadi al Mujib on 21 December 1990.

Coccothraustes coccothraustes
Hawfinch

AR: Bulbul zaytooni
GE: Kernbeißer

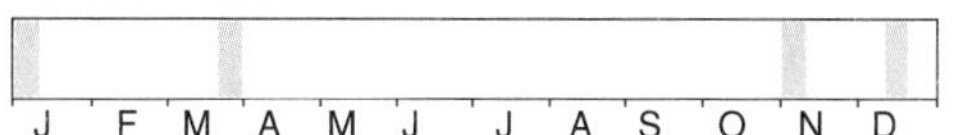

A rare winter visitor to the Northern Highlands, with up to three recorded at Wadi as Sir, Dibbin and the Amman National Park, during early November to late March. At the latter two sites, birds were seen coming to roost with other winter finches.

Emberiza citrinella
Yellowhammer

AR: Derseh safrā'a
GE: Goldammer

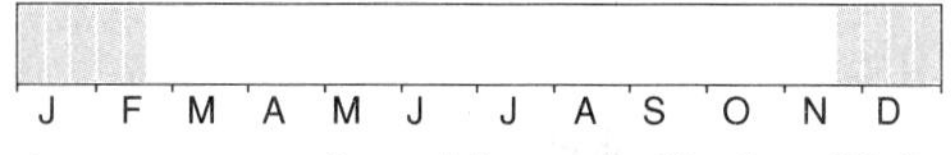

An uncommon winter visitor to the Northern Highlands, especially in open orchards and stony fields. Small flocks of up to 40 have been recorded in the hills above Dibbin, the hills between Na'ur and the Amman National Park, and also at Rumaymin. It has been recorded between late November and mid February.

Emberiza cia
Rock Bunting

AR: Derseh sakhreiyeh
GE: Zippammer

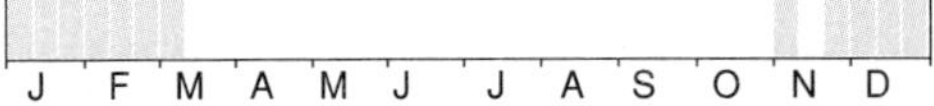

A scarce winter visitor to the Northern Highlands from early November to early March. It frequents stony agricultural land and orchards with other buntings and finches. Up to five have been recorded at Najde, Wadi as Sir and the Amman National Park. Elsewhere, four were seen in Wadi al Wala on 2 March 1990, and three at Shaumari on 1 January 1990.

Emberiza striolata
House Bunting

AR: Derset ad-door
GE: Hausammer

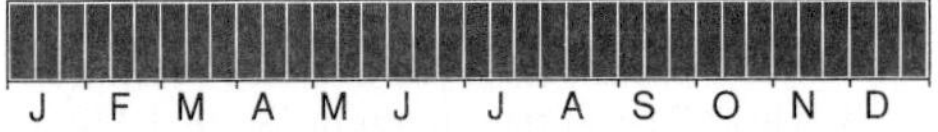

Birds of the striped-headed nominate race *E. s. striolata* are uncommon residents of the Central and Southern Rift Margins, together with the Rum Desert. The favoured habitat is characterised by bare rock, sheer cliffs, and large boulders. At Petra, they breed at low densities (40 pairs/10km^2) throughout the rugged mountainous regions. It can be difficult to observe, and is best located by its loud and monotonous song: 'weDJE-weDi-weDi-weDJE'. As with Sinai Rosefinch, House Buntings frequently drink at watering places.

The species is more likely to wander short distances away from the mountains outside the breeding season. Two seen at Azraq on 4 September 1963 were well east of the species' normal range.

Emberiza cineracea
Cinereous Bunting

AR: Derseh ramadieh
GE: Türkenammer

J F M A M J J A S O N D

A very rare spring migrant, recorded between 24 March and 21 April, with records from the Zarqa River valley, Umm aj Jimal, Qasr Uwaynid, Shaumari, Petra, and Wadi Rum. In addition, a rather early bird was seen at Shaumari on 1 February 1976.

Emberiza hortulana
Ortolan Bunting

AR: Derset aritlan
GE: Ortolan

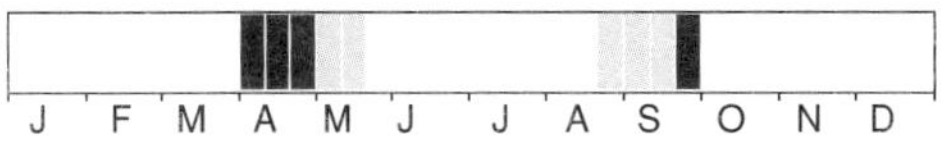

A common migrant in the Northern Highlands, Rift Margin highlands from Amman south to Petra, Wadi Araba, Aqaba, and the Rum Desert. It also occurs in the Eastern Desert; however, despite being the commonest bunting at Azraq in the 1960s, it has been rather scarce there in recent years. It can be seen from early April to mid May (considerably later than Cretzschmar's Buntings), and again from late August to late September, with peaks of 300 at Aqaba on 9-10 April 1990 and 100 at Ghadir Burqu' on 22 September 1991.

Emberiza caesia
Cretzschmar's Bunting

AR: Derseh zarqa'a er-ras
GE: Grauortolan

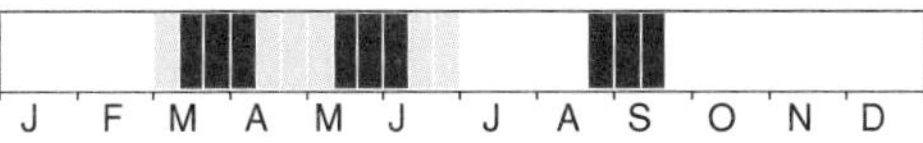

An uncommon migrant breeding species of the Northern Highlands, typically found on sparsely vegetated, bushy wadisides and hillsides, in areas such as Ajlun, Wadi Shu'ayb and Wadi ash Shita. Further south, it also breeds around Dana village, where 10 singing males were recorded in May 1994.

It is perhaps more likely to be seen as a migrant in the Jordan Valley and along the length of the Rift Margins from mid March to early April, and again from late August to mid September. It is a relatively uncommon migrant in the Eastern Desert, with only a few records from Azraq and Shaumari at either season. It seems to occur only rarely at Aqaba.

Emberiza pusilla
Little Bunting

AR: Ad-derseh as-sagheereh
GE: Zwergammer

Vagrant: one at Azraq on 29 October 1989.

Emberiza schoeniclus
Reed Bunting

AR: Derset al-qasab
GE: Rohrammer

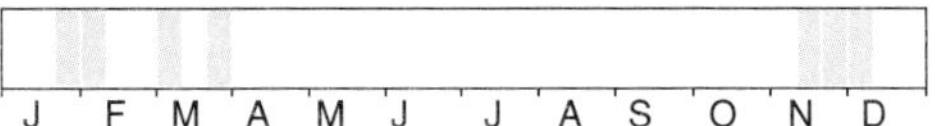

A rare winter visitor, mainly at wetland sites, between mid November and late March, occurring at Azraq, Shaumari, Al Khirba as Samra, and As Safi. It usually occurs only in small numbers, but one flock of 12 has been seen at Shaumari.

Emberiza melanocephala
Black-headed Bunting

AR: Derseh sowda'a er-rās
GE: Kappenammer

J F M A M J J A S O N D

There is a small breeding population of this eastern Mediterranean species in the Northern Highlands west of Amman. The brightly coloured males, perched obviously on tree tops, can be heard giving their descending jingle of a song at sites such as the Amman National Park, Wadi as Sir and Wadi ash Shita from late April. The habitat consists mainly of orchards with hawthorn and other scrub along rocky wadis, but other birds have been recorded in oak woods.

A small number of migrants have been reported from Azraq, Shaumari, Wadi al Butm, At Tafila, Wadi Rum, and Aqaba during mid April to mid May, and again from mid August to mid September. One Shaumari record is of a flock of 45 with 20 Ortolan Buntings on 7 May 1977, but single birds are more normal.

Miliaria calandra
Corn Bunting

AR: Derseh ma'alofa
GE: Grauammer

J F M A M J J A S O N D

A very common winter species, with flocks in the Northern Highlands, desert fringe, and vegetated wadis in the Eastern Desert. Numbers build up from early November, and flocks up to 300 strong can be found at many localities during the winter months. The birds prefer open habitats with isolated trees, bushes, or wires, where they often perch. The largest recorded flocks are: 100 at Al Amiriyya, 250 at Shaumari and 300 at Wadi al Butm. The only site with prolonged observations (Shaumari) shows a dramatic increase in recent years, so this status may be a recent phenomenon. It is absent from the south of the country, except for two records at Petra.

Although the vast majority of birds have left by March, a few lingering birds take up territories in the Jordan Valley and upland grassland (for example at the Zarqa River, Wadi Shu'ayb, Amman National Park, and Wadi al Wala) even as far south as Wadi Dana. Breeding was long suspected, but only proven when an adult and one juvenile were seen in Wadi al Wala on 5 July 1990. Birds are apparently absent during the late summer and autumn, before the winter migrants return.

Appendix 1: *Previously published and unsubstantiated records for species not included in the main list*

Puffinus pacificus
Wedge-tailed Shearwater
GE: Keilschwanz-Sturmtaucher

A party of six large all-dark shearwaters seen off the beach at Aqaba on the evening of 19 June 1992 were probably of this species.

Morus bassanus
Gannet
GE: Baßtölpel

A juvenile gannet seen off Aqaba on 1 December 1992 was either this species or a Cape Gannet *Morus capensis*.

Pelicanus crispus
Dalmatian Pelican
GE: Krauskopfpelikan

Included on the Disi and Bouran List on the basis of distribution maps in a general field guide.

Ardea goliath
Goliath Heron
GE: Goliathreiher

Recorded by the Jordan University Museum from Irbid, Azraq and North Shuna (Disi and Bouran, 1987), but the identification of these specimens has yet to be confirmed.

Cygnus olor
Mute Swan
GE: Höckerschwan

Reported as seen, but not shot, at Azraq in the winter of 1968/69, but no further details are available. Due to the lack of substantive information, this species is not included on the official Jordan list, although it has been accepted by Cramp and Simmons (1979).

Anser fabalis
Bean Goose
GE: Saatgans

Listed by Disi and Bouran (1987), but there are no confirmed sightings.

Anser erythropus
Lesser White-fronted Goose
GE: Zwerggans

Included on the Disi and Bouran List, but there are no confirmed sightings (see page 167).

Bucephala clangula
Goldeneye
GE: Schellente

Reported as seen at Azraq in 1968/69, but there is no further information.

Mergus albellus
Smew
GE: Zwergsäger

Reported at Azraq in 1968/69.

Mergus serrator
Red-breasted Merganser
GE: Mittelsäger

Reported at Azraq in 1968/69.

Elanus caeruleus
Black-shouldered Kite
GE: Gleitaar

There is an unconfirmed report of one at Al Khirba as Samra on a date in September 1992.

Porphyrio porphyrio
Purple Gallinule
GE: Purpurhuhn

Dawydoff (1898) mentions this species for the Jordan Valley, but without sufficient detail to include it in the main list.

Anthropoides virgo
Demoiselle Crane
GE: Jungfernkranich

Local observers have reported this species as a rare migrant and it has also been included on the Disi and Bouran List, based on regional distribution maps.

Charadrius mongolus
Lesser Sand Plover
GE: Mongolenregenpfeifer

Initially, there was some confusion as to whether some or all of the Jordanian sand plovers may have been Lesser Sand Plovers, but all records are now referred to Greater Sand Plover.

Larus hemprichii
Sooty Gull
GE: Hemprichmöwe

Included on the Disi and Bouran List on the basis of regional distribution maps, but there are no confirmed sightings from Aqaba.

Larus melanocephalus
Mediterranean Gull
GE: Schwarzkopfmöwe

There is an unpublished report of one in the Dead Sea area on 12 April 1989.

Larus brunnicephalus
Brown-headed Gull
GE: Braunkopfmöwe

There is an unconfirmed sighting of an immature at Aqaba on 3-4 May 1990.

Sterna paradisaea
Arctic Tern
GE: Küstenseeschwalbe

One observer recorded singles at Azraq on several occasions (and once a group of three) in late April to late May in both 1968 and 1969. However, even the observer admitted that these records could not be fully accepted. Records of four at Azraq on 16 April 1988 and one at Aqaba on 20 April 1989 fall in this same category.

Dendrocopus medius
Middle Spotted Woodpecker
GE: Mittelspecht

A woodpecker with a complete red cap was reported near Jarash on 17 April 1984. Immature Syrian Woodpecker was ruled out, only on the basis of the date being too early.

Eremophila alpestris
Shore Lark
GE: Ohrenlerche

A report of thousands or tens of thousands passing through or resting in the Ma'an/Petra/Aqaba area in 3-5 February 1965 is intriguing. Was this an influx of wintering Shore Larks, or is it possible there was confusion with Temminck's Horned Larks (admittedly not normally that common in this area)?

Oenanthe pleschanka
Pied Wheatear
GE: Nonnensteinschmätzer

There have been several reports of Pied Wheatear in Jordan, and it is possible that it should be included as a rare migrant. However, it is not clear whether these records could refer to the subspecies *cypriaca,* which is considered as a distinct species by some authors. See page 128.

Oenanthe picata
Eastern Pied Wheatear
GE: Elstersteinschmätzer

Following their discovery in the 1960s, the dark wheatears of the Basalt Desert were assigned to the *opistholeuca* race of this species. However, since 1985 it has become accepted that this identification was not correct (see Mourning Wheatear, dark morph, page 130).

Oenanthe leucura
Black Wheatear
GE: Trauersteinschmätzer

The Black Wheatear is listed by Disi and Bouran (1987) and Shafei (1988) as occurring in the Basalt Desert, but the museum specimens and presumably all sightings can be referred to the dark morph of the Mourning Wheatear (see page 130).

Acrocephalus dumetorum
Blyth's Reed Warbler
GE: Buschrohrsänger

There is a report that four were trapped and ringed at Azraq in the springs of 1968 and 1969, but no further details are available.

Sitta europaea
Nuthatch

GE: Kleiber

A report of a few being resident in the woodlands of Ajlun brings to mind Canon Tristram's observations in the woods of northern Israel last century. However, there have been no recent reports from that region.

Sitta neumayer
Rock Nuthatch

GE: Felsenkleiber

Local birdwatchers have reported this species in the rocky wadis of the far north-western Highlands. Sites include the cliffs of the Yarmuk and Umm Qays mountains, where Roman ruins are quoted to be a favoured habitat, as elsewhere in the species' range.

Rhodopechys sanguinea
Crimson-winged Finch

GE: Rotflügelgimpel

Local birdwatchers have reported this species as a rare resident of the highlands around Ajlun, Jarash and As Salt, in areas where there are scattered small trees. Confirmation is preferable before this species is added to the main list.

Emberiza aureola
Yellow-breasted Bunting

GE: Weidenammer

There is a report of one trapped at Azraq in spring 1968 or 1969, but no details were given.

Euodice malabarica
Indian Silverbill

GE: Malabarfasänchen

There are now a few records of this escaped cagebird in the Jordan Valley: eight (one collected) at North Shuna on 21 January 1984, two at South Shuna on 19 March 1989, and a pair nest building at Kafrayn on 1 May 1990. It may eventually become established as a feral species, but at present it is not included in the main list.

Emberiza tahapisi
Cinnamon-breasted Rock Bunting (African Rock Bunting)

GE: Bergammer

A bird reported at Disi on 27 April 1986 needs further confirmation, as it is so far out of range. It was described as having 'a black and white head, black chin and throat, and a bright cinnamon breast'.

APPENDIX 2: *Species likely to occur in Jordan*

DUE TO THE BETTER COVERAGE BY BIRDWATCHERS, THE SPECIES LIST FOR ISRAEL (ESPECIALLY EILAT AND WADI ARAVA) IS FAR IN EXCESS OF THAT SO FAR RECORDED IN JORDAN. AS POSSIBLE FUTURE ADDITIONS TO THE JORDAN LIST, IT IS WORTH MENTIONING (1) SOME OF THE MORE FREQUENT MIGRANTS RECORDED AT EILAT BUT NOT SEEN IN JORDAN, (2) SOME OF THE MORE REGULAR WADI ARAVA AND NORTHERN ISRAEL SPECIES NOT YET RECORDED IN JORDAN, (3) VAGRANTS SEEN WHILST LOOKING OVER THE BORDER FENCE FROM ISRAEL, AND (4) VAGRANT SEABIRDS SEEN AT THE HEAD OF THE GULF OF AQABA.

Gavia arctica
Black-throated Diver
GE: Prachttaucher

A fairly frequent winter vagrant to the Gulf of Aqaba, with records at Eilat most winters; recorded October to February.

Anser erythropus
Lesser White-fronted Goose
GE: Zwerggans

Two adults, with six White-fronted Geese, stayed at Eilat from November 1993 to February 1994. The flock was seen flying to the Aqaba sewage works in Jordan on several occasions.

Tetrax tetrax
Little Bustard
GE: Zwergtrappe

A scarce winter visitor to central and northern Israel, Golan, and the western Negev Desert. The records of 30-40 in the basalt habitat of the Golan is particularly relevant. Birds could well occur in the Basalt Desert in winter.

Pluvialis apricaria
Golden Plover
GE: Goldregenpfeifer

A rare passage bird at Eilat during August to November. It is fairly common elsewhere in Israel in winter, with flocks of up to 300 birds recorded.

Pterocles lichtensteinii
Lichtenstein's Sandgrouse
GE: Wellenflughuhn

Although it has been mapped as a scarce resident in the mountains behind Aqaba, there are no published Jordanian records, despite it's being a scarce resident of the Eilat mountains opposite. A specimen reported as taken near Aqaba in 1914 was actually collected on the Sinai side of the gulf.

Alauda gulgula
Small Skylark (Little or Oriental Skylark)
GE: Kleine Feldlerche

Since 1984, a small number of birds have been wintering in fields at Eilat from late September to early April. A possibility for Jordan?

Anthus hodgsoni
Olive-backed Pipit
GE: Waldpieper

A rare migrant at Eilat in November.

Hypocolius ampelinus
Grey Hypocolius
GE: Seidenwürger

In 1989/90, three birds were first seen in Eilat, but are reported to have spent most of their time in out-of-bounds Jordan.

Prunella collaris
Alpine Accentor
GE: Alpenbraunelle

In the northern parts of Israel, this is a regular winter visitor in small numbers. It frequents wadis and cliffs, sometimes along with the Wallcreeper. There is no Jordan record – as yet.

Cercotrichas podobe
Black Bush Robin (Black Bush Chat)
GE: Rußheckensänger

Better coverage of the southern Wadi Arava of Israel has produced several records of this African species since 1981. It is a bird of acacia savanna, so it could easily turn up in adjacent parts of Jordan.

Loxia curvirostra
Crossbill

GE: Fichtenkreuzschnabel

An irregular and scarce winter visitor to northern and central Israel (December to March), with a few remaining to breed in pine and cypress trees.

Emberiza leucocephalos
Pine Bunting

GE: Fichtenammer

An irregular winter visitor (November to March) in small numbers to the Mount Hermon and Jerusalem areas.

Emberiza rustica
Rustic Bunting

GE: Waldammer

A rare passage migrant at Eilat in October and November.

THE FOLLOWING IS A LIST OF OTHER SEABIRDS RECORDED AS ACCIDENTALS AT THE HEAD OF THE GULF OF AQABA:

Diomedea cauta **Shy Albatross**

Pterodroma incerta **Schlegel's Petrel**

Calonectris leucomelas **Streaked Shearwater**

Puffinus carneipes **Pale-footed Shearwater**

Oceanites oceanicus **Wilson's Petrel**

Oceanodroma leucorhoa **Leach's Petrel**

Oceanodroma monorhis **Swinhoe's Petrel**

Oceanodroma castro **Madeiran Petrel**

Phaethon aethereus **Red-billed Tropicbird**

Stercorarius maccormicki **South Polar Skua**

Larus hemprichii **Sooty Gull**

Larus melanocephalus **Mediterranean Gull**

Larus brunnicephalus **Brown-headed Gull**

Larus sabini **Sabine's Gull**

Rissa tridactyla **Kittiwake**

Sterna paradisaea **Arctic Tern**

Sterna fuscata **Sooty Tern**

Sterna saundersii **Saunder's Little Tern**

BIBLIOGRAPHY

AL EISAWI, D.M. 1985. Vegetation in Jordan. *In*: Hadidi, A. (ed) *Studies in the history and archaeology of Jordan II*. Department of Antiquities, Amman, pages 45-57.

ALOMIA, M.K. 1978. Notes on the present avifauna of Hesban. *In*: Boraas, R.S. and Geraty, L.T. *Heshbon 1976: The Fifth Campaign at Tell Hesban, A Preliminary Report*. Andrews University Monographs, Studies in Religion **10**, 289-303.

ANDREWS, I.J. 1991a. Blue Tits in Jordan. *OSME Bulletin No. 27 (Autumn 1991)*, pages 6-7.

ANDREWS, I.J. 1991b. Is Azraq still an oasis? *OSME Bulletin No. 27 (Autumn 1991)*, pages 13-19.

ANDREWS, I.J. 1994. Description of the black morph Mourning Wheatear *Oenanthe lugens* in Jordan. *Sandgrouse* **16**, 32-35.

ANDREWS, I.J. in press. Preliminary data on raptor passage in Jordan. *Sandgrouse*.

ANDREWS, I.J. in press. Recent additions to the Jordan species and breeding lists. *Sandgrouse*.

BOYD, J.M. 1967. *International Jordan Expedition 1966*. Report for International Biological Programme.

CAMERON, R.A.D. and CORNWALLIS, L. 1966. Autumn notes from Azraq, Jordan. *Ibis* **108**, 284-287.

CARRUTHERS, D. 1910. On a collection of birds from the Dead Sea and north-western Arabia, with contributions to the ornithology of Syria and Palestine. *Ibis* (9th Series) **4**, 475-491.

CLARKE, J.E. 1980. The avifauna of Shaumari Wildlife Reserve, Jordan. *Sandgrouse* **1**, 50-67.

CLARKE, J.E. 1981. The occurrence of Strickland's Wheatear in Jordan. *Sandgrouse* **2**, 98-99.

CLARKE, J.E. 1983 The Houbara Bustard in Jordan. *Sandgrouse* **4**, 111-113.

CONDOR, P. 1981. Birds of the Azraq Wetland Reserve, Jordan: January and February 1979. *Sandgrouse* **2**, 22-32.

CONDOR, P.J. 1981. Water extraction at Azraq. *OSME Bulletin No. 6 (Spring 1981)*, page 8.

CONDOR, P.J. 1982. Azraq Wetland Reserve. *OSME Bulletin No. 8 (Spring 1982)*, pages 4-5.

CRAMP, S., SIMMONS, K.E.L. and PERRINS, C.M. (editors) 1976 to 1994. *The Birds of the Western Palearctic*. 9 volumes. Oxford University Press.

DISI, A.M. and BOURAN, A.H. 1987. *A Check-list of the Birds of the Hashemite Kingdom of Jordan: an Ecological Outlook*. Department of Biological Sciences, University of Jordan, Amman.

DAWYDOFF, K.N. 1898. Beiträge zur ornithologischen Fauna des östlichen Palästina und des Nordens von Petro-Arabien. *Travaux de la Société Impériale des Naturalistes de St.-Pétersbourg (Section de Zoologie et de Physiologie)* **29**, 141-226. St. Petersberg, Russia. [German summary of Russian paper].

EVANS, M.I. (compiler) 1994. *Important Bird Areas of the Middle East*. BirdLife International, Cambridge.

FESTA, E. 1894. Viaggio del Dr E. Festa in Palestina, nel Libano e regioni vicine. *Bolletino dei Musei di Zoologia ed Anatomia comparata della R. Università di Torino* **No. 172**, 1-38 and **No. 174**, 1-7.

FLAXMAN, E.W. 1982. Observations of raptor migration in Jordan, May 1982. *OSME Bulletin No. 9 (Autumn 1982)*, pages 4-5.

GOODMAN, S.M. and MEININGER, P.L. (editors) 1989. *The Birds of Egypt*. Oxford University Press, Oxford.

HARDY, E. 1946. *A Handlist of the Birds of Palestine*. Education Officer-in-Chief, G.H.Q., Middle East Forces.

HART, H.C. 1891. *Fauna and flora of Sinai, Petra and Wadi Arabah*. Watt, London.

HATOUGH-BOURAN, A. and DISI, A.M. 1991. History, distribution and conservation of large mammals and their habitats in Jordan. *Environmental Conservation* **18**, 19-32.

HEMSLEY, J.H. and GEORGE, M. 1965. *Azraq Desert National Park, Jordan: Draft Management Plan*. International Biological Programme, Conservation of Terrestrial Communities.

HEINZEL, H., FITTER, R. and PARSLOW, J. 1972. *The Birds of Britain and Europe with North Africa and the Middle East*. Collins, London.

HOLLOM, P.A.D. 1959. Notes from Jordan, Lebanon, Syria and Antioch. *Ibis* **101**, 183-200.

HOSKING, E. 1970. *An Eye for a Bird*. Arrow Books, London.

HOVEL, H. 1987. *Check-list of the Birds of Israel*. Society for the Protection of Nature in Israel.

HÜE, F. and ETCHÉCOPAR, R.D. 1970. *Les Oiseaux du Proche et du Moyen Orient*. N. Boubée, Paris.

HUNTING TECHNICHAL SERVICES LTD. 1993. *The Soils of Jordan, Level 1: Reconnaissance Soil Survey*. Commission of The European Communities Contract No. SEM/03/628/005. Unpublished report.

JENNINGS, M.C. 1986. The distribution of the extinct Arabian Ostrich *Struthio camelus syriacus* Rothschild, 1919. *Fauna of Saudi Arabia* **8**, 447-461.

KAPPES, E. and KAPPES, W. 1981. Naturkundliche Studien in Jordaniens Wüsten-Nationalpark Azraq – 26 April bis 2 Mai 1980. *Sonderheft Deutscher Bund Für Vogelschutz LV Hamburg* **9**, 139-148.

KIRWAN, G. (compiler) 1992. Around the Region. *OSME Bulletin No. 29 (Autumn 1992)*, pages 35-48.

MEINERTZHAGEN, R. 1924. An account of a journey across the southern Syrian Desert from Amman in Transjordania to Ramadi on the Euphrates. *Ibis* **1924**, 87-100.

MEINERTZHAGEN, R. 1925. A further contribution to the ornithology of Palestine, Transjordania and Petra. *Ibis* (12th Series) 1(2), 305-324.

MILD, K. 1990. *Birds Songs of Israel and the Middle East* (two cassettes and booklet), Stockholm.

MINISTRY OF MUNICIPAL AND RURAL AFFAIRS AND THE ENVIRONMENT (MMRAE). 1991. *National Environmental Strategy for Jordan*. IUCN – The World Conservation Union, Gland, Switzerland.

MOUNTFORD, G. 1965. *Portrait of a Desert*. Collins, London.

NELSON, J.B. 1973. *Azraq: Desert Oasis*. Allen Lane, London.

NELSON, J.B. 1985a. Azraq – a case study. *In*: Hadidi, A. (ed) *Studies in the history and archaeology of Jordan II*. Department of Antiquities, Amman, pages 39-44.

NELSON, J.B. 1985b. Return to Azraq. *Oryx* **19**: 22-26.

PAZ, U. 1987. *The Birds of Israel*. Helm, London.

PHILLIPS, J.C. 1915. Some birds from Sinai and Palestine. *The Auk* **32**(3), 273-289.

RAMADAN BAKIG, A. and HORANI, H.K. 1992. *Birds of Jordan*. Privately published, Amman.

ROYAL SOCIETY FOR THE CONSERVATION OF NATURE, JORDAN. (undated). *The Dana Project*. R.S.C.N., Amman.

SHAFEI, D.M. 1988. [*Wild Birds of Jordan*]. Yarmuk University, Irbid, Jordan. In Arabic.

SHANNON, G.R. 1974. Studies of less familiar birds. 174 Shore Lark and Temminck's Horned Lark. *British Birds* **67**, 502-511.

SHEHADEH, N. 1985. The climate of Jordan in the past and present. *In*: Hadidi, A. (ed) *Studies in the history and archaeology of Jordan II*. Department of Antiquities, Amman, pages 25-37.

SHIRIHAI, H. 1987. Shearwaters and other tubenoses at Eilat. *Dutch Birding* **9**, 152-157.

STEINBACHER, J. 1979. Neue Erkenntnisse über den Fahlkauz (*Stix butleri*). *Natur und Museum* (Frankfurt am Main) **109**, 375.

TRISTRAM, H.B. 1873. *The Land of Moab: travels and discovery on the east side of the Dead Sea and the Jordan*. London.

TRISTRAM, H.B. 1884. *The Flora and Fauna of Palestine*. The Survey of Western Palestine, published by the committee of the Palestine Exploration Fund, London.

TYE, A. 1994. A description of the Middle Eastern black morph of the Mourning Wheatear *Oenanthe lugens*, from museum specimens. *Sandgrouse* **16**, 28-31.

ULLMAN, M. 1991. First record of Little Bunting *Emberiza pusilla* in Jordan. *Sandgrouse* **13**, 53-54.

VERE BENSON, S. 1970. *Birds of Lebanon (and the Jordan area)*. Warne, London.

WALLACE, D.I.M. 1982. Observations of migrant birds at Azraq in north-east Jordan, up to April 1967. *Sandgrouse* **4**, 77-99.

WALLACE, D.I.M. 1983a. The breeding birds of the Azraq oasis and its desert surround, Jordan, in the mid-1960s. *Sandgrouse* **5**, 1-18.

WALLACE, D.I.M. 1983b. The first identification of the Eastern Pied Wheatear in Jordan. *Sandgrouse* **5**, 102-104.

WALLACE, D.I.M. 1984. Selected observations from Lebanon, Syria and Jordan in the springs of 1963 and 1966. *Sandgrouse* **6**, 24-47.

WALLACE, D.I.M. 1989. Arabian Warblers in Jordan in April 1963. *OSME Bulletin No. 22 (Spring 1989)*, pages 9-10.

WITTENBERG, J. 1983. Vogelkundliche Ergebnisse einer naturkundlichen Forschungsreise nach Jordanien (10.4. bis 14.5.1983). *Sonderheft Deutscher Bund Für Vogelschutz LV Hamburg* **11**, 127-153.

WITTENBERG, J. 1987. Zur Vogel-Fauna einer semiariden Gebirgsregion in Süd-Jordanien (Petra und Umgebung) (Aves). *Verh. naturwiss. Ver. Hamburg* **29**, 5-49.

WITTENBERG, J. 1988a. Review of A.M. Disi and A.H. Bouran 1987 (see above). *OSME Bulletin No. 21 (Autumn 1988)*, pages 33-34.

WITTENBERG, J. 1988b. Additional records of the Ring-necked Parakeet, *Psittacula krameri*, from Egypt and the Middle East. *Zoology in the Middle East* **2**, 49-51.

YEKUTIEL, D. 1989. *Birdwatching in Eilat*. International Birdwatching Center, Eilat, Israel.

GAZETTEER OF JORDANIAN LOCALITIES

THE FOLLOWING GAZETTEER CONTAINS ALL OF THE LOCALITIES MENTIONED IN THE TEXT TOGETHER WITH (A) THE AVIFAUNAL REGION IN WHICH THEY ARE SITUATED, AND (B) THE TWO-CHARACTER MAP REFERENCE BY WHICH THEY CAN BE LOCATED ON THE MAPS INSIDE THE FRONT AND BACK COVERS.

SPELLING OF PLACE NAMES

The transliteration of Arabic script into English is notoriously variable and confusing. For consistency, the spellings of most geographic names used in this book are taken from the 1:750,000 scale *Road Map of the Hashemite Kingdom of Jordan* (1989) published by the Royal Jordanian Geographic Centre, Amman. However, the spellings are not necessarily the same as those that appear on road signs. Sites not named on the RJGC road map are located by reference to the nearest landmark which is labelled. In a few cases alternative names or spellings are given in parentheses. Note that an initial al, as, ash etc. has been ignored in the sorting of this gazetteer.

GLOSSARY OF LOCAL GEOGRAPHIC TERMS

Ain	spring
Ghadir	pool
Ghor	valley, in particular the Rift Valley
Jabal	hill, mountain
Qa'	mudflat, pan
Qasr	castle, palace
Wadi	dry or perennial river or river valley, ranging from a broad, shallow depression to a deep, steep-sided gorge
Hammada	rocky desert plain
Hammamat	hot spring
Nahr	river
Sabkha	lagoon flat where mineral evaporites are formed

KEY TO AREA CODES: (See page 15 for their location)

AM Aqaba Mountains	NM Northern Rift Margins
AO Azraq Oasis	NS Northern Steppes
AQ Aqaba	RA Ar Ruwayshid Desert
BD Basalt Desert	RD Rum Desert
CD Central Desert	SG Southern Ghor
CM Central Rift Margins	SH Southern Highlands
ED Eastern Desert	SM Southern Rift Margins
JB Al Jafr Basin	WA Wadi Araba
JV Jordan Valley	WS Wadi as Sarhan
MD Al Mudawwara Desert	YK Yarmuk River valley
NH Northern Highlands	

Abu as Sous, Wadi as Sir (NH)	5D
Abu Dharr, west of Dhiban (NS)	6D
Al Adasiyya (JV)	3D
Ain Musa, east of Wadi Musa (SH)	9C
Ajlun (NH)	4D
Al Amiriyya (NS)	6E
Amman (NH)	5E
Amman National Park, east of Na'ur (NH)	5D
Aqaba (Al Aqaba) (AQ)	11B
Azraq (Al Azraq) (AO)	5G
Al Bahhath, north of Na'ur (NH)	5D
Al Baq'a (NH)	4D
Batn al Ghul, at Qal'at ash Shidiyya (JB/MD)	11D
Al Bayda, Petra (SM)	9C
Bayder Wadi as Sir (NH)	5D
Bayir police post (WS)	8F
Bir al Abwan, NW of Al Bishriyya (BD)	4F
Birket al Rais, east of Al Himma (YK)	3D
Busayra (SM)	8D
Dakhikiya, east of Al Umari (ED)	6G
Damiya (JV)	4D
Dana, west of Al Qadisiyya (SM)	8D
Dayr Alla (JV)	4D
Dead Sea (JV/WA)	5D/6D
Dhiban (NS)	6D
Dibbin Forest, south of Sakib (NH)	4D
Dilagha (SM)	10C
Disi (Ad Disa), NE of Ram (RD)	11D
Druz (Al Azraq ash Shamali) (AO)	5G
Al Fajij, east of Ash Shawbak (SH)	9D
Faqu (NS)	6D
Feinan, east of Qurayqira (WA)	8C
Fidan, west of Qurayqira (WA)	8C
Fifa (SG)	7C
Ghadir Burqu', north of Muqat (BD)	3I
Gharandal (WA)	10C
Ghor Fifa, Fifa (SG)	7C
Ghor Khabid pool, south of Damiya (JV)	4D
Ghor Safi, As Safi (SG)	7C
Hammamat Ma'in (Ma'in springs) (CM)	6D
Al Hashimiyya (JB)	9D
Al Hashimiyya (NS)	4E
Al Himma (YK)	3D
Hisban (NS)	5D
Ibbin (NH)	3D
Iraq al Amir (NH)	5D
Irbid (NH)	3D

INDEXES

In the following species indexes **bold figures** refer to main entries in the Systematic List, *italic figures* refer to colour plates and the remaining figures refer to the introductory chapters and appendixes.

Index to species by English name

Index to species by scientific name

Index of place names

Bold figures refer to significant mentions in the Avifaunal Regions and Birdwatching Sites chapters.

A detailed gazetteer can be found on page 171-173, and maps of northern and southern Jordan are situated inside the front and back covers respectively.

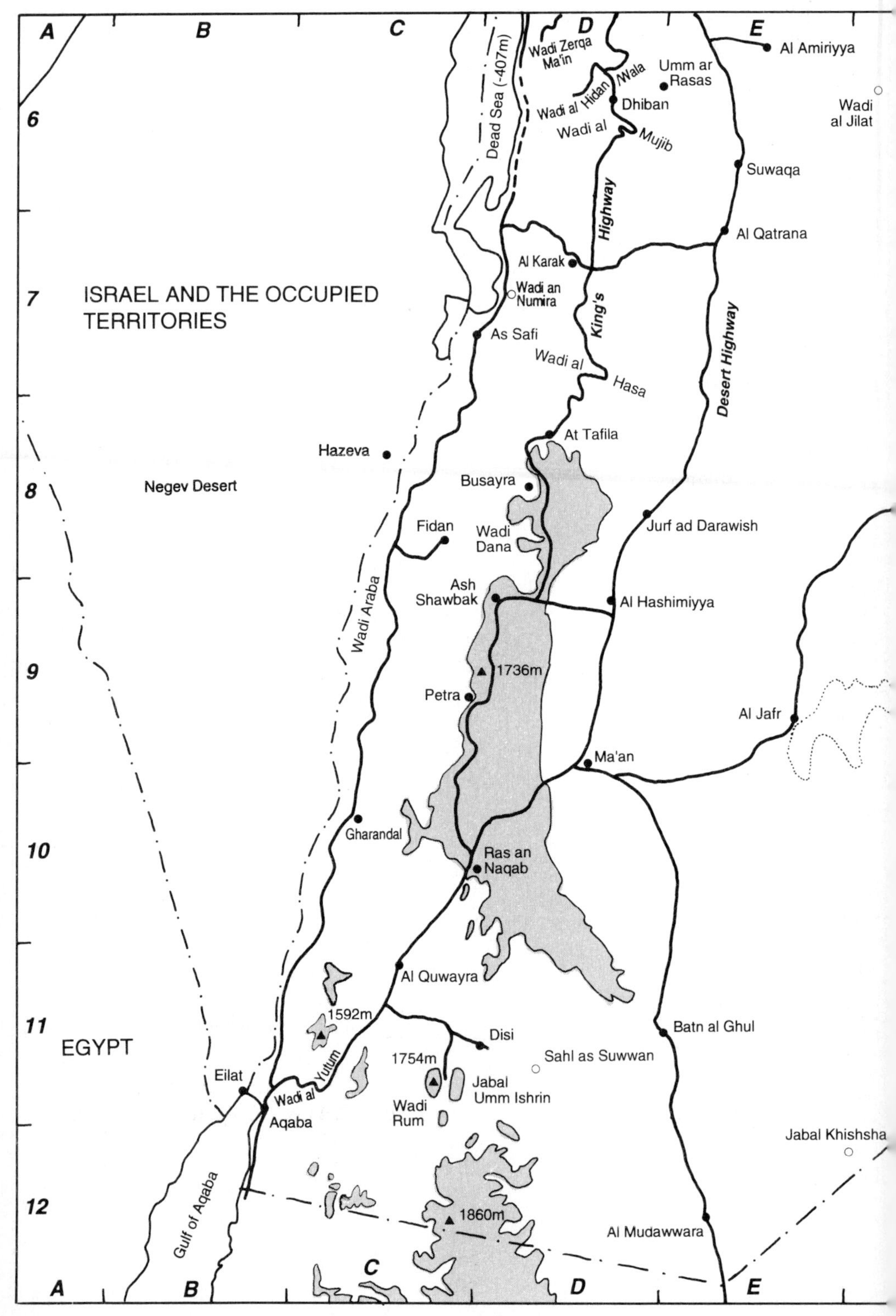
A
B
C
D
E
6
7
8
9
10
11
12
Dead Sea (-407m)
Wadi Zerqa Ma'in
Wadi al Hidan
Wala
Umm ar Rasas
Dhiban
Wadi al
Mujib
Al Amiriyya
Wadi al Jilat
Suwaqa
Highway
Al Qatrana
Al Karak
Wadi an Numira
King's
ISRAEL AND THE OCCUPIED TERRITORIES
As Safi
Wadi al
Hasa
Desert Highway
At Tafila
Hazeva
Negev Desert
Busayra
Jurf ad Darawish
Fidan
Wadi Dana
Ash Shawbak
Al Hashimiyya
Wadi Araba
1736m
Petra
Al Jafr
Ma'an
Gharandal
Ras an Naqab
Al Quwayra
1592m
EGYPT
Disi
1754m
Sahl as Suwwan
Batn al Ghul
Eilat
Wadi al
Yutum
Jabal Umm Ishrin
Wadi Rum
Aqaba
Jabal Khishsha
Gulf of Aqaba
1860m
Al Mudawwara